Edexcel A2 Physics

Miles Hudson

STUDENTS' BOOK

This book also includes Active Book

A PEARSON COMPANY

How to use this book

This book contains a number of great features that will help you find your way around your A2 Physics course and support your learning.

Introductory pages

Each topic has two introductory pages to help you identify how the main text is arranged to cover all that you need to learn. The left-hand page gives a brief summary of the topic, linking the content to three key areas of How Science Works:

What are the theories? What is the evidence? What are the implications?

The right-hand page of the introduction consists of a topic map that shows you how all the required content of the Edexcel specification for that topic is covered in the chapters, and how that content all interlinks. Links to other topics are also shown, including where previous knowledge is built on within the topic.

Main text

The main part of the book covers all you need to learn for your course. The text is supported by many diagrams and photographs that will help you understand the concepts you need to learn.

Key terms in the text are shown in bold type. These terms are defined in the interactive glossary that can be found on the software using the 'search glossary' feature.

UNIT 4 Topic 2
Electric and magnetic fields

Topic 2 Electric and magnetic fields

This rather mathematical topic examines field theory, introducing fields as a way of explaining the behaviour of charged particles influenced by electricity and magnetism. A study of electric fields themselves, capacitance, and the interactions between electric and magnetic fields leads on to the many and varied applications of the models developed.

What are the theories?

This is a necessarily mathematical topic, and you will meet many equations.

The description and calculation of uniform and radial electric fields leads to calculation of the forces between electrically charged particles using Coulomb's law.

Capacitors make use of electric fields to store charge, and the way they behave in electric circuits is investigated. The topic includes a mathematical description of the charge and energy stored, along with the growth and decay of the current that is charging or discharging the capacitor.

When electrically charged particles travel through magnetic fields, they experience a force and their motion is affected. It is this phenomenon that causes electric motors to function, and allows the generation of electricity in power stations. This topic looks at the theory of these interactions and moves on to calculations of these effects.

What is the evidence?

In many areas, these are the theories which explain our modern electrically driven world can operate. fact that electricity can be generated and used to c motors as we wish provides evidence for the accura of the theories. Similarly, capacitor circuits can be to test experimentally that the electric field theorie underlying them are correct. You may have a chan perform some of these experiments yourself.

Some of the experiments which back up these the feature among the archetypal great physics experim from history, performed by some of the most famo physicists. In particular, Michael Faraday undertoo some of the key pioneering work in these fields.

What are the implications?

Since the Industrial Revolution, our society has depended on much of this physics. We expect to h electricity available at all times, made possible by t discovery of Faraday's law.

Additionally, the cutting edge of physics – the par accelerator – could only be conceived in the light o the electromagnetic forces you will find out about i this topic.

The map opposite shows you the knowledge and s you need to have by the end of this topic, and how are linked together. The numbers refer to the secti in the Edexcel specification.

36

Introductory pages

UNIT 4 Topic 3 Particle physics

The bricks of matter Spec 106, 107

Twelve fundamental particles

After a century in which scientists rapidly discovered many subatomic particles, they have developed a theory for how these come together to build up the materials we see around us. This theory is known as the **standard model**. As the idea of the atom as indivisible was swept aside by Rutherford and Thomson, so the idea of the proton and neutron as fundamental has also been overturned. We have probed inside these two nucleons and discovered that each is constructed from smaller particles known as **quarks**. The electron has so far survived as being considered fundamental. However, it has two partners – particles of a similar type – each with a neutrino associated with it, forming a group of six fundamental particles known as **leptons**.

Scientists like to see the Universe as balanced, or symmetrical, and we have now found that quarks are also a group of six, although only the lightest two are found in protons and neutrons. The heavier quarks are found in more exotic particles. The two groups are distinct because quarks can undergo interactions via the **strong nuclear force** (see page 106) whereas leptons do not feel the strong force. It is the strong nuclear force that binds nucleons together. In each group of six there are three pairs with a similar order of magnitude for mass, and these are known as the three generations of matter.

Generation	Name	Symbol	Charge	Mass (MeV/c²)
I	Electron	e⁻	−1	0.511
I	Electron neutrino	νₑ	0	0 (<2.2 × 10⁻⁶)
II	Muon	μ	−1	106
II	Muon neutrino	νμ	0	0 (<0.17)
III	Tau	τ	−1	1780
III	Tau neutrino	ντ	0	0 (<20)

table 3.3.1 The family of leptons. These do not feel the strong nuclear force.

Generation	Name	Symbol	Charge	Mass (GeV/c²)
I	Up	u	+2/3	0.003
I	Down	d	−1/3	0.006
II	Strange	s	−1/3	0.1
II	Charm	c	+2/3	1.3
III	Bottom	b	−1/3	4.3
III	Top	t	+2/3	175

table 3.3.2 The family of quarks. These are subject to the strong nuclear force.

Only the first three quarks were known (up, down, strange) from the early part of the twentieth century, and charm was discovered in 1974. The symmetry of the standard model indicated to scientists that there were other particles they had never observed which should exist – bottom and top quarks. Experiments were carried out to find these and the accelerator experiments at Fermilab discovered bottom in 1977 and top in 1995.

Current particle theory holds that all matter in the Universe is constructed from combinations of some of these 12 particles, and no others. Each of the 12 particles listed in tables 3.3.1 and 3.3.2. also has an antiparticle. The antiparticles have the same mass but all their other properties are opposite to those of the normal matter particle. The symbol for an **antiparticle** is the same as for the normal particle, but with a bar above the symbol. For example, the charge on an anti-down quark is +⅓ and its symbol is d̄. In a few cases, the antiparticle is a different particle in its own right and the bar may not be used. The positron (anti-electron) does not use a bar, but is written as e⁺.

The Higgs boson

One of the great hopes for CERN's Large Hadron Collider (LHC) experiment is that it will discover the Higgs boson. First suggested by Peter Higgs in 1964, this very massive particle (its exact mass is not certain, but lies between the mass of an iron nucleus and that of uranium) is the means by which particles get mass. The Higgs mechanism is considered to be a bit like frictional drag on particles caused by a field called the Higgs field. Thus, an electron suffers less of this drag from the Higgs field than a proton, and so it has less mass. Remember that one of the key points about mass is that it gives objects inertia – the reluctance to change velocity – hence the idea of the frictional drag effect. This is only a model though – the Higgs mechanism is not easy to describe in everyday terms.

UNIT 4 Topic 3 Particle physics

Fig. 3.3.4 The masses of particles in the standard model increase over generations.

Main text

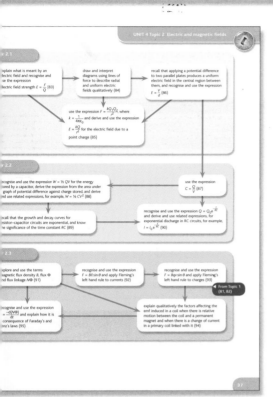

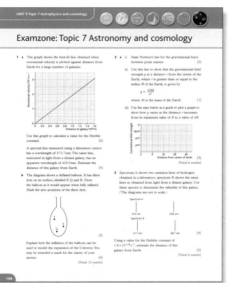

Examzone page

HSW boxes

How Science Works is a key feature of your course. The many HSW boxes within the text will help you cover all the new aspects of How Science Works that you need. These include how scientists investigate ideas and develop theories, how to evaluate data and the design of studies to test their validity and reliability, and how science affects the real world including informing decisions that need to be taken by individuals and society.

Practical boxes

Your course contains a number of core practicals that you may be tested on. These boxes indicate links to core practical work. Your teacher will give you opportunities to cover these investigations.

Question boxes

At the end of each section of text you will find a box containing questions that cover what you have just learnt. You can use these questions to help you check whether you have understood what you have just read, and whether there is anything that you need to look at again.

Examzone pages

At the end of each topic you will find two pages of exam questions from past papers. You can use these questions to test how fully you have understood the topic, as well as to help you practise for your exams.

The contents list shows you that there are two units and five topics in the book, matching the Edexcel A2 specification for physics. Page numbering in the contents list, and in the index at the back of the book, will help you find what you are looking for.

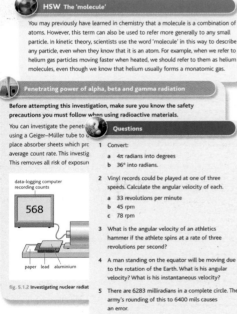

HSW The 'molecule'

You may previously have learned in chemistry that a molecule is a combination of atoms. However, this term can also be used to refer more generally to any small particle. In kinetic theory, scientists use the word 'molecule' in this way to describe any particle, even when they know that it is an atom. For example, when we refer to helium gas particles moving faster when heated, we should refer to them as helium molecules, even though we know that helium usually forms a monatomic gas.

Penetrating power of alpha, beta and gamma radiation

Before attempting this investigation, make sure you know the safety precautions you must follow when using radioactive materials.

You can investigate the penetra... using a Geiger–Müller tube to c... place absorber sheets which pr... average count rate. This investig... This removes all risk of exposure...

data-logging computer recording counts

568

paper   lead   aluminium

fig. 5.1.2 Investigating nuclear radiat...

Questions

1 Convert:
   a 4π radians into degrees
   b $36°$ into radians.

2 Vinyl records could be played at one of three speeds. Calculate the angular velocity of each.
   a 33 revolutions per minute
   b 45 rpm
   c 78 rpm

3 What is the angular velocity of an athletics hammer if the athlete spins at a rate of three revolutions per second?

4 A man standing on the equator will be moving due to the rotation of the Earth. What is his angular velocity? What is his instantaneous velocity?

5 There are 6283 milliradians in a complete circle. The army's rounding of this to 6400 mils causes an error.
   a How far sideways from the target could this rounding cause an artillery shell to be when aimed at a target 20km away?
   b Why does the actual bearing to the target not affect your answer to part a?

How to use your ActiveBook

The ActiveBook is an electronic copy of the book, which you can use on a compatible computer. The CD-ROM will only play while the disc is in the computer. The ActiveBook has these features:

Find Resources

Click on this tab to see menus which list all the electronic files on the ActiveBook.

Student Book tab

Click this tab at the top of the screen to access the electronic version of the book.

Key words

Click on any of the words in **bold** to see a box with the word and what it means. Click 'play' to listen to someone read it out for you to help you pronounce it.

Interactive view

Click this button to see all the icons on the page that link to electronic files, such as documents and spreadsheets. You have access to all of the features that are useful for you to use at home on your own. If you don't want to see these links you can return to **Book view**.

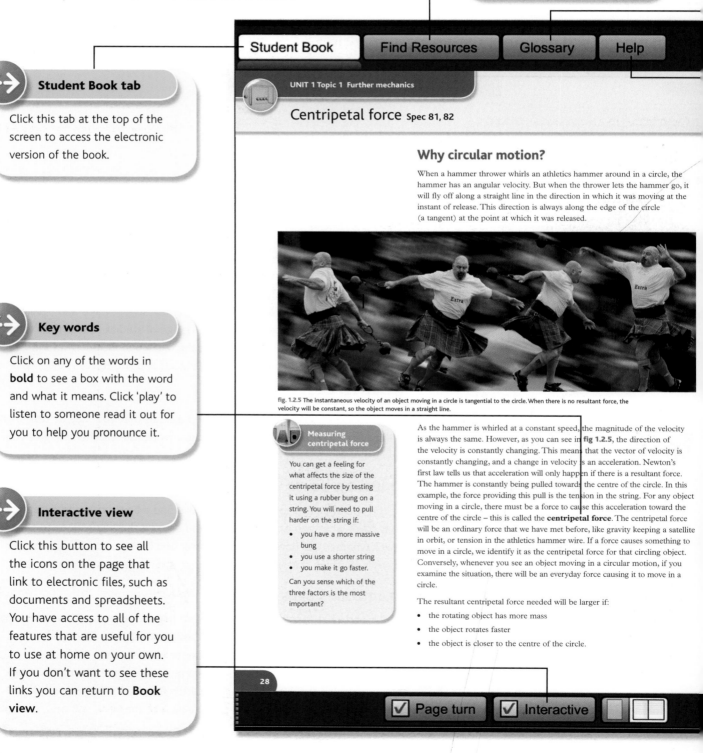

Student Book | Find Resources | Glossary | Help

UNIT 1 Topic 1 Further mechanics

Centripetal force Spec 81, 82

Why circular motion?

When a hammer thrower whirls an athletics hammer around in a circle, the hammer has an angular velocity. But when the thrower lets the hammer go, it will fly off along a straight line in the direction in which it was moving at the instant of release. This direction is always along the edge of the circle (a tangent) at the point at which it was released.

fig. 1.2.5 The instantaneous velocity of an object moving in a circle is tangential to the circle. When there is no resultant force, the velocity will be constant, so the object moves in a straight line.

Measuring centripetal force

You can get a feeling for what affects the size of the centripetal force by testing it using a rubber bung on a string. You will need to pull harder on the string if:

- you have a more massive bung
- you use a shorter string
- you make it go faster.

Can you sense which of the three factors is the most important?

As the hammer is whirled at a constant speed, the magnitude of the velocity is always the same. However, as you can see in **fig 1.2.5**, the direction of the velocity is constantly changing. This means that the vector of velocity is constantly changing, and a change in velocity is an acceleration. Newton's first law tells us that acceleration will only happen if there is a resultant force. The hammer is constantly being pulled towards the centre of the circle. In this example, the force providing this pull is the tension in the string. For any object moving in a circle, there must be a force to cause this acceleration toward the centre of the circle – this is called the **centripetal force**. The centripetal force will be an ordinary force that we have met before, like gravity keeping a satellite in orbit, or tension in the athletics hammer wire. If a force causes something to move in a circle, we identify it as the centripetal force for that circling object. Conversely, whenever you see an object moving in a circular motion, if you examine the situation, there will be an everyday force causing it to move in a circle.

The resultant centripetal force needed will be larger if:

- the rotating object has more mass
- the object rotates faster
- the object is closer to the centre of the circle.

28

☑ Page turn   ☑ Interactive

Glossary

Click this tab to see all of the key words and what they mean. Click 'play' to listen to someone read them out to help you pronounce them.

Help

Click on this tab at any time to search for help on how to use the ActiveBook.

Centripetal force and acceleration

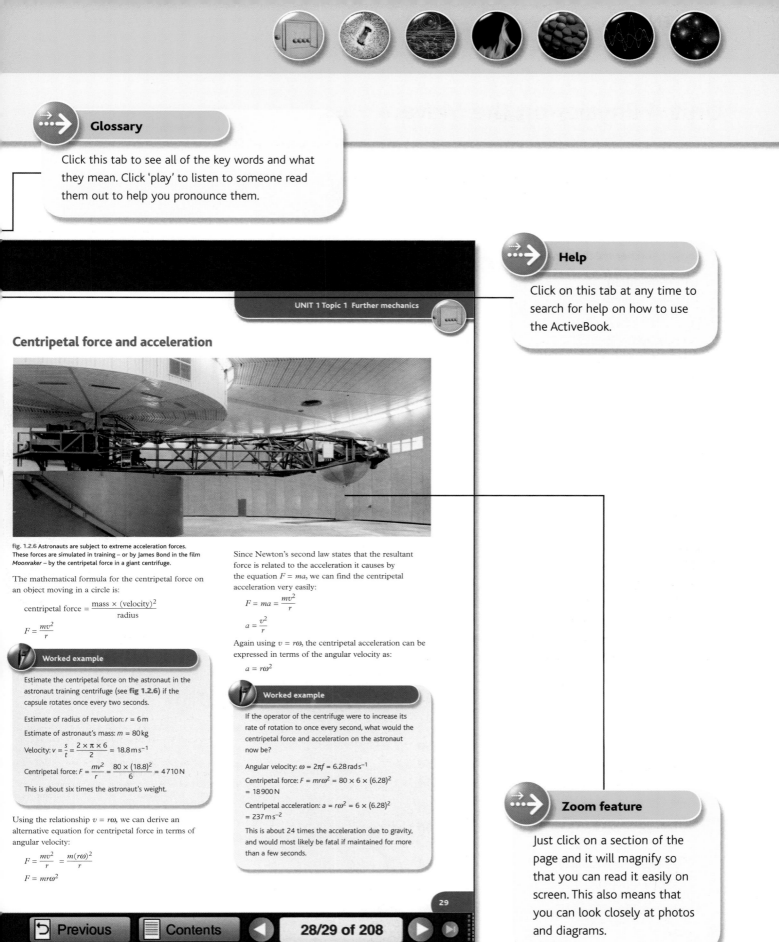

fig. 1.2.6 Astronauts are subject to extreme acceleration forces. These forces are simulated in training – or by James Bond in the film *Moonraker* – by the centripetal force in a giant centrifuge.

The mathematical formula for the centripetal force on an object moving in a circle is:

$$\text{centripetal force} = \frac{\text{mass} \times (\text{velocity})^2}{\text{radius}}$$

$$F = \frac{mv^2}{r}$$

Worked example

Estimate the centripetal force on the astronaut in the astronaut training centrifuge (see **fig 1.2.6**) if the capsule rotates once every two seconds.

Estimate of radius of revolution: $r = 6\,\text{m}$

Estimate of astronaut's mass: $m = 80\,\text{kg}$

Velocity: $v = \dfrac{s}{t} = \dfrac{2 \times \pi \times 6}{2} = 18.8\,\text{m s}^{-1}$

Centripetal force: $F = \dfrac{mv^2}{r} = \dfrac{80 \times (18.8)^2}{6} = 4710\,\text{N}$

This is about six times the astronaut's weight.

Using the relationship $v = r\omega$, we can derive an alternative equation for centripetal force in terms of angular velocity:

$$F = \frac{mv^2}{r} = \frac{m(r\omega)^2}{r}$$

$$F = mr\omega^2$$

Since Newton's second law states that the resultant force is related to the acceleration it causes by the equation $F = ma$, we can find the centripetal acceleration very easily:

$$F = ma = \frac{mv^2}{r}$$

$$a = \frac{v^2}{r}$$

Again using $v = r\omega$, the centripetal acceleration can be expressed in terms of the angular velocity as:

$$a = r\omega^2$$

Worked example

If the operator of the centrifuge were to increase its rate of rotation to once every second, what would the centripetal force and acceleration on the astronaut now be?

Angular velocity: $\omega = 2\pi f = 6.28\,\text{rad s}^{-1}$

Centripetal force: $F = mr\omega^2 = 80 \times 6 \times (6.28)^2$
$= 18\,900\,\text{N}$

Centripetal acceleration: $a = r\omega^2 = 6 \times (6.28)^2$
$= 237\,\text{m s}^{-2}$

This is about 24 times the acceleration due to gravity, and would most likely be fatal if maintained for more than a few seconds.

Zoom feature

Just click on a section of the page and it will magnify so that you can read it easily on screen. This also means that you can look closely at photos and diagrams.

CONTENTS

Unit 4 Physics on the Move

TOPIC 1
Further mechanics

TOPIC 2
Electric and magnetic fields

TOPIC 3
Particle physics

Unit 5 Physics from Creation to Collapse

TOPIC 4
Thermal energy

TOPIC 5
Nuclear decay

TOPIC 6
Oscillations

TOPIC 7
Astrophysics and cosmology

Topic 1 Further mechanics

This topic builds on the work in mechanics covered at AS, developing the scope of the calculations used to describe and predict the movements of objects. It looks at more complex motions such as circular motion and collisions between objects. In this topic you will learn how to describe mathematically the journey of an object, like a satellite, moving in a circular orbit; you will also learn what momentum is and how to calculate its value before and after a collision.

What are the theories?

As you discovered at AS, Newton's laws of motion can be used to work out the movement of everyday objects. This topic examines these laws in greater depth and shows how they define momentum and its conservation during collisions. You will meet the equations used to calculate kinetic energy and force in terms of momentum, and learn how to calculate the changes in these quantities that occur as a result of an impact.

The mathematical description of changing angular position is fundamental to understanding the movement of an object around a circular path. Using the concept of angular velocity, you will learn how to calculate a centripetal acceleration, and how Newton's second law then determines the associated centripetal force.

What is the evidence?

Newton's laws of motion, when he published them in 1687, referred to acceleration in terms of a change in momentum. These laws have been well tested by experiment ever since. You may have a chance to investigate momentum transfers in collision experiments of your own. With modern ICT recording of data, the reliability of such experiments is much improved over traditional methods.

Similarly, the equations for circular motion have been well tested experimentally, and you may have the chance to confirm them experimentally for yourself. Calculations of the motions of planets in the Solar System can also confirm their veracity.

What are the implications?

Combining the mathematical rules presented in this topic allows us to describe and predict the motion of objects in more complicated situations than can be dealt with simply in terms of velocity and acceleration. It becomes possible to incorporate multiple objects crashing into each other, or the sort of circular movements that govern the movements of planets and moons, and provide a simplistic account of electrons in atomic orbits.

The application of these equations is tested in an extensive investigation into an idea for protecting the Earth from a collision with an asteroid. The spread at the end of chapter 1.2 presents some everyday examples of circular motion physics in action at the fairground.

When combined with the electromagnetic forces in the next topic, the mechanics presented here also allows the calculation of the trajectories of subatomic particles in circular accelerators.

The map opposite shows you the knowledge and skills you need to have by the end of this topic, and how they are linked together. The numbers refer to the sections in the Edexcel specification.

Chapter 1.1

calculate linear momentum using the expression $p = mv$ (73)

apply the principle of conservation of linear momentum to problems in one dimension (74)

analyse and interpret data to calculate momenta of (non-relativistic) particles and apply the principle of conservation of momentum in one and two dimensions (77)

explain and apply the principle of conservation of energy, and determine whether a collision is elastic or inelastic (78)

relate net force to rate of change of momentum in situations where the mass is constant (Newton's second law of motion) (75)

derive and use the expression $E_k = \dfrac{p^2}{2m}$ for the kinetic energy of a non-relativistic particle (76)

Chapter 1.2

express angular displacement in radians and in degrees, and convert between those units (79)

explain that a resultant force (centripetal force) is required to produce and maintain circular motion (81)

To Topic 3 ▶ (99, 100)

explain the concept of angular velocity and recognise and use the relationships $v = r\omega$ and $T = \dfrac{2\pi}{\omega}$ (80)

use the expression for centripetal force $F = \dfrac{mv^2}{r}$ and hence derive and use the expressions for centripetal acceleration, $a = \dfrac{v^2}{r} = r\omega^2$ (82)

1.1 Momentum Spec 73, 75

How much is it moving?

In previous studies in physics, we have seen how we can measure movement by considering displacement, velocity and acceleration Another measure of motion that is very useful is **momentum**, which is defined mathematically as the product of mass and velocity:

momentum = mass × velocity

Or in symbol form:

$p = mv$

As mass is a scalar quantity, whilst velocity is a vector, this relationship means that momentum is a vector quantity. Momentum always has both magnitude and direction. The relationship also gives us the units for momentum, as mass multiplied by velocity gives kilogram metres per second, $kg\,m\,s^{-1}$.

fig. 1.1.1 Which has more momentum?

Worked example

Estimate the momentum of the rugby player and the cricket ball shown in fig. 1.1.1.

Rugby player

estimated mass = 120 kg   estimated velocity = 5 m s^{-1} (towards me!)

$p = mv = 120 \times 5 = 600\,kg\,m\,s^{-1}$ (towards me!)

Cricket ball

estimated mass = 200 g = 0.200 kg
estimated velocity = 25 m s^{-1} (towards me!)

$p = mv = 0.200 \times 25 = 5.0\,kg\,m\,s^{-1}$ (towards me!)

Newton's second law

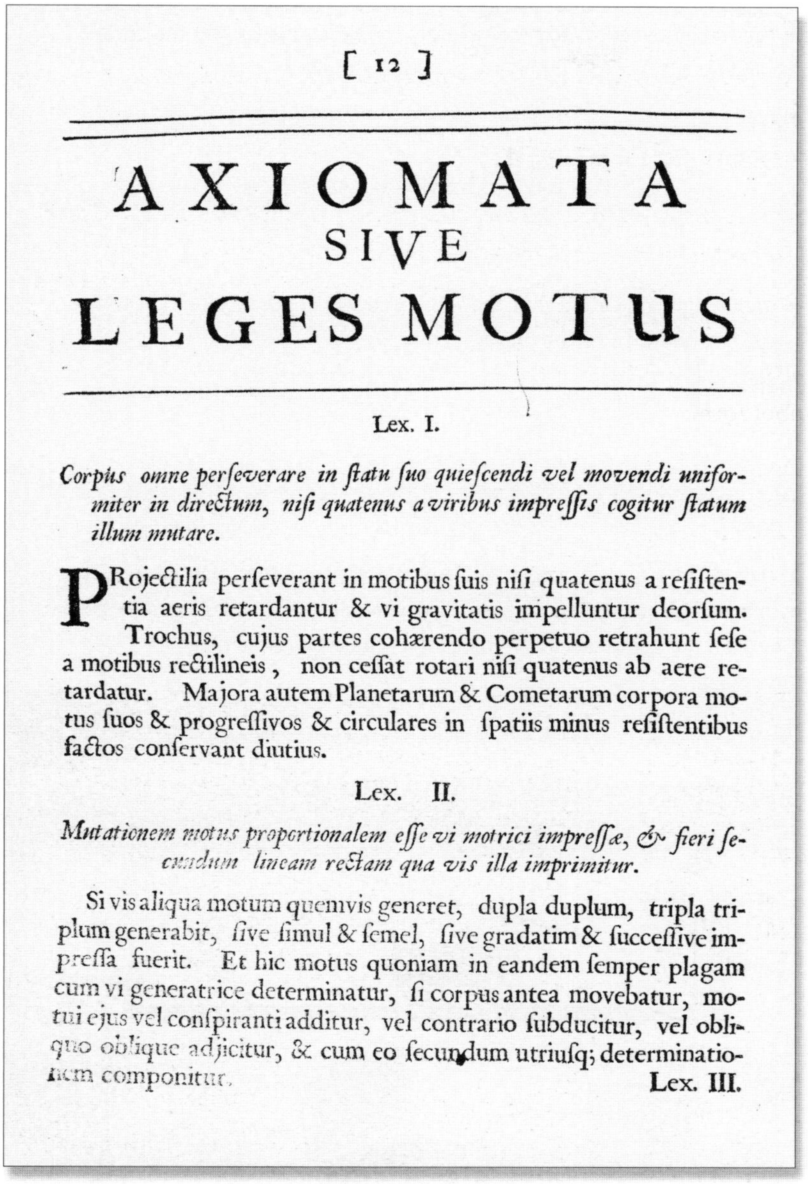

[12]

AXIOMATA
SIVE
LEGES MOTUS

Lex. I.

Corpus omne perseverare in statu suo quiescendi vel movendi unifor-miter in directum, nisi quatenus a viribus impressis cogitur statum illum mutare.

PRojectilia perseverant in motibus suis nisi quatenus a resisten-tia aeris retardantur & vi gravitatis impelluntur deorsum. Trochus, cujus partes cohærendo perpetuo retrahunt sese a motibus rectilineis, non cessat rotari nisi quatenus ab aere re-tardatur. Majora autem Planetarum & Cometarum corpora mo-tus suos & progressivos & circulares in spatiis minus resistentibus factos conservant diutius.

Lex. II.

Mutationem motus proportionalem esse vi motrici impressæ, & fieri se-cundum lineam rectam qua vis illa imprimitur.

Si vis aliqua motum quemvis generet, dupla duplum, tripla tri-plum generabit, sive simul & semel, sive gradatim & successive im-pressa fuerit. Et hic motus quoniam in eandem semper plagam cum vi generatrice determinatur, si corpus antea movebatur, mo-tui ejus vel conspiranti additur, vel contrario subducitur, vel obli-quo oblique adjicitur, & cum eo secundum utriusq; determinatio-nem componitur. **Lex. III.**

fig. 1.1.2 Newton's laws of motion as he originally wrote them.

If we think about bringing an object to rest, or accelerating it to a certain velocity, the requirements will be different for different situations. A golf ball is accelerated in a very different way to a ferry. We need to consider the forces needed, and the time for which they act. This brings us to another way of considering momentum. The momentum of an object is a measure of the accelerating force, applied over a period of time, that is needed to bring the object from rest to the speed at which it is moving. An object's momentum is also the force required, over a period of time, to bring the moving object to rest.

In AS mechanics, we learned that **Newton's second law of motion** can be written mathematically as $F = ma$. In fact, this formula only holds true if the mass remains constant. When Newton originally wrote his second law in the 1687 book, *Philosophiae naturalis principia mathematica* (**fig. 1.1.2**), he actually wrote it as:

> **The rate of change of momentum of a body is directly proportional to the resultant force applied to the body, and is in the same direction as the force.**

This can be written mathematically as:

$$F = \frac{dp}{dt} = \frac{d(mv)}{dt}$$

Here, F is the applied force, and $\frac{dp}{dt}$ is the rate of change of momentum in the direction of the force.

The $\frac{d(x)}{dt}$ term is a mathematical expression meaning the rate of change of x, or how quickly x changes. If the quantities are not constantly changing, we can express this as:

$$F = \frac{\Delta p}{\Delta t}$$

The product of a force applied for a certain time $(F \times \Delta t)$ is known as the **impulse**, and we can now see that this is equal to a change in momentum:

$$\text{impulse} = F \times \Delta t = \Delta p$$

To stop something moving, we need to remove all of its momentum. This idea allows us to calculate the impulse needed to stop a moving object. And if we know for how long a force is applied, we can work out the size of that force.

Worked example

Calculate the force needed to stop completely the rugby player and the cricket ball shown in **fig. 1.1.1** if this force is applied for a tenth of a second.

Rugby player

$$\Delta p = -600 \, \text{kg m s}^{-1} \quad \Delta t = 0.1 \, \text{s}$$

$$F = \frac{\Delta p}{\Delta t} = \frac{-600}{0.1}$$

$$F = -6000 \, \text{N}$$

Note the minus sign, indicating that the force is in the opposite direction to the velocity (and momentum) of the player.

Cricket ball

$$\Delta p = -8.0 \, \text{kg m s}^{-1} \quad \Delta t = 0.1 \, \text{s}$$

$$F = \frac{\Delta p}{\Delta t} = \frac{-8.0}{0.1}$$

$$F = -80 \, \text{N}$$

The force needed to stop the cricket ball is much less than that needed to stop the rugby player. This is the main reason why batsmen don't usually get knocked over if they stop the ball dead, unlike tackling a rugby player, where everybody ends up in a heap.

Recording momentum change

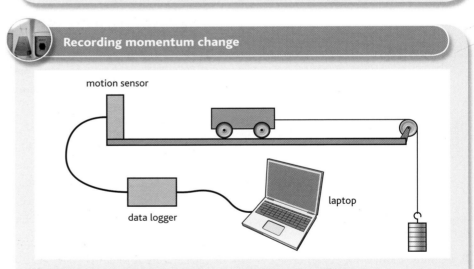

fig. 1.1.3 Measuring how a force changes the momentum of a trolley.

You can investigate the rate of change of momentum in the laboratory (**fig. 1.1.3**). If you record the movement of the trolley over time as a force makes it move from rest, you can find its velocity each second. If you then calculate the momentum each second, you will be able to plot a graph of momentum against time. It should be a straight line. As $p = Ft$, the gradient of this line will be equal to the accelerating force (**fig. 1.1.4**).

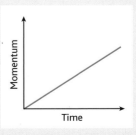

fig. 1.1.4 Accelerating from rest, momentum will be proportional to time.

Questions

1 What is the momentum of:

 a a plane of mass 2×10^5 kg flying at $270 \, \text{m s}^{-1}$?

 b a horse of mass 400 kg carrying a rider of mass 75 kg, galloping at $10 \, \text{m s}^{-1}$?

2 In the worked example on page 12, it was estimated that a cricket batsman might need to use 80 N to stop a ball dead.

 a Explain why a batsman hitting a ball so that it travels away at the same speed might need less than 80 N force to play his shot.

 b Explain why the same batsman playing the same ball might need more than 80 N force to play a shot.

3 An 800 kg car is travelling at $33 \, \text{m s}^{-1}$. How much force must the brakes apply, if they are to stop the car completely in four seconds?

4 a In a car crash, a passenger with a mass of 82 kg is not wearing a seatbelt. The car is travelling at $45 \, \text{km h}^{-1}$. What impulse must the car's airbag provide in order to stop the passenger's motion?

 b Explain why hitting an airbag will cause less injury than if a passenger hits the dashboard.

5 A wooden mallet is being used to hammer a tent peg into hard ground.

fig. 1.1.5

 a The head of the mallet is a cylinder of diameter 0.100 m and length 0.196 m. The density of the wood is $750 \, \text{kg m}^{-3}$. Show that the mass of the head is approximately 1.2 kg.

 b The head strikes the tent peg as shown at a speed of $4.20 \, \text{m s}^{-1}$ and rebounds at $0.58 \, \text{m s}^{-1}$. Calculate the magnitude of its momentum change in the collision.

 c The head is in contact with the peg for 0.012 s. Estimate the average force exerted on the peg by the head during this period.

 d Give a reason why your value for the force will only be approximate.

 e With reference to your calculations above, discuss whether a mallet with a rubber head of the same mass would be more or less effective for hammering in tent pegs.

Collisions Spec 74

Conservation of linear momentum

When objects collide, the laws of physics allow us to calculate where they will go after the collision. The **principle of conservation of linear momentum** can be used to predict the motion of objects after a collision. This tells us that if we calculate the momentum of each object before the collision, the sum total of these momenta (accounting for their direction) will be the same as the sum total afterwards (**fig. 1.1.6**).

This principle is dependent on the condition that no external force acts on the objects in question. An external force would provide an additional acceleration, so the motion of the objects would not be dependent on the collision alone. As we saw in the previous section, a resultant force will cause a change in momentum, so it makes sense that momentum is only conserved if no external force acts. Imagine if a juggler's upward moving ball collided with one coming down. Momentum conservation would suggest that the one falling down would bounce back with an upward velocity after the collision. Common sense tells us that all balls will still end up back on the ground. The external force of gravity means that the law of conservation of momentum alone cannot be used to predict the motions after the collision.

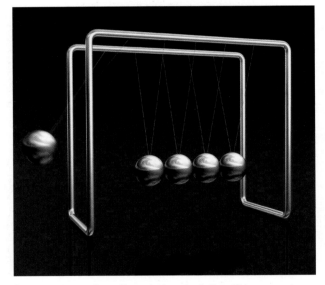

fig. 1.1.6 Newton's cradle: each time the balls collide, momentum is transferred from one to another, but the total momentum remains constant.

Explosions

If a stationary object explodes, then the total momentum of all the shrapnel parts added up (taking account of the direction of their movements) must be zero. The object had zero momentum at the start, so the principle of conservation of linear momentum tells us this must be the same total after the **explosion**. In physics terms, any such event is termed an explosion, although it may not very dramatic. For example, if the two trapeze artists in **fig 1.1.7** simply let go their hands and swing apart, they have zero total horizontal momentum before and will have equal and opposite horizontal momenta afterwards, which when added together will total zero again. Again, the external force of gravity will introduce vertical momentum.

fig. 1.1.7 If these trapeze artists let go of each other, they will 'explode' – they will fly apart with equal and opposite momenta.

Worked examples

fig. 1.1.8 Isaac Bruce of the St Louis Rams feels the full force of the conservation of linear momentum.

fig. 1.1.9 Caution: explosions may make you wet!

1 In an American football match, a stationary player is tackled by a defender who dives through the air at $4.0\,\text{m s}^{-1}$ and, in mid-air, grabs the quarterback (**fig. 1.1.8**). Both players then fly backwards together. Ignoring any friction effects, calculate how fast the players fly back if the tackler has a mass of 140 kg and the first player has a mass of 95 kg.

Before

quarterback stationary so zero momentum

$p_{\text{tackler}} = mv = 140 \times 4.0 = 560\,\text{kg m s}^{-1}$

momentum after = momentum before = $560\,\text{kg m s}^{-1}$

After

$p_{\text{both}} = m_{\text{both}} \times v_{\text{both}}$

$v_{\text{both}} = \dfrac{p_{\text{both}}}{m_{\text{both}}} = \dfrac{560}{(140 + 95)} = \dfrac{560}{235}$

$v_{\text{both}} = 2.4\,\text{m s}^{-1}$

2 A boy tries to step out of a boat onto the jetty, forgetting the principle of conservation of momentum.

If the boy has a mass of 55 kg and steps forward at a speed of $1.5\,\text{m s}^{-1}$, what will happen to the boat, which has a mass of 66 kg? (Ignore friction effects.)

This situation is an explosion, so:

total momentum before = total momentum after
= 0

Therefore:

$p_{\text{boat}} = -p_{\text{boy}}$

This means that when the two are added together, the total momentum is still zero.

$p_{\text{boat}} = -(55 \times 1.5) = -82.5\,\text{kg m s}^{-1}$

$m_{\text{boat}} \times v_{\text{boat}} = -82.5\,\text{kg m s}^{-1}$

$v_{\text{boat}} = \dfrac{-82.5}{m_{\text{boat}}} = \dfrac{-82.5}{66}$

$v_{\text{boat}} = -1.25\,\text{m s}^{-1}$

So the boat moves at $1.25\,\text{m s}^{-1}$ in the opposite direction to the boy.

Conservation of linear momentum in two dimensions

So far we have only considered collisions where both objects are moving along the *same* straight line. When the objects are moving along *different* lines, we can resolve the velocity vectors into perpendicular directions and carry out the momenta sums for the component directions.

Worked example

A rocket is moving through empty space at $8\,\text{m}\,\text{s}^{-1}$. A meteoroid travelling at $15\,\text{m}\,\text{s}^{-1}$ comes from behind and at an angle of 45° to the line of movement of the rocket, crashes into the rocket and becomes embedded in it (**fig. 1.1.10**). The rocket has a mass of 350 kg and the meteoroid's mass is 20 kg. Calculate the velocity of the rocket and embedded meteoroid after the collision.

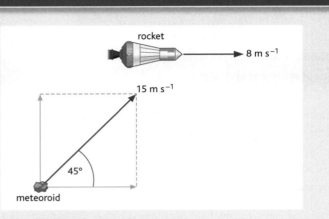

fig. 1.1.10 A collision in two dimensions.

Before

Parallel to rocket motion:

$v_{\text{meteoroid}} = 15\cos 45° = 10.6\,\text{m}\,\text{s}^{-1}$

$P_{\text{meteoroid}} = 20 \times 10.6 = 210\,\text{kg}\,\text{m}\,\text{s}^{-1}$

$P_{\text{rocket}} = 350 \times 8.0 = 2800\,\text{kg}\,\text{m}\,\text{s}^{-1}$

$P_{\text{parallel}} = 2800 + 210 = 3010\,\text{kg}\,\text{m}\,\text{s}^{-1}$

Perpendicular to rocket motion:

$v_{\text{meteoroid}} = 15\sin 45° = 10.6\,\text{m}\,\text{s}^{-1}$

$P_{\text{meteoroid}} = 20 \times 10.6 = 210\,\text{kg}\,\text{m}\,\text{s}^{-1}$

$P_{\text{rocket}} = 350 \times 0 = 0$

$P_{\text{perpendicular}} = 0 + 210 = 210\,\text{kg}\,\text{m}\,\text{s}^{-1}$

After

Vector sum of momenta (**fig. 1.1.11**):

$P_{\text{total}} = \sqrt{3010^2 + 210^2} = 3020\,\text{kg}\,\text{m}\,\text{s}^{-1}$

$$v_{\text{after}} = \frac{P_{\text{total}}}{(m_{\text{rocket}} + m_{\text{meteoroid}})}$$

$$= \frac{3020}{(350 + 20)}$$

$$= 8.2\,\text{m}\,\text{s}^{-1}$$

Angle of momentum (i.e. direction of velocity) after collision:

$$\theta = \tan^{-1}\left(\frac{210}{3010}\right) = 4.0°$$

So, the rocket with embedded meteoroid carries on at $8.2\,\text{m}\,\text{s}^{-1}$ at an angle of 4.0° to the original direction of motion.

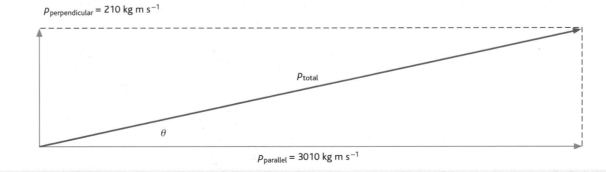

fig. 1.1.11 Vector sum of total momenta in two dimensions.

Investigating transfer of momentum

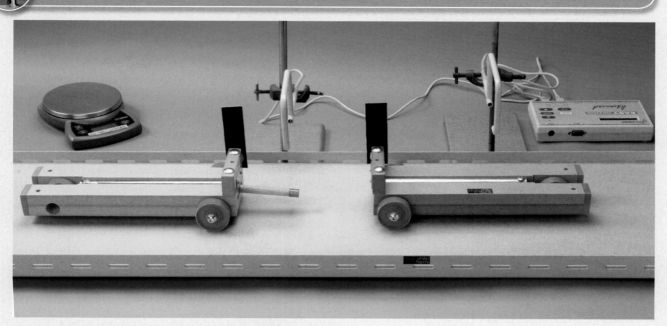

fig. 1.1.12 Verifying the principle of conservation of linear momentum.

You can investigate the transfer of momentum in collisions in the laboratory (**fig. 1.1.12**). By recording the movement of one trolley crashing into another, you can find the momentum of each one before and after the collision. Summing the total momenta before and after the collision will allow you to verify the principle of conservation of linear momentum. Try different types of collision, and trolleys with different masses. You could also try an explosion, in which the trolleys spring apart from a stationary position (**fig. 1.1.13**).

In experiments, we often find that momentum is actually not conserved in the measurements we make. What might be the reasons for that?

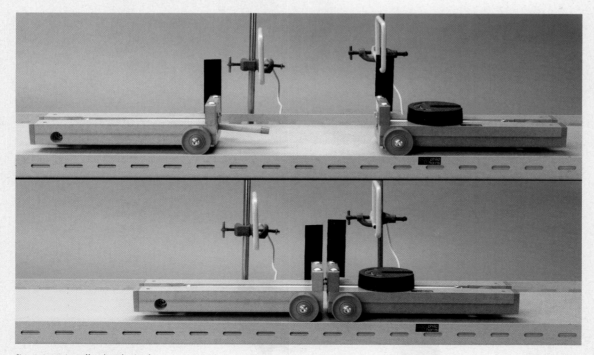

fig. 1.1.13 A trolley 'explosion'.

Newton's third law

Conservation of momentum is directly responsible for **Newton's third law of motion**. Remember, this law told us that for every force, there is an equal and opposite force. If we think of a force as a means to change momentum (as expressed by $F = \dfrac{dp}{dt}$), then a force changing momentum in one direction must be countered by an equal and opposite force to ensure that overall momentum is conserved. For example, if the gravitational pull of the Earth causes an apple to fall from a tree, the apple gains momentum towards the Earth (**fig. 1.1.14**). To conserve overall momentum, the Earth must gain an equal and opposite momentum. This is caused by an equal and opposite gravitational force on the Earth from the apple. The immense mass of the Earth means that its acceleration is imperceptible to us.

momentum increase down

momentum increase up

fig. 1.1.14 **Conservation of momentum causes equal and opposite forces, as Newton explained in his third law of motion.**

Questions

1   A movie stuntman with a mass of 90 kg stands on a stationary 1 kg skateboard. An actor shoots the stuntman with a 9 mm pistol. The 8-gram bullet leaves the pistol at $358 \, ms^{-1}$ and embeds completely in the stuntman's bulletproof vest. At what speed will the stuntman roll away?

2   A girl in a stationary boat on a still pond has lost her oars in the water. To get the boat moving again, she throws her rucksack horizontally out of the boat with a speed of $4 \, ms^{-1}$.

   Mass of boat = 60 kg; mass of girl = 40 kg; mass of rucksack = 5 kg.

   a   How fast will this action make the boat move?

   b   If she throws the rucksack by exerting a force on it for 0.2 s, how much force does she exert?

3   How can Newton's third law help to explain the problem suffered by the boy stepping out of the boat in Worked example 2 on page 15?

4   In a stunt for an action movie, the 100 kg actor jumps from a train which is crossing a river bridge. On the river below, the heroine is tied to a raft floating towards a waterfall at $3 \, ms^{-1}$. The raft and heroine have a total mass of 200 kg.

   a   If the hero times his jumps perfectly so as to land on the raft, and his velocity is $12 \, ms^{-1}$ at an angle of 80° to the river current, what will be the velocity of the raft immediately after he lands? Draw a vector diagram to show the momentum addition. (Ignore any vertical motion.)

   b   If the waterfall is 100 m downstream, and the hero landed when the raft was 16 m from the bank, would they plummet over the fall? (Assume the velocity remains constant after the hero has landed.)

5   a   Define linear momentum.

   The principle of conservation of linear momentum is a consequence of Newton's laws of motion. An examination candidate is asked to explain this, using a collision between two trolleys as an example. He gives the following answer, which is correct but incomplete. The lines of his answer are numbered on the left for reference.

   i   During the collision the trolleys push each other.

   ii   These forces are of the same size but in opposite directions.

   iii   As a result, the momentum of one trolley must increase at the same rate as the momentum of the other decreases.

   iv   Therefore the total momentum of the two trolleys must remain constant.

   b   In which line of his argument is the candidate using Newton's second law?

   c   In which line is he using Newton's third law?

   d   The student is making one important assumption which he has not stated. State this assumption. Explain at what point it comes into the argument.

   e   Describe how you could check experimentally that momentum is conserved in a collision between two trolleys.

Energy in collisions Spec 78, 76, 74

We have seen that linear momentum is always conserved in any collision between objects, but what about the kinetic energy?

fig. 1.1.15 Damaging a car uses energy, so what can we say about the conservation of kinetic energy in a car crash?

Elastic collisions

In a collision between one snooker ball and another, the first ball stops dead and the second then moves away from the collision. As both snooker balls have the same mass, the law of conservation of momentum tells us that the velocity of the second must be identical to the initial velocity of the first. This means that the kinetic energy of this system before and after the collision must be the same. A collision in which kinetic energy is conserved is called an **elastic collision**. In life, these are rare. Newton's cradle is an example that is nearly perfectly elastic (**fig.1.1.16**). A collision caused by non-contact forces, such as alpha particles being scattered by a nucleus (caused by electrostatic repulsion), is perfectly elastic.

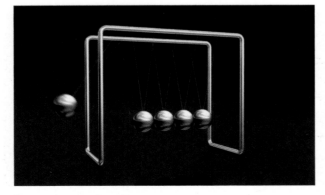

fig. 1.1.16 Newton's cradle

Inelastic collisions

In a crash between two dodgems at the fair (**fig. 1.1.17**), the total momentum after the collision must be identical to the total momentum before the collision. However, if we calculate the total kinetic before and after, we invariably find that the total momentum is reduced by the collision. Some of the kinetic energy is converted into other forms such as heat and sound. A collision in which kinetic energy is not conserved is called an **inelastic collision**.

Worked example

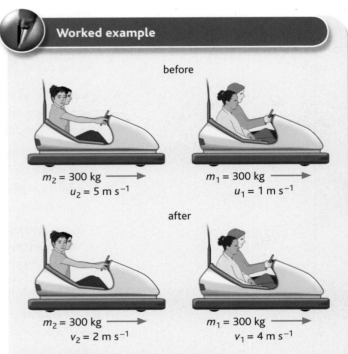

fig. 1.1.17 The fun of inelastic collisions.

If you calculate the total momentum before and after the collision shown in **fig. 1.1.17**, you will see that it is conserved. But what happens to the kinetic energy?

Before $E_{k1} = \frac{1}{2} m_1 u_1^2 = \frac{1}{2} \times 300 \times 1^2 = 150\,J$

$E_{k2} = \frac{1}{2} m_2 u_2^2 = \frac{1}{2} \times 300 \times 5^2 = 3750\,J$

total kinetic energy = 3900 J

After $E_{k1} = \frac{1}{2} m_1 v_1^2 = \frac{1}{2} \times 300 \times 4^2 = 2400\,J$

$E_{k2} = \frac{1}{2} m_2 v_2^2 = \frac{1}{2} \times 300 \times 2^2 = 600\,J$

total kinetic energy = 3000 J

Loss in kinetic energy = 900 J – an inelastic collision.

This 'lost' energy will have been transferred into heat and sound energy.

Particle collisions

We know that the formula for calculating kinetic energy is $E_k = \frac{1}{2}\,mv^2$ and that the formula for momentum is $p = mv$. By combining these relationships we can get an equation that gives kinetic energy in terms of the momentum and mass.

$$E_k = \frac{1}{2}\,mv^2 \qquad \text{and} \qquad v = \frac{p}{m}$$

$$\therefore E_k = \frac{1}{2}\,m\left(\frac{p}{m}\right)^2$$

$$E_k = \frac{1}{2}\,\frac{p^2}{m}$$

$$E_k = \frac{p^2}{2m}$$

This is a particularly useful formula when dealing with the kinetic energy of subatomic particles travelling at non-relativistic speeds (i.e. much slower than the speed of light).

The de Broglie wavelength

The formula $E_k = p^2/2m$ offers an alternative way of calculating the de Broglie wavelength (see **chapter 1.3.1**) for a particle if we know its energy and mass:

$$\lambda = \frac{h}{p}$$

$$\lambda = \frac{h}{\sqrt{2E_k m}}$$

Worked examples

What is the kinetic energy of an electron which has a momentum of $2.7 \times 10^{-24}\,\text{kg m s}^{-1}$?

$$E_k = \frac{p^2}{2m} = \frac{(2.7 \times 10^{-24})^2}{2 \times (9.11 \times 10^{-31})}$$

$$E_k = 4.0 \times 10^{-18}\,\text{J}$$

Investigating elastic and inelastic collisions

This practical is additional to those suggested in the specification.

fig. 1.1.18 Crash testing the elasticity of collisions.

You can investigate elastic and inelastic collisions in the laboratory. If you cause head-on collisions between trolleys, and record the mass and velocity of each trolley before and after the collisions, you can calculate the momentum at each stage. This should be conserved. You can also calculate the kinetic energy before and after the collisions. Real cars are designed to absorb as much kinetic energy as possible when they crash. This reduces the energy available to cause injury to the passengers. What is the best design on your experimental trolleys for a crumple zone to fulfil this idea of kinetic energy absorption (**fig. 1.1.18**)?

The electronvolt

The **electronvolt** is a unit used to measure a tiny amount of energy. It is the amount of energy gained by an electron when it is accelerated through a potential difference of 1 volt. $1\,\text{eV} = 1.6 \times 10^{-19}\,\text{J}$

Energies of subatomic particles are typically quoted in electronvolts, in MeV, or even in GeV.

Questions

1 A bowling ball travelling at $5\,\text{m s}^{-1}$ strikes the only standing pin straight on. The pin flies backward at $7\,\text{m s}^{-1}$. Calculate:

   a the velocity of the bowling ball after the collision

   b the loss of kinetic energy in this collision.
   (Mass of bowling ball = 6.35 kg; mass of pin = 1.5 kg.)

2 Calculate the kinetic energy of an alpha particle which has a momentum of $1.08 \times 10^{-19}\,\text{kg m s}^{-1}$

   a in joules   b in electronvolts

   c in MeV. (Mass of neutron = mass of proton = $1.67 \times 10^{-27}\,\text{kg}$)

3 Explain why the slingshot orbit of a satellite passing near a planet and then flying away at a different angle as a result of the effect of the planet's gravity would be an elastic collision.

Deep space collisions

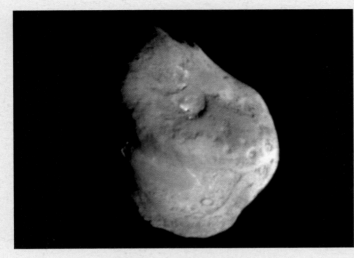

fig. 1.1.19 The comet Tempel 1 was hit by NASA's Deep Impact probe.

On 4 July 2005, NASA's Deep Impact mission succeeded in crashing a spacecraft into a comet called Tempel 1 (**fig. 1.1.19**). For that mission, the impactor spacecraft had a mass of 370 kg compared with the comet's mass of 7.2×10^{13} kg, so there would have been an insignificant change in the comet's trajectory. Deep Impact was purely intended to study the comet's composition. However, there is an asteroid named Apophis which has a small chance of colliding with Earth in 2035, 2036, or maybe 2037, and there have been some calls for a mission to crash a spacecraft into Apophis in order to deviate it out of harm's way. The mass of this asteroid is 2×10^{10} kg and it is travelling at 12.6 km s^{-1}. It has been claimed that a collision by a 4000 kg impactor craft travelling at 6 km s^{-1} could alter the path of this asteroid enough to ensure it would not hit Earth. If this impactor collided with Apophis at right angles, we can calculate the change in angle of the asteroid's velocity (**fig. 1.1.20**).

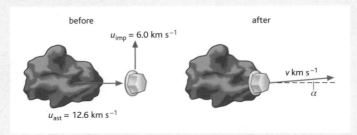

before   after

$u_{imp} = 6.0$ km s^{-1}

v km s^{-1}

α

$u_{ast} = 12.6$ km s^{-1}

fig. 1.1.20 Could we hit an asteroid hard enough to save Earth from Asteroid Impact Hazards?

Before collision

$$p_{ast} = m_{ast}u_{ast} = 2 \times 10^{10} \times 12.6 \times 10^3 = 2.52 \times 10^{14}\,\text{kg m s}^{-1}$$

$$p_{imp} = m_{imp}u_{imp} = 4 \times 10^3 \times 6 \times 10^3 = 2.4 \times 10^7\,\text{kg m s}^{-1}$$

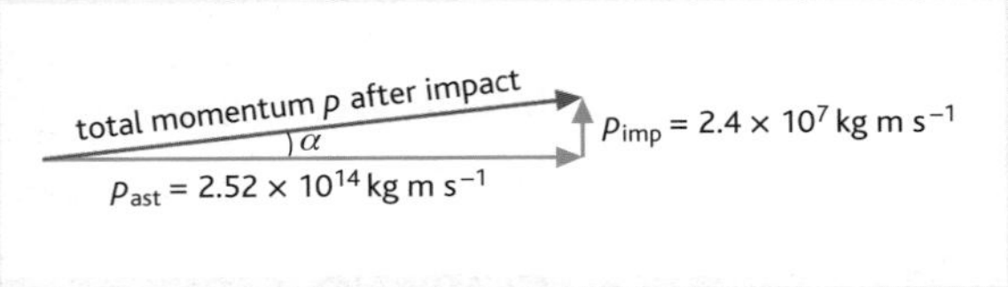

total momentum p after impact

α

$p_{imp} = 2.4 \times 10^7$ kg m s^{-1}

$p_{ast} = 2.52 \times 10^{14}$ kg m s^{-1}

fig. 1.1.21 The vector sum of momentum components after the asteroid impact.

The momentum of the combined object after the impactor embeds in the asteroid is the vector sum of the two initial momenta, which are at right angles to each other (**fig. 1.1.21**).

After collision

$$p_{after} = \sqrt{p_{ast}^2 + p_{imp}^2}$$
$$= \sqrt{(2.52 \times 10^{14})^2 + (2.4 \times 10^7)^2}$$
$$= 2.52 \times 10^{14}\,\text{kg m s}^{-1}$$

$$\therefore v_{after} = \frac{p_{after}}{m_{total}}$$
$$= \frac{2.52 \times 10^{14}}{(2 \times 10^{10} + 4 \times 10^3)}$$
$$= 12.6\,\text{km s}^{-1} \qquad \text{(3 significant figures)}$$

There is no significant change in the magnitude of the asteroid's velocity – what about its direction?

Angle of momentum after collision:

$$\alpha = \tan^{-1}\left(\frac{2.4 \times 10^7}{2.52 \times 10^{14}}\right)$$
$$= 5.46 \times 10^{-6\circ}$$

Although five and a half microdegrees sounds like an insignificantly small angle, this would represent a change in position of nearly 30 km as Apophis crosses the Earth's orbit from one side of the Sun to the other. This might be just enough to avert a collision with us equivalent to 4 megatonnes of TNT!

Particle collisions

In experiments to determine the nature of fundamental particles, physicists will detect the movements of many unknown particles. The Large Hadron Collider experiment at CERN, deep underground near Geneva in Switzerland, can produce 600 million particle interactions in its detector every second. By colliding the particles produced in the experiment with known particles in the detector, and applying the principle of the conservation of momentum, the masses of these particles can be calculated. This information can then be used to help towards their identification.

Worked example

Suppose the detector registers an elastic collision with one of its neutrons, in which the neutron's velocity is changed from stationary to $3.4 \times 10^6 \, \text{m s}^{-1}$ in a head-on collision with an unknown particle. If the unknown particle was initially moving

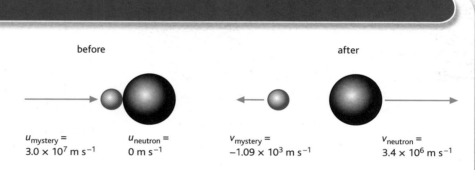

fig. 1.1.22 **Discovering mystery particles from their momentum and collisions.**

at 10% of the speed of light, and leaves the collision in the opposite direction at $1.09 \times 10^3 \, \text{m s}^{-1}$ (**fig. 1.1.22**), what is the mass of the mystery particle?

Before

$$p_{\text{mystery}} = m_{\text{mystery}} \times 3.0 \times 10^7$$

$$= p_{\text{total}} \quad (p_{\text{n}} = \text{zero})$$

After

$$p_{\text{total after}} = (m_{\text{mystery}} \times v_{\text{mystery}}) + (m_{\text{n}} \times v_{\text{n}})$$

$$= (m_{\text{mystery}} \times -1.09 \times 10^3) + (1.67 \times 10^{-27} \times 3.4 \times 10^6)$$

$$= p_{\text{total before}} = m_{\text{mystery}} \times 3.0 \times 10^7$$

Thus:

$$(m_{\text{mystery}} \times -1.09 \times 10^3) + (1.67 \times 10^{-27} \times 3.4 \times 10^6) = m_{\text{mystery}} \times 3.0 \times 10^7$$

$$(1.67 \times 10^{-27} \times 3.4 \times 10^6) = (m_{\text{mystery}} \times 3.0 \times 10^7) - (m_{\text{mystery}} \times -1.09 \times 10^3)$$

$$5.678 \times 10^{-21} = m_{\text{mystery}} \times 30\,001\,090$$

So:

$$m_{\text{mystery}} = \frac{5.678 \times 10^{-21}}{30\,001\,090}$$

$$= 1.89 \times 10^{-28} \, \text{kg}$$

This is approximately 207 times the mass of an electron. This mass identifies the particle as a muon.

Questions

1   An alpha particle moving at 3% of the speed of light collides elastically with a stationary aluminium nucleus (atomic number 13 and mass number 27). If the alpha particle bounces backwards at 0.1% of the speed of light, what is the velocity of the aluminium nucleus after the collision?

2   In a pool shot, the cue ball of mass 0.17 kg travels at $6 \, \text{m s}^{-1}$ and hits the stationary black ball in the middle of the table. The black ball, also of mass 0.17 kg, travels away at 45° with a speed of $4.24 \, \text{m s}^{-1}$, ending up in the corner pocket. By resolving the components of the black ball's momentum, find out what happens to the cue ball.

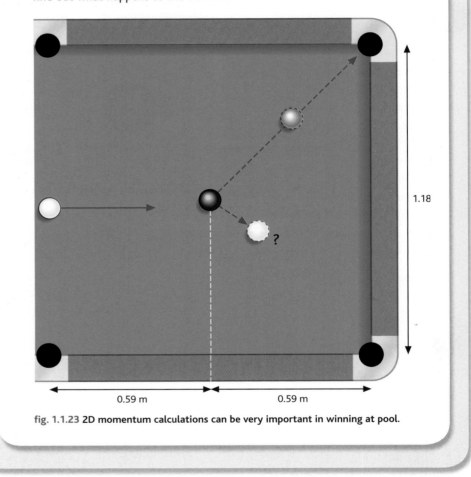

1.18

0.59 m   0.59 m

fig. 1.1.23 **2D momentum calculations can be very important in winning at pool.**

1.2 Circular motion Spec 79, 80

Angular displacement

Going round in circles

In geometry you will have learned how to measure angles in degrees. Angles are used extensively in geography to locate places according to their latitude and longitude, and as bearings to describe the path to be taken from starting point to destination. Each degree is subdivided into 60 'minutes' and each of those minutes into 60 'seconds'.

When we are measuring rotation, we often use an alternative measure of angle called the **radian**. This is defined by the nature of the circle itself. Imagine an object moving around the circumference of a circle. The angle through which the object moves, measured in radians, is defined as the distance it has travelled along the circumference divided by its distance from the centre of the circle (the radius). For a circle of radius one metre, the distance an object travels around the circumference (also in metres) would be the same as the angle swept out in radians:

$$\text{angle (in radians)} = \frac{\text{length of arc}}{\text{radius of arc}}$$

$$\theta = \frac{s}{r}$$

Thus for movement around a complete circle, for which the circumference is equal to $2\pi r$, the angle swept out would be:

$$\theta = \frac{2\pi r}{r}$$

$$= 2\pi \text{ radians}$$

fig. 1.2.1 Measuring angles in degrees.

This means that an angle of 1 radian (rad) corresponds to movement of a distance around the circle equal to the radius – just over ⅙ of the distance around the circumference.

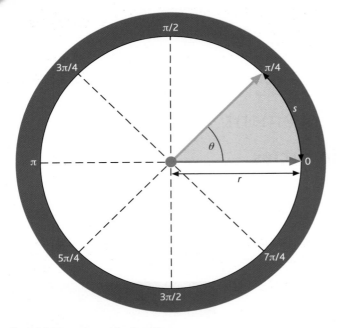

fig. 1.2.2 Measuring angles in radians.

Angular displacement is the vector measurement of the angle through which something has turned. The standard convention is that anticlockwise rotation is a positive number and clockwise rotation is a negative number.

Angular velocity

An object moving in a circle sweeps out a certain angle in a certain time, depending upon how fast it is moving. The rate at which the angular displacement changes is called the angular velocity, ω. So, (constant) angular velocity is defined mathematically by:

$$\omega = \frac{\theta}{t}$$

If the object completes a full circle (2π radians) in a time period T, then the angular velocity is given by:

$$\omega = \frac{\theta}{t}$$

$$\omega = \frac{2\pi}{T}$$

The frequency of rotation is the reciprocal of the time period:

$$f = \frac{1}{T}$$

So:

$$\omega = 2\pi f$$

Military angles

The British Army uses a system for angle measurement in which a complete circle is divided into 6400 'mils'. This is an abbreviation for milliradian. The numbers are rounded for ease of use, as strictly speaking there should be 6283 milliradians in a complete circle. The idea is that at a distance of 1 kilometre, an angle of 1 mil would represent a sideways distance of 1 metre. Thus for aiming artillery fire, a horizontal adjustment of 1 mil in angle of fire should move the point of impact 1 metre sideways for every kilometre distance away.

fig. 1.2.3 Measuring angles in mils.

Angle in radians	0	π/4	π/2	3π/4	π	5π/4	3π/2	7π/4	2π
Angle in degrees	0	45	90	135	180	225	270	315	360

table 1.2.1 Angles measured in degrees and radians.

Worked example

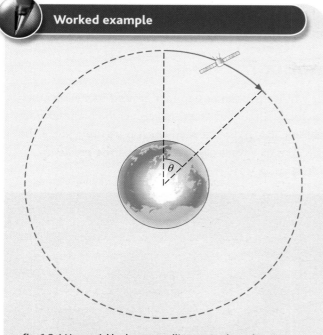

fig. 1.2.4 How quickly does a satellite rotate through a certain angle?

Figure 1.2.4 shows a geostationary satellite orbiting the Earth. What is its angular velocity?

To find its angular velocity, remember that the satellite completes an orbit at the same rate as the Earth revolves, so it completes one full revolution every 24 hours.

$$\omega = \frac{2\pi}{T}$$

$$\omega = \frac{2\pi}{(24 \times 60 \times 60)}$$

$$= \frac{2\pi}{86\,400}$$

$$= 7.27 \times 10^{-5}\,\text{rad}\,\text{s}^{-1}$$

Rather than thinking about the angular movement, let's consider the actual velocity through space of the moving object (sometimes called the 'instantaneous velocity'). We know that $v = \frac{s}{t}$ and from the definition of the angle in radians (see **fig. 1.2.2**) $\theta = \frac{s}{r}$, so that $s = r\theta$. Thus:

$$v = \frac{r\theta}{t}$$

$$v = r\omega$$

Worked example

If the radius of the Earth is 6400 km and the satellite in **fig. 1.2.4** is in orbit 35 600 km above the surface, what is the velocity of the satellite?

From before:

$$\omega = 7.27 \times 10^{-5}\,\text{rad}\,\text{s}^{-1}$$

$$v = r\omega = (6400 + 35\,600) \times 10^3 \times 7.27 \times 10^{-5}$$

$$v = 3050\,\text{m}\,\text{s}^{-1}$$

Questions

1   Convert:

    a 4π radians into degrees

    b   36° into radians.

2   Vinyl records could be played at one of three speeds. Calculate the angular velocity of each.

    a   33 revolutions per minute

    b   45 rpm

    c   78 rpm

3   What is the angular velocity of an athletics hammer if the athlete spins at a rate of three revolutions per second?

4   A man standing on the equator will be moving due to the rotation of the Earth. What is his angular velocity? What is his instantaneous velocity?

5   There are 6283 milliradians in a complete circle. The army's rounding of this to 6400 mils causes an error.

    a   How far sideways from the target could this rounding cause an artillery shell to be when aimed at a target 20 km away?

    b   Why does the actual bearing to the target not affect your answer to part **a**?

Centripetal force Spec 81, 82

Why circular motion?

When a hammer thrower whirls an athletics hammer around in a circle, the hammer has an angular velocity. But when the thrower lets the hammer go, it will fly off along a straight line in the direction in which it was moving at the instant of release. This direction is always along the edge of the circle (a tangent) at the point at which it was released.

fig. 1.2.5 The instantaneous velocity of an object moving in a circle is tangential to the circle. When there is no resultant force, the velocity will be constant, so the object moves in a straight line.

Measuring centripetal force

You can get a feeling for what affects the size of the centripetal force by testing it using a rubber bung on a string. You will need to pull harder on the string if:

- you have a more massive bung
- you use a shorter string
- you make it go faster.

Can you sense which of the three factors is the most important?

As the hammer is whirled at a constant speed, the magnitude of the velocity is always the same. However, as you can see in **fig 1.2.5**, the direction of the velocity is constantly changing. This means that the vector of velocity is constantly changing, and a change in velocity is an acceleration. Newton's first law tells us that acceleration will only happen if there is a resultant force. The hammer is constantly being pulled towards the centre of the circle. In this example, the force providing this pull is the tension in the string. For any object moving in a circle, there must be a force to cause this acceleration toward the centre of the circle – this is called the **centripetal force**. The centripetal force will be an ordinary force that we have met before, like gravity keeping a satellite in orbit, or tension in the athletics hammer wire. If a force causes something to move in a circle, we identify it as the centripetal force for that circling object. Conversely, whenever you see an object moving in a circular motion, if you examine the situation, there will be an everyday force causing it to move in a circle.

The resultant centripetal force needed will be larger if:

- the rotating object has more mass
- the object rotates faster
- the object is closer to the centre of the circle.

Centripetal force and acceleration

fig. 1.2.6 Astronauts are subject to extreme acceleration forces. These forces are simulated in training – or by James Bond in the film *Moonraker* – by the centripetal force in a giant centrifuge.

The mathematical formula for the centripetal force on an object moving in a circle is:

$$\text{centripetal force} = \frac{\text{mass} \times (\text{velocity})^2}{\text{radius}}$$

$$F = \frac{mv^2}{r}$$

> ### Worked example
>
> Estimate the centripetal force on the astronaut in the astronaut training centrifuge (see **fig 1.2.6**) if the capsule rotates once every two seconds.
>
> Estimate of radius of revolution: $r = 6\,\text{m}$
>
> Estimate of astronaut's mass: $m = 80\,\text{kg}$
>
> Velocity: $v = \dfrac{s}{t} = \dfrac{2 \times \pi \times 6}{2} = 18.8\,\text{ms}^{-1}$
>
> Centripetal force: $F = \dfrac{mv^2}{r} = \dfrac{80 \times (18.8)^2}{6} = 4710\,\text{N}$
>
> This is about six times the astronaut's weight.

Using the relationship $v = r\omega$, we can derive an alternative equation for centripetal force in terms of angular velocity:

$$F = \frac{mv^2}{r} = \frac{m(r\omega)^2}{r}$$

$$F = mr\omega^2$$

Since Newton's second law states that the resultant force is related to the acceleration it causes by the equation $F = ma$, we can find the centripetal acceleration very easily:

$$F = ma = \frac{mv^2}{r}$$

$$a = \frac{v^2}{r}$$

Again using $v = r\omega$, the centripetal acceleration can be expressed in terms of the angular velocity as:

$$a = r\omega^2$$

> ### Worked example
>
> If the operator of the centrifuge were to increase its rate of rotation to once every second, what would the centripetal force and acceleration on the astronaut now be?
>
> Angular velocity: $\omega = 2\pi f = 6.28\,\text{rad s}^{-1}$
>
> Centripetal force: $F = mr\omega^2 = 80 \times 6 \times (6.28)^2$
> $= 18\,900\,\text{N}$
>
> Centripetal acceleration: $a = r\omega^2 = 6 \times (6.28)^2$
> $= 237\,\text{ms}^{-2}$
>
> This is about 24 times the acceleration due to gravity, and would most likely be fatal if maintained for more than a few seconds.

Verifying the centripetal force equation

fig. 1.2.7 Verifying the centripetal force equation.

You can investigate the centripetal force equation by spinning a rubber bung on a string in a circle (**fig. 1.2.7**). The tension in the string, which is the centripetal force, will be provided by the hanging masses and thus will be known. Spin the rubber bung around in a circle at a speed that keeps the paperclip marker in a constant position. The paperclip marker allows you to keep a fixed length of string (radius), which you can measure. You will also need to measure the mass of the rubber bung. Your partner can time ten revolutions in order to give you the angular velocity. Take angular velocity measurements for different forces (different numbers of hanging masses).

$$F = mr\omega^2$$
$$\therefore \omega^2 = \frac{F}{mr}$$

A graph of ω^2 plotted against F should give a straight line of best fit. The gradient of this line will be $\frac{1}{mr}$.

Questions

1   A roller coaster has a complete (circular) loop with a radius of 20 m. A 65 kg girl rides the roller coaster and the car travels once round the loop in 4.5 seconds. What centripetal force does the girl experience?

2   A man of mass 75 kg standing on the equator is moving because of the rotation of the Earth.

   a   What centripetal force is required to keep him moving in this circle?
   b   How does this compare with his weight?
   c   How would the reaction force with the ground be different if he went to the South Pole? (Assume the Earth is a perfect sphere.)

Swings and roundabouts

fig. 1.2.8 Centripetal force can be a fun thing!

The swing carousel is a fairground ride which is common in theme parks and fairs around the world (**fig. 1.2.8**). As there is little rider protection in the chair, engineering design is paramount in creating a safe ride. The points that would need to be considered by a manufacturer of such a ride include:

- the speed of rotation must be low enough to avoid nausea
- the internal friction must be low enough for the motor to drive the ride
- the seat chains must be strong enough for the maximum possible tension generated.

Table 1.2.2 gives some example technical data for a swing carousel.

Specification parameter	Whirler model value
Seats/chairs	64
Hourly capacity	960
Total weight	195 kN
Volume	120 m³
Shaft bearing friction	<3500 N
Total height	12.1 m
Rotation speed	12 rpm anticlockwise
Seat chain length	5 m
Maximum chain angle	45°
Top radius	7 m
Base radius	10 m

table 1.2.2 Data for the 'Whirler' swing carousel.

Angular velocity

The physiology behind motion sickness involves three different systems within the body, and their interaction under different conditions of movement is not well understood. Quick head movements by jet fighter pilots can induce nausea; similar symptoms can be experienced on fairground rides which involve high centripetal accelerations. As many as 50% of astronauts suffer motion sickness. In the 1960s, NASA undertook experiments on subjects in a slowly rotating room, which produced various results depending on the exact conditions. The results suggested that a centripetal acceleration of more than $12\,\mathrm{m\,s^{-2}}$ maintained for more than 10 minutes could induce nausea in many subjects.

From the technical specifications given in **table 1.2.2**, the Whirler swing carousel rotates at '12 rpm anticlockwise' – 12 complete circles every minute. This equates to 2π radians every 5 seconds, or:

$$\omega = \frac{12 \times 2\pi}{60} = 1.26\,\mathrm{rad\,s^{-1}}$$

Thus the centripetal acceleration is:

$$a = \frac{v^2}{r}$$

which can be expressed in terms of the angular velocity as:

$$a = r\omega^2$$

The actual radius of rotation of a rider is shown in **fig. 1.2.9** as R and is the sum of the top radius and the horizontal distance that the chair swings outward (Here the actual radius R will be 10.5 m):

$$a = R\omega^2 = 10.5 \times (1.26)^2 = 17\,\mathrm{m\,s^{-2}}$$

Based on the NASA research, the operators of the Whirler will need to ensure that each ride lasts less than ten minutes (probably significantly less) in order that they do not upset a considerable proportion of their customers. With an hourly capacity of 960 riders and 64 seats, there must be 15 rides per hour, which means that no ride will last more than four minutes, significantly less than ten minutes.

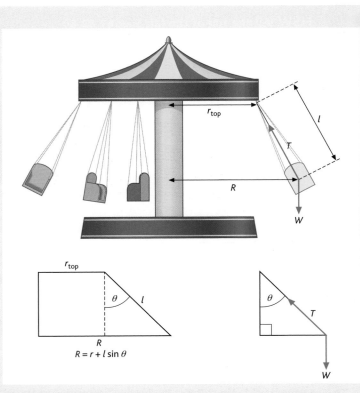

fig. 1.2.9 Resolving force vectors and length geometry for a swing carousel.

Motor power

For an object moving at a uniform speed, v, against a friction force, F, the driving power required, P, is given by:

$$P = Fv$$

Applying this to the swing carousel, with $\omega = 1.26\,\mathrm{rad\,s^{-1}}$ and $v = r\omega$, we can calculate the instantaneous velocity that is being maintained. However, as the various parts of the carousel have different radii, the speed varies from zero up to a maximum at the furthest radius (shown by R in **fig. 1.2.9**). To find the average instantaneous velocity we will need to use the average radius, $\dfrac{R + r_{\text{top}}}{2}$.

$$v = r\omega = \frac{R + r_{\text{top}}}{2} \times \omega = \frac{17.5 \times 1.26}{2} = 11.0\,\mathrm{m\,s^{-1}}$$

Thus, the driving motor power needed to overcome a maximum frictional force of 3500 N (central shaft friction as quoted by the manufacturers; see **table 1.2.2**) will be:

$$P = Fv = 3500 \times 11.0 = 38.5\,\mathrm{kW}$$

Chain strength

Common engineering practice is to make the breaking tension in any component 2.5 times the maximum possible force it is required to withstand. To work out the maximum possible tension in one of the seat chains, the manufacturers work on the expectation that a person with a mass greater than 120 kg will be unable to fit into the hanging seat and this will therefore be the maximum mass of any rider. When the ride is stationary, the four chains supporting any given seat only need to support the rider's weight. As the ride spins, the seat swings out at an angle. The tension in the chain will then be a vector sum of a vertical component to balance the weight, T_w, and a horizontal component to provide the centripetal force needed for continuous circular motion, T_c.

$$\text{centripetal force} = \frac{\text{mass} \times (\text{velocity})^2}{\text{radius}}$$

$$F = \frac{mv^2}{r}$$

From **fig. 1.2.9**, the radius of revolution:

$$R = 10.5 \, \text{m}$$

Seat velocity:

$$v = R\omega = 10.5 \times 1.26 = 13.2 \, \text{m s}^{-1}$$

Maximum rider weight:

$$m = 120 \, \text{kg} \qquad T_w = 120 \times 9.81 = 1180 \, \text{N}$$

Centripetal force:

$$T_c = \frac{mv^2}{r} = \frac{120 \times (13.2)^2}{10.5} = 1991 \, \text{N}$$

The ride's maximum speed of rotation causes a maximum swing angle of 45°.

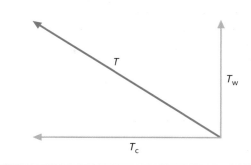

fig. 1.2.10 **Vector sum of tension components.**

Thus the overall tension is the vector sum of T_w, which balances the weight of the rider, and T_c, which acts to provide the centripetal force (**fig. 1.2.10**):

$$T = \sqrt{(1180)^2 + (1991)^2} = 2314 \, \text{N}$$

This force is split across four chains, so each chain can be expected not to suffer a tension exceeding 580 N. Using the safety standard of 2.5 times the maximum expected tension, the chains must be constructed such that they are each able to withstand a tension of 1450 N.

Questions

1 In times gone by, safety regulations were much less stringent than they are today, as evidenced by the old photograph in **fig. 1.2.11**.

   a Estimate the combined mass of the car, driver and lion. Hence calculate their weight.

   b Estimate the radius of the circular wall they are driving around.

   c To avoid slipping down the wall, the friction force between the tyres and the wall must exceed the weight. The centripetal force provided by the wall pushing against the tyres will affect the friction according to the equation:

   $$F_{\text{friction}} = 0.6 F_{\text{centripetal}}$$

Using your estimates from **a** and **b**, work out how fast they must drive in order to avoid slipping down the wall.

fig. 1.2.11 **The Wall of Death.**

Examzone: Topic 1 Further mechanics

1 State Newton's second law of motion. **(2)**

A student says, incorrectly, "Momentum is conserved completely in elastic collisions, but not in inelastic collisions." Rewrite this sentence to make a correct statement about momentum conservation. **(1)**

In what circumstance is kinetic energy conserved in a collision? **(1)**

(Total 4 marks)

2 Describe an experiment you would perform to provide a *single* illustration of the principle of conservation of linear momentum.

i) Sketch and label a diagram of the apparatus you would use. **(2)**

ii) List the physical quantities you would measure and state how you would measure them. **(4)**

iii) How would you use this information to provide a single illustration of the law? **(2)**

(Total 8 marks)

3 Explain why a body moving at constant speed in a circular path needs a resultant force acting on it. **(2)**

The diagram shows a student at the equator standing on a set of weighing scales, and a free-body force diagram for the student.

Identify the bodies applying forces A and B. **(2)**

Because of the Earth's daily rotation the student is performing circular motion about the Earth's axis. Calculate the angular speed of the student. **(2)**

The radius of the Earth is 6400 km. The student's mass is 55 kg. Calculate the resultant force on the student. **(3)**

Force A is 539 N. Calculate the value of force B. State, with a reason, the force indicated by the weighing scales. **(3)**

(Total 12 marks)

4 A car travelling at $30\,\mathrm{m\,s^{-1}}$ collides with a wall. The driver, wearing a seatbelt, is brought to rest in 0.070 s.

The driver has a mass of 50 kg. Calculate the momentum of the driver before the crash. **(2)**

Calculate the average resultant force exerted on the driver during impact. **(3)**

Explain why the resultant force is not the same as the force exerted on the driver by the seatbelt. **(1)**

(Total 6 marks)

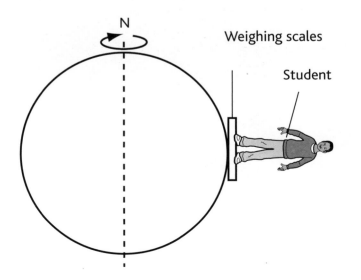

N

Weighing scales

Student

A

B

5

Palaeontologists are able to deduce much about the behaviour of dinosaurs from the study of fossilised footprints.

The tracks below show the path of a *Tyrannosaurus rex* as it attacks a stationary *Triceratops*.

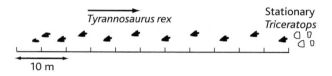

The time between footprints is 0.62 s. Show that the maximum speed of the *Tyrannosaurus rex* is about 10 m s^{-1}. (2)

Tyrannosaurus rex is believed to have attacked its prey by charging and locking its jaws on the prey. *Tyrannosaurus rex* would be at its maximum speed when it hit the stationary prey.

This *Tyrannosaurus rex* has a mass of 7000 kg. Calculate its momentum just before it hits the *Triceratops*. (2)

Triceratops has a mass of 5000 kg. Calculate their combined speed immediately after the collision. (3)

The skull of *Tyrannosaurus rex* is heavily reinforced to withstand the force produced in such a collision.

Calculate the force exerted on the *Tyrannosaurus rex* if the time taken to reach their combined speed after the collision is 0.30 s. (3)

(Total 10 marks)

6 A neutron of mass 1.7×10^{-27} kg travelling at 2.96×10^7 m s^{-1} collides with a stationary nucleus of nitrogen of mass 23.3×10^{-27} kg. Calculate the magnitude of the momentum of the neutron before it collides with the nucleus of nitrogen. (2)

Given that the neutron 'sticks' to the original nucleus after the collision, calculate the speed of the new heavier nucleus of nitrogen. (3)

An elastic collision is one where kinetic energy is conserved. Make suitable calculations to determine whether this collision is elastic. (3)

(Total 8 marks)

Topic 2 Electric and magnetic fields

This rather mathematical topic examines field theory, introducing fields as a way of explaining the behaviour of charged particles influenced by electricity and magnetism. A study of electric fields themselves, capacitance, and the interactions between electric and magnetic fields leads on to the many and varied applications of the models developed.

What are the theories?

This is a necessarily mathematical topic, and you will meet many equations.

The description and calculation of uniform and radial electric fields leads to calculation of the forces between electrically charged particles using Coulomb's law.

Capacitors make use of electric fields to store charge, and the way they behave in electric circuits is investigated. The topic includes a mathematical description of the charge and energy stored, along with the growth and decay of the current that is charging or discharging the capacitor.

When electrically charged particles travel through magnetic fields, they experience a force and their motion is affected. It is this phenomenon that causes electric motors to function, and allows the generation of electricity in power stations. This topic looks at the theory of these interactions and moves on to calculations of these effects.

What is the evidence?

In many areas, these are the theories which explain how our modern electrically driven world can operate. The fact that electricity can be generated and used to drive motors as we wish provides evidence for the accuracy of the theories. Similarly, capacitor circuits can be used to test experimentally that the electric field theories underlying them are correct. You may have a chance to perform some of these experiments yourself.

Some of the experiments which back up these theories feature among the archetypal great physics experiments from history, performed by some of the most famous physicists. In particular, Michael Faraday undertook some of the key pioneering work in these fields.

What are the implications?

Since the Industrial Revolution, our society has depended on much of this physics. We expect to have electricity available at all times, made possible by the discovery of Faraday's law.

Additionally, the cutting edge of physics – the particle accelerator – could only be conceived in the light of the electromagnetic forces you will find out about in this topic.

The map opposite shows you the knowledge and skills you need to have by the end of this topic, and how they are linked together. The numbers refer to the sections in the Edexcel specification.

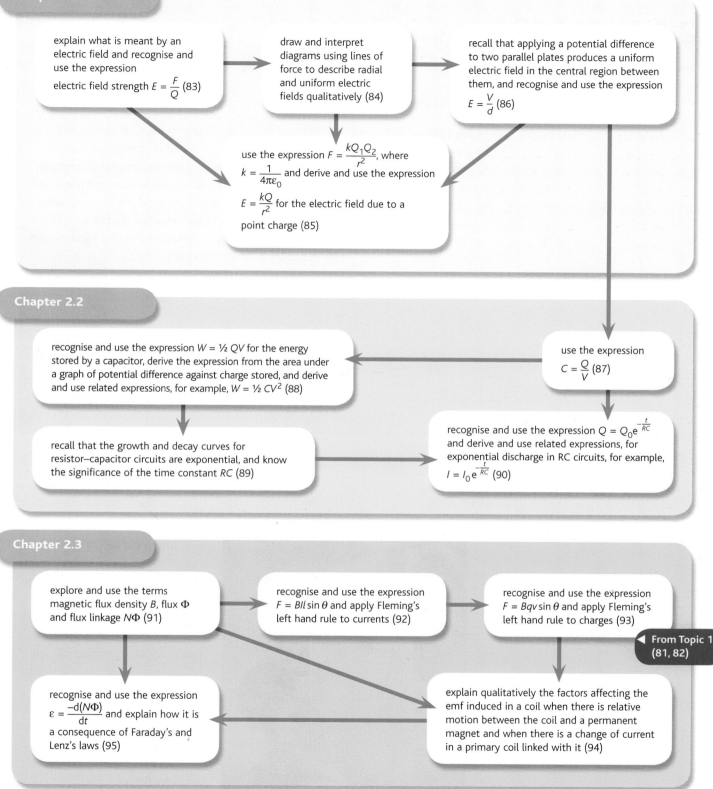

Chapter 2.1

explain what is meant by an electric field and recognise and use the expression

electric field strength $E = \frac{F}{Q}$ (83)

draw and interpret diagrams using lines of force to describe radial and uniform electric fields qualitatively (84)

recall that applying a potential difference to two parallel plates produces a uniform electric field in the central region between them, and recognise and use the expression

$E = \frac{V}{d}$ (86)

use the expression $F = \frac{kQ_1Q_2}{r^2}$, where $k = \frac{1}{4\pi\varepsilon_0}$ and derive and use the expression

$E = \frac{kQ}{r^2}$ for the electric field due to a point charge (85)

Chapter 2.2

recognise and use the expression $W = \frac{1}{2}QV$ for the energy stored by a capacitor, derive the expression from the area under a graph of potential difference against charge stored, and derive and use related expressions, for example, $W = \frac{1}{2}CV^2$ (88)

use the expression

$C = \frac{Q}{V}$ (87)

recall that the growth and decay curves for resistor–capacitor circuits are exponential, and know the significance of the time constant RC (89)

recognise and use the expression $Q = Q_0 e^{-\frac{t}{RC}}$ and derive and use related expressions, for exponential discharge in RC circuits, for example, $I = I_0 e^{-\frac{t}{RC}}$ (90)

Chapter 2.3

explore and use the terms magnetic flux density B, flux Φ and flux linkage $N\Phi$ (91)

recognise and use the expression $F = BIl\sin\theta$ and apply Fleming's left hand rule to currents (92)

recognise and use the expression $F = Bqv\sin\theta$ and apply Fleming's left hand rule to charges (93)

◄ From Topic 1 (81, 82)

recognise and use the expression $\varepsilon = \frac{-d(N\Phi)}{dt}$ and explain how it is a consequence of Faraday's and Lenz's laws (95)

explain qualitatively the factors affecting the emf induced in a coil when there is relative motion between the coil and a permanent magnet and when there is a change of current in a primary coil linked with it (94)

2.1 Electric fields Spec 83, 84, 86

Pushing charges

Many machines function through the use of fast-moving charged particles. For example, in a hospital X-ray machine high-speed electrons are crashed into a metal target to produce the X-rays. So how do we cause the electrons to move at high speed? A region of space which will cause charged particles to accelerate is said to have an **electric field**.

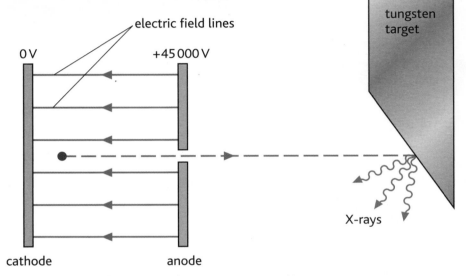

fig. 2.1.1 **An electric field accelerates electrons in an X-ray machine.**

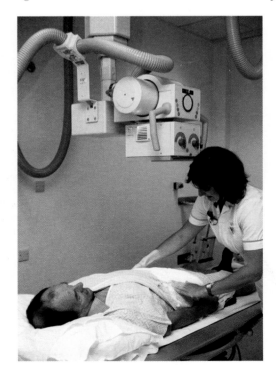

A charged particle will experience a force when it is in an electric field. To visualise the forces caused by the field, we draw **electric field lines** which show the direction in which a positively charged particle will be pushed by the force the field produces. Like magnetic field patterns – indeed like all field patterns – the closer the lines are together, the stronger the field is. And a stronger field causes stronger forces.

The force that a charged particle will feel is the **electric field strength** (E) multiplied by the amount of charge on the particle in coulombs (Q), as given by the equation:

$$F = EQ$$

From this force equation, we can also find how quickly a charge would accelerate. Newton's second law states that $F = ma$, so we can equate the two equations for force:

$$F = EQ = ma$$

So:

$$a = \frac{EQ}{m}$$

Worked example

a What force will an electron feel when it is in the electric field of an X-ray machine which has a strength of $4.5 \times 10^5\,\text{Vm}^{-1}$?

$$F = EQ$$

$$= 4.5 \times 10^5 \times -1.6 \times 10^{-19}$$

$$= -7.2 \times 10^{-14}\,\text{N}$$

The minus sign indicates that the electron will feel a force trying to accelerate it towards the more positive end of the field. This is in the opposite direction to the conventional field direction which, like electric current, goes from positive to negative.

b How fast will the electron be travelling if this field accelerates it from rest and it is within the field for a distance of 10 cm?

From the equations of motion we know that $v^2 = u^2 + 2as$. 'From rest' means that $u = 0$, so:

$$v = \sqrt{2as} = \sqrt{\frac{2EQs}{m}}$$

$$= \sqrt{\frac{2 \times (4.5 \times 10^5) \times (-1.6 \times 10^{-19}) \times 0.1}{9.11 \times 10^{-31}}}$$

$$= -1.26 \times 10^8\,\text{ms}^{-1}$$

Again, the minus sign indicates that the motion is in the opposite direction to the electric field, i.e. towards the positive end of the field.

In the worked example above, the kinetic energy gained by the electron was provided in a transfer from the electrical potential energy the electron had by virtue of its location within the electric field. Every location within a field has a certain **potential**. The difference between the potential at an electron's original location and the potential at a new location is the **potential difference** through which the electron moves.

You may remember that we previously defined potential difference for a device in an electrical circuit as the energy transferred per coulomb of charge passing through the device. In an electric field, we can follow exactly the same idea in order to find out how much kinetic energy a charged particle will gain by moving within the field. This is given by the equation:

$$E = VQ$$

 Worked example

a What is the kinetic energy of the electron in part **b** of the worked example on page 39?

$E_k = \frac{1}{2} mv^2$

$= \frac{1}{2} \times (9.11 \times 10^{-31}) \times (1.26 \times 10^8)^2$

$= 7.2 \times 10^{-15}$ J

b What is the kinetic energy gained by an electron as it is accelerated through a potential difference of 45 kV?

$E_k = VQ$

$= 45 \times 10^3 \times 1.6 \times 10^{-19}$

$= 7.2 \times 10^{-15}$ J

These two answers are the same because they are actually calculations of the same thing, looked at from different perspectives.

Uniform fields

An electric field exists between any objects which are at a different electrical potential. Thus, if we connect parallel metal plates to a power supply we can set up a potential difference, and therefore an electric field, between them. This is shown in fig. 2.1.2.

The strength of a uniform electric field is a measure of how rapidly the potential changes. The equation which describes this divides the potential difference by the distance over which the potential difference exists:

$$E = \frac{V}{d}$$

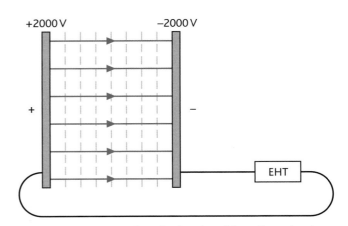

fig. 2.1.2 The blue arrows show the direction of the uniform electric field produced between parallel plates which have a potential difference between them.

 Worked example

In the X-ray machine shown in **fig. 2.1.1**, there is a potential difference of 45 000 V between a cathode and an anode which are 10 cm apart. What is the electrical field strength between these two plates?

$$E = \frac{V}{d} = \frac{45\,000}{0.1} = 4.5 \times 10^5 \, V\,m^{-1}$$

HSW Units for electric field strength

Electric field strength can be defined in two ways:

$$E = \frac{F}{Q}$$

$$E = \frac{V}{d}$$

This gives rise to two equally valid SI units for electric field strength: $N\,C^{-1}$ and $V\,m^{-1}$.

Investigating electric fields

fig. 2.1.3 Finding field lines in the lab.

Ensure you know how to safely use an EHT power supply before conducting this experiment.

You can investigate the shapes of electric fields using an EHT power supply to provide a potential difference, and castor oil with floating semolina to show the field lines. In the castor oil, the semolina becomes slightly charged. The forces on the charged semolina grains cause the grains to line up, showing the lines of action of the forces produced by the field. Try this investigation with different shaped electrodes to see uniform and non-uniform fields.

Questions

1 What is the force on an electron in an electric field of $300 \, V \, m^{-1}$?

2 What is the strength of an electric field that will put a force of $1.28 \times 10^{-15} \, N$ on a proton?

3 How much acceleration will an alpha particle undergo whilst in an electric field of $10 \, kV \, m^{-1}$?

4 In the electron beam of a cathode ray oscilloscope, electrons are accelerated through a potential difference of 3000V which is set up between electrodes which are 3 cm apart.

   a Calculate the electric field strength between these electrodes, assuming it is a uniform field.

   b How fast will the electrons be moving when they emerge from this field?

   c Draw a picture to illustrate the field produced by these plates.

   d Describe and explain how the field's effects would be different if a proton were placed in it.

Uniform and radial fields Spec 86, 84, 83

Equipotentials

As we move through an electric field, the electrical potential changes from place to place. Those locations which all have the same potential can be connected by lines called **equipotentials**. These are very much like the contours on a map, which show lines of equal height and thus indicate lines of gravitational equipotential. The field will always be perpendicular to the equipotential lines, as a field is defined as a region which changes the potential. Remember that field lines can never cross each other.

Investigating equipotentials

This is additional to the practicals suggested in the Edexcel specification.

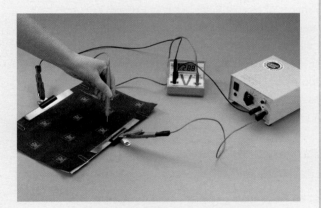

fig. 2.1.4 **Apparatus for investigating equipotentials.**

You can investigate how electrical potential varies across an electric field by measuring the voltage between zero and the point within the field that you are interested in. A simple experiment using conducting paper and a battery pack to set up an electric field allows you to map out equipotentials which you can use to produce a picture of the electric field. Try it with differently shaped electrodes to see how they change the field shape.

Radial fields

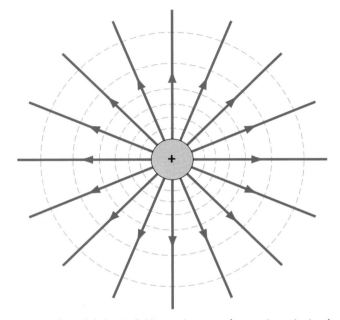

fig. 2.1.5 **The radial electric field around a proton (or any charged sphere).**

In the region around a positively charged sphere, or a point charge like a proton, the electric field will act outwards in all directions away from the centre of the sphere, as shown in **fig 2.1.5**. You will see that the arrows in the diagram get further apart as you move further away from the sphere, indicating that the field strength reduces as you move away from the centre. This means that the distance between equipotentials also increases. The field is the means by which the potential changes, so if it is weaker, then the potential changes less quickly.

Combination electric fields

In a region where there are electric fields caused by more than one charged object, the overall field is the vector sum at each point of the contributions from each field. If you imagine building the overall field up from the force effects of each contributing field, you can see that at every point you have to work out the resultant force, which will tell you how a charged particle would be affected at that point. The sum of all of these individual force effects is the overall electric field.

a   b   c   d

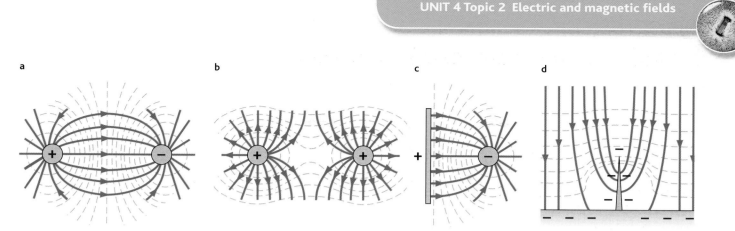

fig. 2.1.6 Complex fields still have their equipotentials perpendicular to the field lines at all points.

Charge is particularly concentrated in regions around spikes or points on charged objects. The field lines are close together at these places and the field will be strong around them. This is why lightning conductors are spiked. The concentrated charge at the point will attract the lightning more strongly, so it is more likely to hit the lightning conductor than the building being protected. In fact, the field around a spiked lightning conductor is often strong enough that it can cause charge leakage through the conductor before charge builds up to a point to produce a lightning strike. The likelihood of lightning occurring is reduced, further protecting the building.

Questions

1 Explain what would happen to an electron which found itself at the exact centre of the electric field shown in fig 2.1.6 b.

2 Draw a pair of electrons 8 cm apart. On your diagram, add field lines to show the shape of the electric field produced by these two electrons. Draw in several equipotential lines.

3 A pair of flat, square metal plates are held parallel to each other 10 cm apart. One is connected to earth, and the other is connected to a 2000 V supply.

 a What would the electrical potential be at a point between the centres of the plates, which is 3 cm from the earthed one?

 b What difference in effect would there be on electrons placed within the field, one 1 cm from the earthed plate, and the other in the exact midpoint of the field?

4 Why is the electric field in fig 2.1.6 d strongest near the point of the steeple?

5 If fig. 2.1.6 a shows a hydrogen atom, then the separation of the charges would be 5.3×10^{-11} m. If the potential difference from the proton to the electron's position is 27.2 V, what is the strength of the electric field along the line between the two particles? (Assume the field is uniform, although this is a simplification.)

Coulomb's law Spec 85, 78

Charged particle interactions

The attraction between a proton and an electron can be imagined as the proton creating an electric field because of its positive charge, and the electron feeling a force produced by the proton's field. (Note that it could also be thought of the other way round, with the proton feeling a force caused by the electron's electric field.)

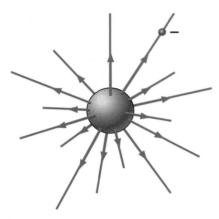

fig. 2.1.7 A proton's field will produce a force on a negatively charged electron.

The force between two charged particles, Q_1 and Q_2, which are separated by a distance r, is described by Coulomb's law and is given by the expression:

$$F = \frac{kQ_1Q_2}{r^2}$$

where $k = \frac{1}{4\pi\varepsilon_0} = 8.99 \times 10^9 \, \text{N}\,\text{m}^2\,\text{C}^{-2}$. Here ε_0 is a constant known as the **permittivity of free space**, which is a measure of how easy it is for an electric field to pass through space.

Investigating Coulomb's law

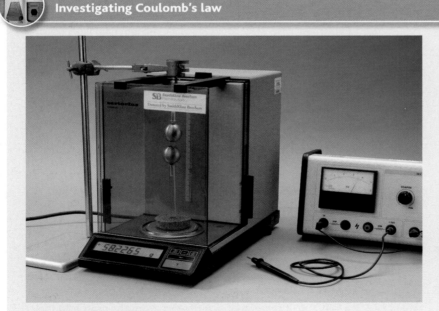

fig. 2.1.8 Measuring the force between two charges.

You can investigate the force between two charges using an electronic balance. You can charge a pair of insulated metallised spheres using a van der Graaf generator, or simply by induction using a charged plastic rod. Clamping the spheres close to each other will cause a force between them which can be measured using an electronic balance. By adjusting the distance of separation and measuring the force at each distance, this setup can be used to confirm that Coulomb's law follows an inverse square law. An alternative method for verifying Coulomb's law is shown on page 47.

Worked example

All materials are made of atoms, and the outer part of the atom is considered to be the region of electron orbits and thus the location of the negative charge. We can therefore imagine any surface to consist of a sheet of negative charges. Thus the surface of the floor and the bottom of a man's shoe will both be planes covered with negative charge. The repulsion between these two surfaces will cause the man to levitate ever so slightly above the floor, rather than actually touching it. Estimate the height at which a man levitates.

Estimate of weight = 800 N; thus each shoe supports 400 N

Estimate of shoe surface area = 10 cm by 30 cm

$$= 0.1 \times 0.3 = 0.03\,m^2$$

Estimate of average radius of atoms in each surface = 1.5×10^{-10} m

Cross-sectional area of each atom = πr^2

$$= \pi \times (1.5 \times 10^{-10})^2$$

$$= 7.07 \times 10^{-20}\,m^2$$

Number of atoms in bottom surface of shoe = $\dfrac{\text{area of shoe}}{\text{area one atom}}$

$$N = \frac{0.03}{7.07 \times 10^{-20}}$$

$$= 4.24 \times 10^{17}\,atoms$$

Force supported by each shoe atom = $\dfrac{\text{force supported by shoe}}{N}$

$$F_{atom} = \frac{400}{4.24 \times 10^{17}}$$

$$= 9.42 \times 10^{-16}\,N$$

Assume that each shoe atom electron repels a corresponding atom in the floor surface, and that oxygen, with eight electrons, is the most abundant element. From this, estimate that the force per atom is shared between four electrons (with the other four being on the opposite side of the atom at any given moment). Thus:

$$F_{electron} = \frac{F_{atom}}{4}$$

$$= 2.36 \times 10^{-16}\,N$$

$F_{electron}$ = Coulomb force repelling shoe electron and floor electron

$$= \frac{kQ_1Q_2}{r^2}$$

$$\therefore r = \sqrt{\frac{kQ_1Q_2}{F_{electron}}}$$

$$= \sqrt{\frac{(8.99 \times 10^9) \times (-1.6 \times 10^{-19}) \times (-1.6 \times 10^{-19})}{2.36 \times 10^{-16}}}$$

$$r = 9.9 \times 10^{-7}\,m$$

So the man will float about one micrometre above the floor surface – a distance equal to about a tenth of the size of a human red blood cell, or the size of a bacterium like *Escherichia coli*.

There are a number of assumptions in this calculation, not least of which is that the positive charge of the nuclei of the atoms involved has not been considered. Also, the compression of atomic bonds will mean that the force is supported across more atoms than just those considered. However, it is true that the repulsion of atomic electrons, which increases with the square of a decreasing separation, provides the majority of contact forces with which we are familiar in everyday life, and does mean that you can never truly touch anything!

Radial field calculations

We have seen that an electric field can be defined as a region of space which will produce a force on a charged particle. This definition allows us to come up with an expression for the strength of a radial electric field using the expressions for force on a charged particle met earlier:

$$F_{coulomb} = E_1Q_2 = \frac{kQ_1Q_2}{r^2}$$

Thus, the radial field strength at a distance r from a charge Q is given by:

$$E = \frac{kQ}{r^2}$$

Worked example

Calculate the electric field strength at a distance of 1 angstrom (1×10^{-10} m) from a proton.

$$E = \frac{kQ}{r^2}$$

$$= \frac{(8.99 \times 10^9) \times (1.6 \times 10^{-19})}{(1 \times 10^{-10})^2}$$

$$= 1.44 \times 10^{11}\,Vm^{-1}$$

Powers of ten

You will have noticed that a detailed study of Physics requires us to deal with very large and very small numbers. Scientists have devised a system of adapting the names of units to account for these very large or small numbers without having to 'speak' in standard form. You will have seen that a thousand of anything can be referred to by adding the prefix 'kilo'. For example, a thousand metres is a kilometre, a thousand grams a kilogram, and so on. Similarly, a thousandth part of a unit can use the prefix 'milli'. Think of the millimetre, or a milliamp.

There are 20 standard prefixes for use with SI units. These are shown in table 2.1.1.

You may not use more than one prefix at a time. 'Kilogram' is the SI unit but already includes the prefix, so we have to change multiples of this so that they relate to the gram.

For example, 10^{-6} kg = 1 mg (one milligram), but we don't write 10^{-6} kg = 1 μkg (one microkilogram).

Nelson's Column is 51.66 m tall, or 5166 cm, or 51660 mm, or 0.05166 km tall.

Factor	Name	Symbol	Factor	Name	Symbol
10^{24}	yotta	Y	10^{-1}	deci	d
10^{21}	zetta	Z	10^{-2}	centi	c
10^{18}	exa	E	10^{-3}	milli	m
10^{15}	peta	P	10^{-6}	micro	μ
10^{12}	tera	T	10^{-9}	nano	n
10^{9}	giga	G	10^{-12}	pico	p
10^{6}	mega	M	10^{-15}	femto	f
10^{3}	kilo	k	10^{-18}	atto	a
10^{2}	hecto	h	10^{-21}	zepto	z
10^{1}	deka	da	10^{-24}	yocto	y

table 2.1.1 **Powers of ten prefixes for use with SI units.**

Questions

1 What is the force of attraction between a uranium nucleus (atomic number 92) and an electron at a distance of 0.1 nm?

2 a What is the strength of the electric field caused by a gold nucleus (atomic number 79) at a distance of 1×10^{-12} m from the centre of the nucleus?

 b What is the force of repulsion between an alpha particle and a gold nucleus when the alpha particle passes by the nucleus at a distance of 1 pm?

3 Describe and explain a potential problem with the experimental set-up in fig 2.1.8 when comparing results with Coulomb's law that $F = \dfrac{kQ_1Q_2}{r^2}$. (*Hint:* What would the metre ruler be measuring?)

4 Estimate the distance that you float above your bed at night as a result of the Coulomb repulsion between the electrons in the bedsheets and those in your pyjamas.

Finding the electronic charge Spec 83, 85, 86

This is additional to the practicals suggested in the Edexcel specification.

In 1785, Charles Augustine de Coulomb published a paper in which he provided experimental evidence for the equation for calculating the force between two charges. His experiments involved measuring the force between charged spheres on a torsion (rotating) balance and fixed charged spheres. A simplification of his method, which can be carried out in a school lab, is shown in fig. 2.1.9.

fig. 2.1.9 A simple method to verify Coulomb's law.

You can investigate the force between charged spheres and confirm that there is an inverse square law involved, and that the force is proportional to the product of the charges.

Figure 2.1.10 shows the forces on the hanging ball. By resolving and equating the horizontal and vertical components, we can develop a method for verifying Coulomb's law.

The horizontal component of the tension balances the Coulomb force:

$$F_{coulomb} = T\sin\theta$$

and the vertical component of the tension balances the weight:

$$mg = T\cos\theta$$

Dividing the two equations gives:

$$\frac{F_{coulomb}}{mg} = \frac{T\sin\theta}{T\cos\theta}$$

$$= \tan\theta$$

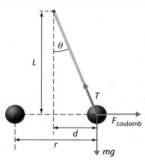

fig. 2.1.10 Forces on the hanging charged ball.

For small angles $\tan\theta \approx \frac{d}{L}$ (you will need a long piece of thread to allow this simplification to be made):

$$\frac{F_{coulomb}}{mg} = \frac{d}{L}$$

$$F_{coulomb} = \frac{mgd}{L}$$

$$\frac{kQ_1Q_2}{r^2} = \frac{mgd}{L}$$

For a fixed amount of charge on the spheres, you could vary r and measure d, from which a plot of $1/r^2$ against d should produce a straight line. It is very difficult to control specifically the amount of charge placed on the spheres, but having charged them both up, touching one with a third, uncharged, sphere can remove half the charge on that one. Doing this several times, and measuring d in each case, will allow you to confirm that $F_{coulomb}$ is proportional to the product of the two charges.

Jasmin and Izaac undertook an experiment to test Coulomb's law, following the method of fig. 2.1.9. The measurements they took are given in table 2.1.2. Draw an appropriate graph to analyse their results to show that the Coulomb force follows an inverse square relationship.

d/m	0.002	0.004	0.006	0.008	0.010	0.012	0.014	0.016
r/m	0.036	0.028	0.024	0.021	0.019	0.018	0.016	0.014

table 2.1.2 Experimental results from a Coulomb's law experiment.

Millikan's oil drop experiment

In experiments to determine the nature of fundamental particles, scientists can use a mass spectrometer (see page 66) to find the ratio of charge to mass for particles. This ratio is a fundamental property of a charged particle and identifies it uniquely, but until the determination of the value of the charge on an electron, it was impossible to break down the

fig. 2.1.11 Millikan's oil drop apparatus for finding the charge on an electron. The chamber shown was suspended in a trough of motor oil to reduce heat transfer within it, and thus reduce any problems of convection currents affecting falling oil droplets within the chamber.

ratio and find the mass of that particle. In 1909, Robert Millikan developed an experiment which determined the charge on a single electron.

Although he had a variety of extra bits and pieces to make it function successfully, the basic essence of Millikan's experiment is pure simplicity. The weight of a charged droplet of oil is balanced by the force from a uniform electric field, so that the oil drop remains stationary. Using the same apparatus, Millikan undertook variations, one in which there was no field and the downward terminal velocity of the oil drop was measured, and another in which the field was adjusted to provide a stronger force than gravity and the terminal velocity upwards was measured.

When oil is squirted into the upper chamber from the vaporiser, friction gives the droplets an electrostatic charge. This will be some (unknown) multiple of the charge on an electron, because electrons have been added or removed due to the friction. As the drops fall under gravity, some will go through the anode and enter the uniform field created between the charged plates. If the field is switched off, they will continue to fall at their terminal velocity.

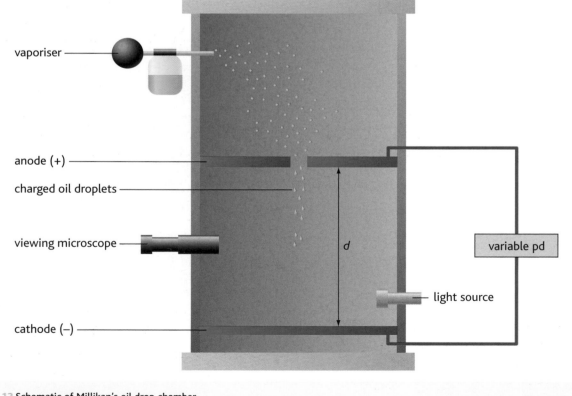

fig. 2.1.12 Schematic of Millikan's oil drop chamber.

Stokes' law

Sir George Gabriel Stokes investigated fluid dynamics and derived an equation for the viscous drag (F) on a small sphere moving through a fluid at low speeds:

$$F = 6\pi\eta v r$$

where r is the radius of the sphere, v is the velocity of the sphere, and η is the coefficient of viscosity of the fluid.

For Millikan's oil drops, the density of air in the chamber is so low that the upthrust is generally insignificant (although it would have to be considered if we wanted to do really accurate calculations). At the terminal velocity, the weight equals the viscous drag force:

$$mg = 6\pi\eta v_{term} r \qquad \text{where } \eta \text{ is the viscosity of air and } r \text{ is the radius of the drop.}$$

When held stationary by switching on the electric field and adjusting the potential, V, until the drop stands still:

weight = electric force

$$mg = QE$$
$$= \frac{QV}{d}$$

By equating the expressions for weight from the two situations, it is found that:

$$6\pi\eta v_{term} r = \frac{QV}{d}$$

or

$$Q = \frac{6\pi\eta v_{term} r d}{V}$$

Millikan could not measure r directly, so had to eliminate it from the equations. Further development of Stokes' law tells us that a small drop falling at a low terminal velocity will follow the equation:

$$v_{term} = \frac{2r^2 g(\rho_{oil} - \rho_{air})}{9\eta}$$

which, if we again ignore the density of air, rearranges to:

$$r = \left(\frac{9\eta v_{term}}{2g\rho_{oil}}\right)^{\frac{1}{2}}$$

Overall then:

$$Q = \frac{6\pi\eta v_{term} d}{V} \times \left(\frac{9\eta v_{term}}{2g\rho_{oil}}\right)^{\frac{1}{2}}$$

Millikan did the experiment several hundred times, including repeated measurements on each drop, over and over again letting it fall, halting it with a field, and then lifting it up again with a stronger field, before letting it fall again. From these data, he found that the charges on the droplets were always a multiple of 1.59×10^{-19} C, which is less than 1% away from the currently accepted value of 1.602×10^{-19} C. For this (and work on the photoelectric effect) Millikan was awarded the 1923 Nobel Prize for Physics.

Extension question

Figure 2.1.13 shows a positively charged oil drop held at rest between two parallel conducting plates A and B.

oil droplet

A

2.50 cm

B

fig. 2.1.13

a The oil drop has a mass 9.79×10^{-15} kg. The potential difference between the plates is 5000 V and plate B is at a potential of 0 V. Is plate A positive or negative?

b Draw a labelled free-body force diagram which shows the forces acting on the oil drop.

c Calculate the electric field strength between the plates.

d Calculate the magnitude of the charge Q on the oil drop.

e How many electrons would have to be removed from a neutral oil drop for it to acquire this charge?

2.2 Capacitors Spec 87, 88

Storing charge

Electric fields in circuits

We have seen in Chapter 2.1 that an electric field can cause charged particles to move. Indeed, this is why a current flows through a circuit – an electric field is set up within the conducting material and this causes electrons to feel a force and thus move through the wires and components of the circuit. Where there is a gap in a circuit, although the effect of the electric field can be felt by charges across the empty space, conduction electrons are generally unable to escape their conductor and move across the gap. This is why a complete path is needed for a simple electric circuit to function.

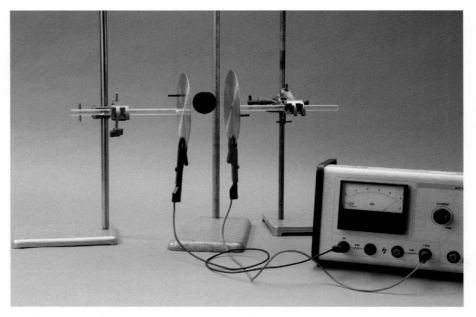

fig. 2.2.1 An electric field acts across a space. You could test this by hanging a charged sphere near the plates and observing the field's force acting on the sphere.

However, charge can be made to flow in an incomplete circuit. This can be demonstrated by connecting two large metal plates in a circuit with an air gap between them (fig. 2.2.1). The circuit shown in fig. 2.2.2 represents the situation shown by the photo in fig. 2.2.1. When the power supply is connected, the electric field created in the conducting wires causes electrons to flow towards the positive terminal. Since the electrons cannot cross the gap between the plates they build up on the plate connected to the negative terminal, which becomes negatively charged. Electrons in the plate connected to the positive terminal flow towards the positive terminal, resulting in a positive charge on that plate. The attraction between the opposite charges across the gap creates an electric field between the plates which increases until the pd across the plates is equal to the pd of the power supply.

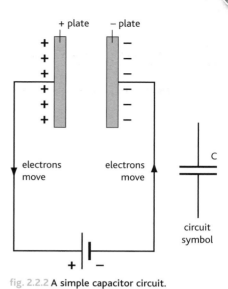

A pair of plates like this with an insulator between them is called a **capacitor**. As we have seen, charge will build up on a capacitor until the pd across the plates equals that provided by the power supply to which it is connected. At that stage it is said to be fully charged. The capacitor is acting as a store of charge. The amount of charge a capacitor can store, per volt applied across it, is called its **capacitance**, C, and is measured in farads (F). The capacitance depends on the size of the plates, their separation, and the nature of the insulator between them.

Capacitance can be calculated from the equation:

$$C = \frac{Q}{V}$$

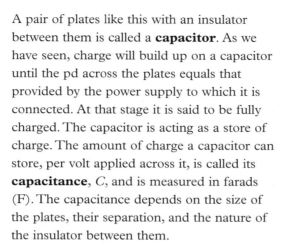

fig. 2.2.2 A simple capacitor circuit.

Worked example

a What is the capacitance of a capacitor which can store 18 mC of charge when the pd across it is 6V?

$$C = \frac{Q}{V}$$

$$= \frac{18 \times 10^{-3}}{6}$$

$$= 3 \times 10^{-3}$$

$$C = 3\,mF$$

b How much charge will be stored on this capacitor if the voltage is increased to 20 V?

$$Q = CV$$

$$= 3 \times 10^{-3} \times 20$$

$$= 60 \times 10^{-3}$$

$$= 0.06\,C$$

Using a coulombmeter to measure charge stored

A device which will measure the amount of charge directly is called a coulombmeter. By charging a capacitor to various different voltages, and discharging through the coulombmeter each time, you can verify the basic capacitor equation that $C = \frac{Q}{V}$. A graph of charge (on the y-axis) against pd (on the x-axis) should produce a straight line through the origin. The gradient of this line will equal the capacitance.

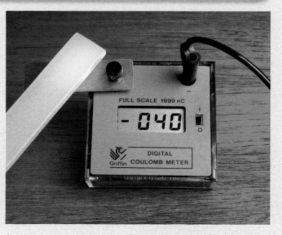

fig. 2.2.3 A coulombmeter will measure how much charge is stored on a capacitor.

Energy stored on a charged capacitor

A charged capacitor is a store of electrical potential energy. When the capacitor is discharged, this energy can be transferred into other forms. Our definition of voltage gives the energy involved as $E = QV$. However, the energy stored in a charged capacitor is given by $E = \frac{1}{2}QV$. So where has the missing half of the energy gone? This is a trick question, because our original equation assumes that the charge and voltage are constant. However, in order to charge a capacitor, it begins with zero charge stored on it and slowly fills up as the pd increases, until the charge at voltage V is given by Q. This can be seen on the graph in fig 2.2.4.

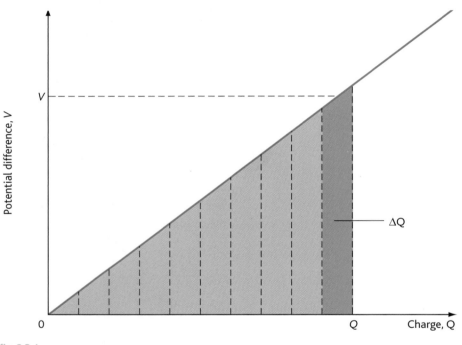

fig. 2.2.4

Each time we add a little extra charge (ΔQ) this has to be done by increasing the voltage and pushing the charge on, which requires energy (we are doing work against the repulsion between like charges).

By finding the area of each roughly rectangular strip, we find $V\Delta Q$, which is the amount of extra energy needed for that extra charge. Thus, the sum of all the strips, or the area under the line, will give us the total energy stored. This is the area of a triangle, so its area is $\frac{1}{2} \times$ base $\times$ height, which from the graph is $\frac{1}{2}QV$. Thus:

$$E = \frac{1}{2}QV$$

But $Q = CV$, so we can use this to find two other versions of the equation for the stored energy:

$$E = \frac{1}{2}QV$$
$$= \frac{1}{2}(CV)V$$
$$= \frac{1}{2}CV^2$$

or

$$E = \frac{1}{2}QV = \frac{1}{2}Q\left(\frac{Q}{C}\right) = \frac{1}{2}\frac{Q^2}{C}$$

Worked example

What is the energy stored on a 100 μF capacitor which has 3 mC of charge on it?

$$E = \frac{1}{2}\frac{Q^2}{C}$$

$$= \frac{1}{2} \times \frac{(3 \times 10^{-3})^2}{(100 \times 10^{-6})}$$

$$= 0.045\,J$$

Investigating energy stored on a capacitor

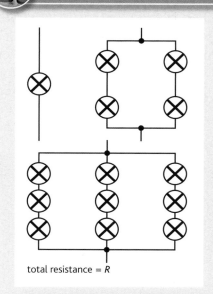

total resistance = R

fig. 2.2.5 **Investigating how energy stored on a capacitor can be altered.**

You can investigate how the energy stored on a capacitor changes with the voltage used to charge it. Various combinations of identical series and parallel bulbs will have different overall resistances. If we add an extra parallel branch and increase the number of bulbs on each branch by one, we can keep the total resistance, R, constant, but have more bulbs to light up (fig 2.2.5). By allowing our charged capacitor to discharge through these, and altering the voltage to keep the bulb brightness constant, we can confirm our equation $E = \frac{1}{2}CV^2$ for the energy stored on the capacitor.

Questions

1   What is the capacitance of a capacitor which stores 2 coulombs of charge for every 100 volts applied to it?

2   A 0.01 F capacitor is charged by and then isolated from an 8 V power supply.

   a   Calculate the charge stored.

   b   The capacitor is then connected across another identical capacitor which is uncharged. Describe and explain what will happen to the charge and voltage on each capacitor.

3   How much energy is stored on a 50 μF capacitor which is charged to 12 V?

4   A 1200 μF capacitor is connected to a voltage supply until fully charged with 10.8 mC. If this capacitor is then disconnected and reconnected across a 100 W light bulb, for how long could it light the bulb?

Charging and discharging capacitors Spec 89, 90

Growth and decay curves

Investigating current flow through a capacitor

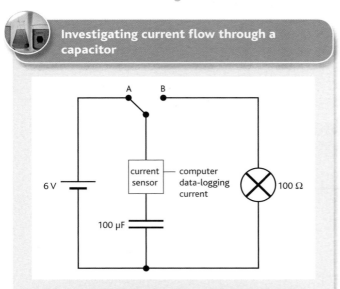

fig. 2.2.6 **Investigating how the current through a capacitor changes over time.**

You can investigate how the current through a capacitor changes over time by connecting a data logger which senses current to the capacitor, and then charging and discharging the capacitor. A suitable setup for this is shown in fig 2.2.6. This setup could be altered to log the pd across the capacitor over time, using a voltage sensor.

If the capacitor in fig. 2.2.6 is fully charged it will be at 6 V, and from $Q = CV$ we know it will be storing 0.6 mC of charge. Recall that in the previous spread we looked at how the electrons in a circuit are influenced by the electric field caused by the supply voltage. If the two-way switch in fig 2.2.6 is moved to position B, the electrons on the capacitor will be able to move under the influence of the electric field towards the positive side of the capacitor. To do this they will flow through the lamp. As it has 100 Ω resistance, their progress will be slowed, but they will still flow and the lamp will light for as long as some current flows through it.

At first, the rush of electrons as the capacitor discharges is as high as it can be – the current starts at a maximum. We can calculate this current using Ohm's law, which gives a value of 0.06 A. As electrons flow from the discharging capacitor, the pd across it is reduced and the electric field and hence the push on the remaining electrons is weaker. The current (V/R) is less and the light will be dimmer. Some time later, the flow of electrons is so small that the current is down to a trickle, and the lamp will be so dim that it may appear to be off. Eventually, the capacitor will be fully discharged and there will be no more electrons moving from one side of the capacitor to the other – the current will be zero. If we put this story together over time, the discharging current, pd across the capacitor, and charge remaining on the capacitor will follow the patterns shown in the three graphs in fig. 2.2.7.

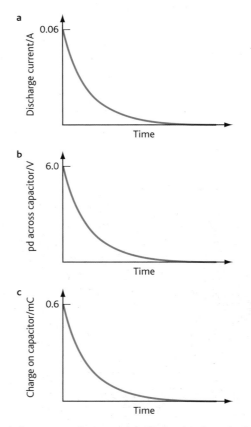

fig. 2.2.7 **Discharge curves for a capacitor discharging through a lamp.**

How could we make the lamp light up for longer, given the same power supply? There are two possibilities:

1 store more charge on the capacitor
2 decrease the rate at which the capacitor discharges.

For the same maximum pd, increasing the capacitance, C, will increase the charge stored, as $Q = CV$. Alternatively, the charge would flow more slowly if the resistance, R, in the lamp circuit was greater.

An overall impression of the rate of discharge of a capacitor can be gained by working out the **time constant**, τ. This is calculated from $\tau = RC$, and with resistance in ohms and capacitance in farads, the answer is in seconds. In fact, the time constant tells you how many seconds it takes for the current to fall to 37% of its starting value. We will see the mathematics of how 37% comes about shortly, but for now we just need to understand that RC indicates how quickly a charged capacitor will discharge.

HSW Car courtesy lights

Modern cars often have a light in the cabin which comes on when the door is opened, and remains on for a short time after the door is closed. This is useful when it is dark, allowing the driver to see to put the key in the ignition. The light functions by having a capacitor discharge through the light bulb so that it dims and goes off as the charge runs out. In some cars, the length of time for which the light remains on after the door is closed is adjustable and can be set by the vehicle owner. This adjustable setting makes use of the idea of the time constant, RC. The owner will be able to adjust a switch connected to the courtesy light circuit which connects more or less resistance to the discharging circuit. Thus for the same fully charged capacitor, the time taken to discharge completely will vary and the courtesy light illuminates the cabin for more or less time.

fig. 2.2.8 Capacitor discharge is used in a car courtesy light.

By considering the charging process in the same way as we did the discharge of the capacitor in fig 2.2.6, we can quickly work out that the charging process produces graphs like those in fig 2.2.9.

When charging through a resistor, the time constant RC has exactly the same implications. A greater resistance, or a larger capacitance, or both, means the circuit will take longer to charge up the capacitor.

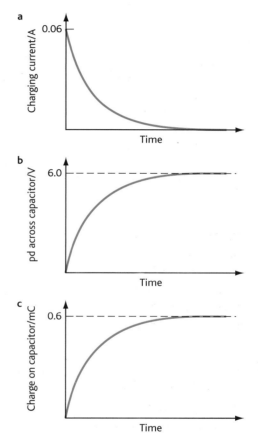

fig. 2.2.9 Charging curves for a capacitor connected to a 6V supply.

Worked example

What is the time constant for the capacitor in the circuit shown in fig. 2.2.6?

$$\tau = RC$$
$$= 100 \times 100 \times 10^{-6}$$
$$= 0.01\,s$$

Thus, in reality, the lamp shown in fig. 2.2.6 might flash on and off so quickly that we could not spot it!

Discharging capacitor maths

We have seen that the charging and discharging of a capacitor follows curved graphs in which the current is constantly changing, and so the rate of change of charge and pd are also constantly changing. These graphs are known as **exponential** curves. The shapes can be produced by plotting mathematical formulae which have power functions in them. In the case of discharging a capacitor, C, through a resistor, R, the function which describes the charge remaining on the capacitor, Q, at a time, t, is:

$$Q = Q_0 e^{-\frac{t}{RC}}$$

where Q_0 is the initial charge on the capacitor, and e is the special mathematical number which is used in the inverse function of natural logarithms (e $\approx$ 2.718).

Worked example

A 0.03 F capacitor is fully charged by a 12V supply and is then connected to discharge through a 900 Ω resistor. How much charge remains on the capacitor after 20 seconds?

Initial charge, $Q_0 = CV = 0.03 \times 12 = 0.36\,C$

$$Q = Q_0 e^{-\frac{t}{RC}}$$
$$Q = 0.36 \times e^{\left(\frac{-20}{900 \times 0.03}\right)}$$
$$= 0.36 \times e^{\left(\frac{-20}{27}\right)}$$
$$= 0.36 \times 0.477$$
$$= 0.172\,C$$

The pd across a discharging capacitor will fall as the charge stored falls. By substituting the equation $Q = CV$ into our exponential decay equation, we can show that the formula that describes voltage on a discharging capacitor has exactly the same form as that for the charge itself:

$$Q = Q_0 e^{-\frac{t}{RC}} \quad \text{and} \quad Q = CV$$

(which also means that, initially, $Q_0 = CV_0$). Therefore:

$$CV = CV_0 e^{-\frac{t}{RC}}$$

from which the capacitance term, C, can be cancelled, leaving:

$$V = V_0 e^{-\frac{t}{RC}}$$

Worked example

A 0.03 F capacitor is fully charged by a 12 V supply and is then connected to discharge through a 900 Ω resistor. What is the pd on the capacitor after 20 seconds?

Initial voltage is the same as the supply at 12 V.

$$V = V_0 e^{-\frac{t}{RC}}$$
$$V = 12 \times e^{\left(\frac{-20}{900 \times 0.03}\right)}$$
$$= 12 \times e^{\left(\frac{-20}{27}\right)}$$
$$= 12 \times 0.477 = 5.72V$$

As we saw in **fig. 2.2.7 a**, the discharging current also dies away following an exponential curve. Ohm's law tells us that $V = IR$, and hence $V_0 = I_0 R$.

$$V = V_0 e^{-\frac{t}{RC}}$$
$$IR = I_0 R e^{-\frac{t}{RC}}$$

from which the resistance term, R, will cancel on both sides:

$$I = I_0 e^{-\frac{t}{RC}}$$

Worked example

A 0.03 F capacitor is fully charged by a 12 V supply and is then connected to discharge through a 900 Ω resistor. What is the discharge current after 20 seconds?

Initial voltage is the same as the supply at 12 V, so the initial current is:

$$I_0 = \frac{V_0}{R}$$
$$= \frac{12}{900}$$
$$= 0.013A$$
$$I = I_0 e^{-\frac{t}{RC}}$$
$$I = 0.013 \times e^{\left(\frac{-20}{900 \times 0.03}\right)}$$
$$= 0.013 \times e^{\left(\frac{-20}{27}\right)}$$
$$= 0.013 \times 0.477 = 0.006\,2A$$

HSW Using a spreadsheet to investigate time constant

In order to create a timing circuit which fulfils the needs of a certain situation (like a car courtesy light staying on for the desired length of time), we can model the circuit using a spreadsheet. This allows us to type in different possible values for the circuit components and see what the outcome will be, before building the circuit. Figure 2.2.10 shows how such a spreadsheet could be set up.

The spreadsheet can be created without any experimentation being done. The various cells are given formulae to calculate what capacitor theory tells us will happen, using the mathematics you have seen above. For example, the cell giving the time constant, τ, does not require input from the user – it is programmed to display the multiplication of the capacitance and the discharge resistance. This value is then used in the formula for calculating the values in the current column, using the equation, $I = I_0 e^{-\frac{t}{RC}}$.

	A	B	C	D	E	F	G	H
1	**Capacitor discharge curves**							
2								
3	Time (s)	Current (A)		C, Capacitance (µF)	100			
4	0	0.03000		V, Power supply (V)	6			
5	5	0.02336		R, Discharge resistance (Ω)	200			
6	10	0.01820		T, time constant (s)	20			
7	15	0.01417						
8	20	0.01104						
9	25	0.00860						
10	30	0.00669						
11	35	0.00521						
12	40	0.00406						
13	45	0.00316						
14	50	0.00246						
15	55	0.00192						
16	60	0.00149						

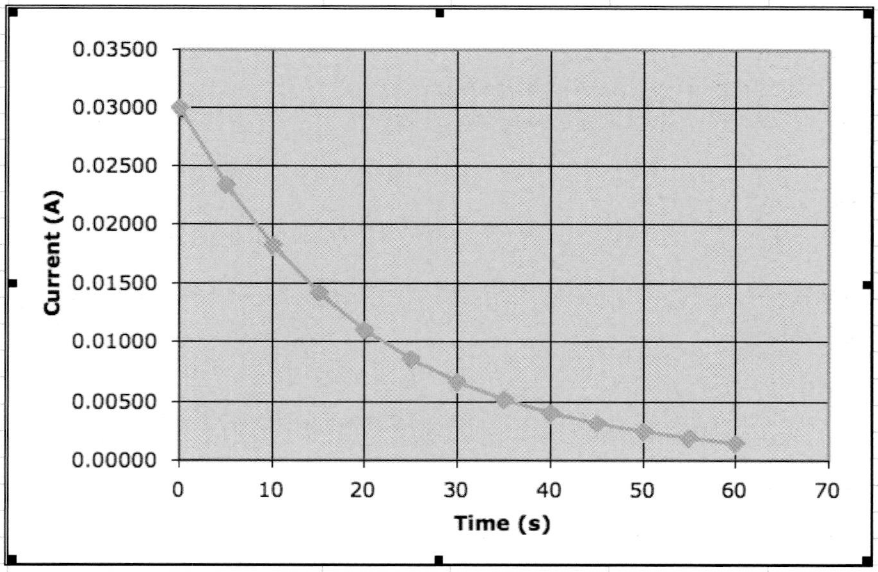

fig. 2.2.10 A spreadsheet to calculate the discharge curve for a capacitor circuit.

Capacitor calculus

The equation for the charge on a discharging capacitor is the solution to a differential equation based on considering **Kirchhoff's second law** around the discharging circuit. With only the capacitor, C, and resistance, R, in the circuit, the emf is zero. So:

$$0 = V_C + V_R$$

$$-IR = \frac{Q}{C}$$

The current is the rate of change of charge:

$$I = \frac{dQ}{dt}$$

So:

$$-R\frac{dQ}{dt} = \frac{Q}{C}$$

$$\frac{dQ}{Q} = \frac{-dt}{RC}$$

Integrating this from the start to time t, i.e. from capacitor charge Q_0 to Q:

$$\int_{Q_0}^{Q}\frac{dQ}{Q} = \int_{0}^{t}\frac{-dt}{RC}$$

gives

$$\ln Q - \ln Q_0 = \frac{-t}{RC}$$

or

$$\ln\left(\frac{Q}{Q_0}\right) = \frac{-t}{RC}$$

Applying the inverse function of natural logarithms gives:

$$\frac{Q}{Q_0} = e^{-\frac{t}{RC}}$$

or

$$Q = Q_0\, e^{-\frac{t}{RC}}$$

The '37% life'

If we consider the charge at time τ:

$$t = \tau = RC$$

so

$$\frac{-t}{RC} = \frac{-RC}{RC} = -1$$

Thus:

$$Q = Q_0\, e^{\frac{-RC}{RC}}$$

$$Q = Q_0\, e^{-1}$$

and

$$e^{-1} = 0.37$$

So $Q = 0.37Q_0$, which means the charge is 37% of its original value.

This calculation shows that the time constant describes the decay of charge on a discharging capacitor in the same way as radioactive half-life describes the number of radioactive nuclei remaining (see chapter 5.1), except that instead of describing the time taken to reach half of the initial value, τ is the time taken to reach 37% of the initial value. This similarity comes from the fact that radioactive decay also follows an exponential equation: $N = N_0\, e^{-\lambda t}$.

Questions

1 What is the time constant for a car courtesy light in which a 2 mF capacitor discharges through a 15 kΩ resistor?

2 How much charge remains on a 0.04 F capacitor after 8 seconds, if it is discharging through a 500 Ω resistance and initially held 2 C of charge?

3 a Use the graph in fig. 2.2.10 to find the current through the capacitor after 30 s.

   b If this were a model of an automatic hand dryer circuit which requires 4.0 V to operate, use the graph to work out for how long it will remain on.

   c How would you alter the circuit so that the dryer remains on for 30 s?

4 Draw an accurate sketch graph for the current through a discharging 50 μF capacitor which is fully charged by a 6 V supply and then discharged through a 10 kΩ resistance, over a period of 2 seconds.

5 A defibrillator is a machine that is used to correct irregular heartbeats by passing a large current through the heart for a short time. The machine uses a 6000 V supply to charge a capacitor of capacitance 20 μF. The capacitor is then discharged through metal electrodes (defibrillator paddles) placed on the chest of the patient.

   a Calculate the charge on the capacitor plates when charged to 6000 V.

   b Calculate the energy stored in the capacitor.

   c When the capacitor is discharged, there is an initial current of 40 A through the patient. Calculate the electrical resistance of the body tissue between the metal electrodes of the paddles.

   d Assuming a constant discharge rate of 40 A, calculate how long it would take to discharge the capacitor.

   e In practice the time for discharge is longer than this calculated time. Suggest a reason for this.

2.3 Electromagnetic effects Spec 91, 92

Magnetic fields

Pushing poles

In chapter 2.1 we saw how an electric field can be represented by lines which show how a charge will feel a force when placed in the field. You are probably more familiar, though, with the everyday effects of magnetic fields such as attracting a fridge with a magnetic souvenir from Florida. Usually the fridge magnet moves towards the fridge rather than the other way around, but Newton's third and second laws of motion explain this outcome. Electric and magnetic fields are very similar (and utterly intertwined), as Maxwell's work on the nature of electromagnetic radiation taught us.

Where an electric field affects charges, a **magnetic field** affects magnetic poles. A region of space which will cause a **magnetic pole** to feel a force is called a magnetic field.

Maxwell's equations

Maxwell's theoretical research on electromagnetic radiation essentially unified moving electric and magnetic fields to explain how light moves and interacts with matter. His equations are quite complex but, for fixed fields, there are some quite simple outcomes which have important applications for us here:

- an electric field can exert a force on a charged particle
- a magnetic field can exert a force on a charged particle if it is moving.

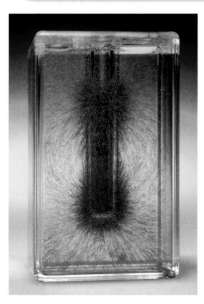

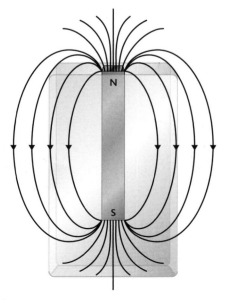

fig. 2.3.1 The magnetic field around a permanent bar magnet.

When we represent a magnetic field, the field lines show the direction in which a lone north pole will be pushed. In reality, poles always exist in north and south pairs, but the convention is to take the field as acting from north to south, and this is the direction of arrows drawn onto magnetic field lines (also called lines of **magnetic flux**). Like electric field patterns, indeed like all field patterns, the closer the lines are together, the stronger the field is. The term referring to the strength of a magnetic field is the **magnetic flux density, B**, and the SI unit is the **tesla (T)**.

Looking at fig. 2.3.1, you can see that the field lines all go in and out of the ends of the bar magnet. This forces them to be closer together at those points, which means that the field is stronger there. This is why a paperclip picked up by a bar magnet would jump to one of its ends. The quantity of flux, Φ (measured in **weber, Wb**), through any given area indicates the strength of the effect of the field there. This can be determined for a particular region by multiplying the area enclosed by the region by the component of flux density perpendicular to the area:

$$\Phi = B\sin\theta \times A$$

Worked example

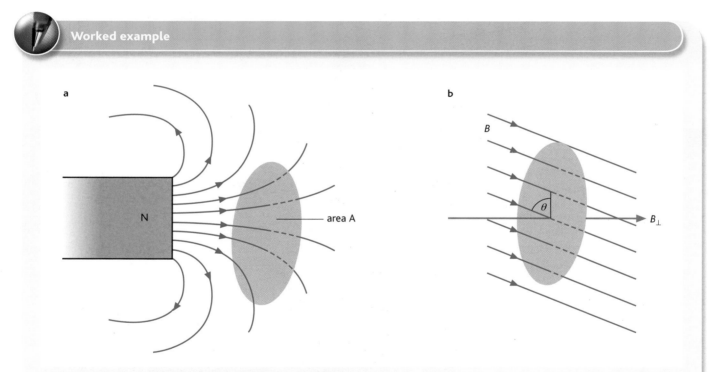

a

b

fig. 2.3.2 **Magnetic flux contained in a small region, A.**

If the bar magnet in fig. 2.3.2a causes a magnetic field with a strength of 20 mT perpendicular to the region of area A, how much flux will be contained by this region if it has an area of 10 cm²?

$A = 10\,\text{cm}^2$

$\quad = 10 \times 10^{-4}\,\text{m}^2$

$\Phi = B \times A$

$\quad = 20 \times 10^{-3} \times 10 \times 10^{-4}$

$\quad = 2 \times 10^{-5}\,\text{Wb}$

Fleming's left hand rule

Magnetic fields can affect moving charges as well as magnetic poles. If you place a wire in a magnetic field and pass a current through it, the wire will feel a force on it (fig. 2.3.3). This is called the **motor effect**. The effect is greatest when the wire and the magnetic field are at right angles. In this instance, the force will be at right angles to both, in the third dimension, as shown by **Fleming's left hand rule** in fig. 2.3.4.

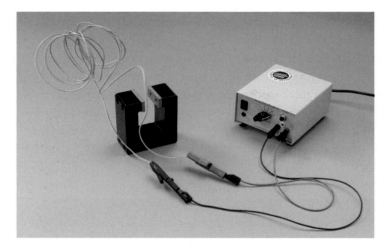

fig. 2.3.3 **The jumping wire experiment illustrates the motor effect in action.**

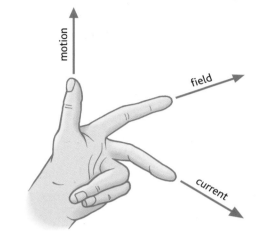

fig. 2.3.4 Fleming's left hand rule gives the relative directions of the field, current and movement in the motor effect.

The motor effect

This is additional to the practicals suggested in the Edexcel specification.

The forced movement of a current-carrying conductor within a magnetic field is the fundamental principle that causes motors to work. From Fleming's left hand rule, it is clear that if a coil of wire carrying a current were placed in a magnetic field it would feel a turning force. The current travels in opposite directions on opposite sides of the coil, thus causing forces in opposite directions, tending to twist the coil. If it is free to move, then the coil (or motor) will spin continuously (fig. 2.3.5).

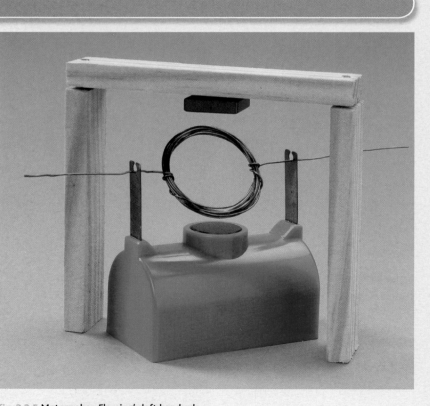

fig. 2.3.5 **Motors obey Fleming's left hand rule.**

HSW The tiniest motor in the world?

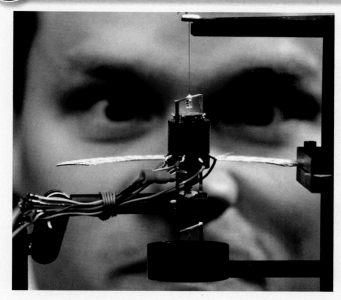

fig. 2.3.6 A fully functional micro-motor, with a human hair lying across it.

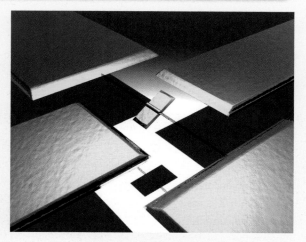

fig. 2.3.7 Computer-generated image of a nano-motor – a tiny gold rotor spins on a carbon nanotube axle. The entire setup would fit within one wavelength of red light. Courtesy Zettl Research Group, Lawrence Berkeley National Laboratory and University of California at Berkeley.

There was some amazement amongst scientists when the University of Berkeley in California produced an electric motor which was little more than 100 µm across (fig. 2.3.6). However, this 'micromotor' now seems like a lumbering clunky giant, when compared with the Berkeley lab's 'nanomotor'. In 2003, the same Zettl Lab at Berkeley produced a motor which is less than 500 nanometres across (fig. 2.3.7).

Questions

1 Describe the use of Fleming's left hand rule.

2 Copy the diagrams in fig. 2.3.8 and draw an arrow to show the direction of any force acting on the wire in each case.

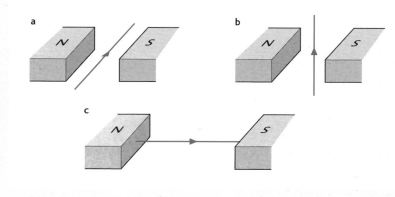

fig. 2.3.8

3 Many real motors use electromagnets to create the magnetic field that causes their rotor to spin. Give one advantage and one disadvantage of building a motor which uses electromagnets rather than permanent magnets.

The strength of electromagnetic forces Spec 81, 82, 92, 93

Fred = BIl

Investigating magnetic force on a current-carrying conductor

You can investigate how much force there is on a wire subjected to the motor effect. In the experiment shown in fig. 2.3.9, it is easy to alter the current through the wire, the length of current-carrying wire which is within the magnetic field, and the angle at which the wire cuts across the field.

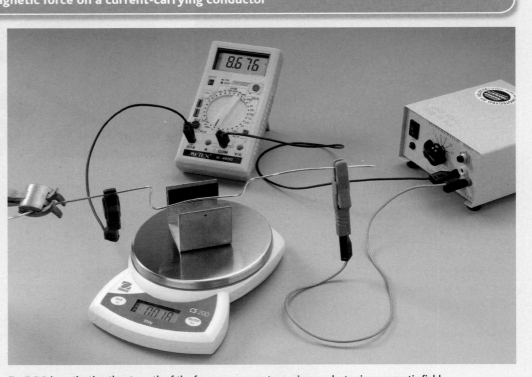

fig. 2.3.9 **Investigating the strength of the force on a current-carrying conductor in a magnetic field.**

The strength of the force, F, on a wire which has a current, I, through it whilst it is in a magnetic field, B, is given by the equation:

$$F = B \times I \times l \times \sin\theta$$

where l is the length of the wire within the field, and θ is the angle the current makes with the lines of magnetic field. For simplicity, we will only consider uniform magnetic fields in which the field lines are all parallel.

It is common to set up situations in which the angle θ is 90° so that $\sin\theta$ is a maximum and equals 1. This reduces the formula to $F = BIl$ which is often remembered by students as '*Fred = BIl*'.

Worked example

Hannah sets up a jumping wire demonstration to impress her younger cousin. She uses a wire with a current of 2A running through it, and a pair of Magnadur magnets which have a magnetic field of 0.5 mT. She is not too careful in setting up and 5 cm of the wire actually hangs across the field at an angle of 80°. How much force does Hannah's wire experience? If it has a mass of 9 grams, how fast will it initially accelerate?

$F = BIl\sin\theta$

$\quad = 0.5 \times 10^{-3} \times 2 \times 0.05 \times \sin80°$

$\quad = 4.92 \times 10^{-5}\,N$

$a = \dfrac{F}{m}$

$\quad = \dfrac{4.92 \times 10^{-5}}{0.009}$

$\quad = 5.5 \times 10^{-3}\,m\,s^{-2}$

A consequence of the expression $F = BIl$ is that a motor can be made more powerful, or faster, by:

*   increasing the current through the motor (I)
*   increasing the number of turns of wire in the motor (l)
*   increasing the magnetic field within the motor (B).

The magnetic field strength is usually maximised by making the central rotating core out of soft iron. Some motors use electromagnets to provide the field, and these could be strengthened by increasing the current through them.

Fred = Bev

The motor effect happens because a charged particle moving at right angles to a magnetic field feels a force on it at right angles to its direction of motion and also at right angles to the field. If the charged particle is constrained – like an electron in a current in a wire – then the force will be transferred to the wire. If the particle is flying freely, its direction will change and it will travel a circular path whilst in the magnetic field (fig. 2.3.10).

It turns out that the strength of the force on a charged particle moving across a magnetic field is given by the equation:

$$F = B \times q \times v \times \sin\theta$$

where q is the charge on the particle, v is its velocity, and θ is the angle between the velocity and the magnetic field lines. A simplified situation which is often considered is that of an electron (charge 'e') moving at right angles to the field ($\sin 90° = 1$). This reduces the formula to $F = Bev$, which is often remembered by students as '$Fred = Bev$'.

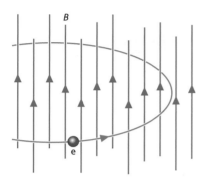

fig. 2.3.10 **Charged particles moving in a magnetic field follow a circular path as the motor effect provides a centripetal force.**

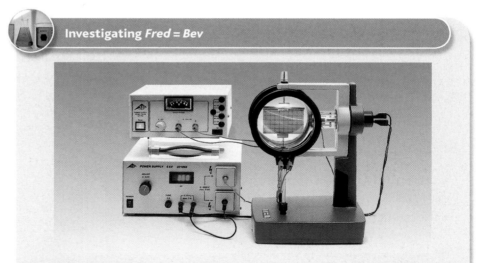

Investigating Fred = Bev

fig. 2.3.11 **Investigating the force on a charge moving in a magnetic field. Image © 3B Scientific GmbH, Hamburg.**

You can investigate the size of the force on an electron moving across a magnetic field using equipment like that shown in fig. 2.3.11. The grid allows you to observe the path travelled by the electrons and there is a standard formula for calculating the magnetic field strength provided by a pair of parallel electromagnetic coils, often referred to as Helmholtz coils.

As the force on the charged particle is always at right angles to the direction of its velocity, it acts as a centripetal force, and the particle follows a circular path. This means that, given the right combination of conditions, a moving charged particle could be held in place by a magnetic field, continuously orbiting a central point. This is the principle by which artificially generated antimatter is contained to save it from annihilation, for future use or study.

HSW The mass spectrometer

Scientists often need to identify unknown chemicals. This is particularly important, for example, in the field of forensic science, where a crime scene technician will take a sample of unknown material that needs to be identified. A machine called a mass spectrometer (fig. 2.3.12) can separate chemicals according to their mass, which allows unique identification of each substance within a sample.

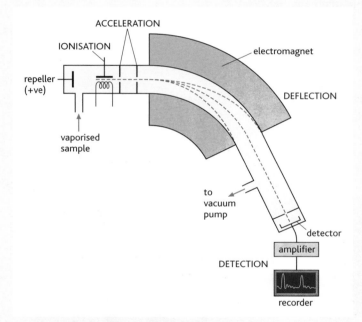

fig. 2.3.12 Schematic of the basic parts of a mass spectrometer.

A chemical to be identified enters the machine and is ionised. This charge will then allow it to be accelerated in two different ways within the mass spectrometer. An electric field increases its speed. Then it feels a force when travelling through the field of the electromagnet, which changes its direction.

The force on a charged particle moving at right angles to a magnetic field is given by:

$$F = Bqv$$

Centripetal force is given by:

$$F = \frac{mv^2}{r}$$

Only particles that follow the central dotted path in fig. 2.3.12 will reach the detector. For these particles:

$$Bqv = \frac{mv^2}{r}$$

where r is the radius of the circular path. This rearranges to:

$$\frac{q}{m} = \frac{v}{Br}$$

The charge/mass ratio will identify the particles involved, so with B and r known from the calibration of the machine, all we need to know is how fast the particles were moving when they entered the electromagnet. They are accelerated to this speed by an electric field acting on their charge, and the kinetic energy gained comes from the potential difference, V, that they pass through according to:

$$\tfrac{1}{2} mv^2 = qV$$

which gives:

$$v = \sqrt{\frac{2qV}{m}}$$

Substituting this into our equation for the mass/charge ratio:

$$\frac{q}{m} = \frac{\sqrt{2qV/m}}{Br}$$

Squaring gives:

$$\frac{q^2}{m^2} = \frac{\sqrt{2qV/m}}{B^2r^2}$$

$$\frac{m}{q} \times \frac{q^2}{m^2} = \frac{2V}{B^2r^2}$$

$$\frac{q}{m} = \frac{2V}{B^2r^2}$$

Thus, by adjusting the accelerating voltage and the strength of the electromagnet (by altering the current through it) we can identify the various chemicals contained within a sample as each is registered in the detector. The intensity of the current in the detector can indicate the proportion of a given chemical within the sample.

Worked example

A company selling sea salt for cooking wanted to find out if its ratio of chlorine isotopes was different from the usual abundance ratio. In nature, the ^{35}Cl isotope is more common than the ^{37}Cl one by a factor of 3:1. They analysed a sample of their product using a mass spectrometer which would ionise the chlorine atoms into single minus ions. What would be the difference between the radii of curvature caused for the chlorine isotopes, if the mass spectrometer operated at an accelerating potential of 3.0 kV and had a magnetic field strength of 3.0 T?

$$\frac{q}{m} = \frac{2V}{B^2 r^2}$$

$$r^2 = \frac{2Vm}{qB^2}$$

$$r = \sqrt{\frac{2Vm}{qB^2}}$$

For ^{35}Cl$^-$:

$$r = \sqrt{\frac{(35 \times 1.67 \times 10^{-27}) \times 2 \times 3000}{1.6 \times 10^{-19} \times (3.0)^2}}$$

$$r = 0.0156\,m$$

For ^{37}Cl$^-$:

$$r = \sqrt{\frac{(37 \times 1.67 \times 10^{-27}) \times 2 \times 3000}{1.6 \times 10^{-19} \times (3.0)^2}}$$

$$r = 0.0160\,m$$

So the difference in the radius of curvature of the path of these two ions is 0.4 mm.

Questions

1   a   How much force would be felt by a 12 cm wire carrying 0.8 A at right angles to the Earth's surface magnetic field of 5×10^{-5} T?

    b   How much force would be felt by a proton travelling across the Earth's magnetic field at 500 m s^{-1}?

    c   How fast would a proton need to travel in order for the electromagnetic force on it to be sufficient to make it orbit the Earth at the surface? (Radius of Earth = 6.4×10^6 m.) Comment on your answer.

2   Speed = distance/time and current = charge/time. Explain how $F = BIl$ is actually the same equation as $F = Bqv$ but considered for many charges in a group.

3   For the investigation on table salt in the worked example above, calculate the difference in the radii of curvature that would be found if the company investigated the two isotopes of sodium: ^{23}Na$^+$ and ^{22}Na$^+$. Explain why such small differences can be easily detected by a machine like that shown in fig. 2.3.12.

Generating electricity Spec 93, 94, 95

Electromagnetic induction

We have seen that the movement of a charged particle in a magnetic field causes it to feel a force. Newton's third law of motion reminds us that this force must have a counterpart which acts equally in the opposite direction. Moreover, this pair of electromagnetic forces is generated whenever there is relative motion between a charge and a magnetic field. Thus, a magnetic field moving past a stationary charge will create the same force. The velocity term in the expression $F = Bqv$ actually refers to the relative (perpendicular) velocity between the magnetic field lines and q. (Also remember that if the movement is not at right angles, then we need to work out the component of it that is at right angles by including the $\sin \theta$ term: $F = Bqv \sin \theta$.)

This means that if we move a magnet near a wire, the electrons in the wire will feel a force tending to make them move through the wire. This is an emf – if the wire is in a complete circuit, then the electrons will move, forming an electric current (fig. 2.3.13). This is one principle by which we generate electricity. Reversing the direction of the magnetic field, or the direction of the relative motion, will reverse the direction of the force on the electrons, reversing the polarity of the emf.

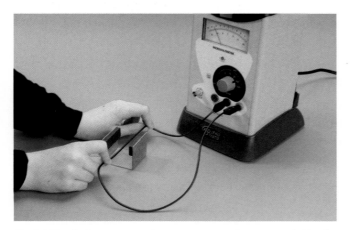

fig. 2.3.13 Relative movement between a wire and a magnetic field will induce an emf.

Flux linkage

The **induced emf** may well be tiny and only detectable by the most sensitive voltmeter. However, by coiling the wire up the magnetic field can influence a much greater length of the wire and thus have a greater effect. A stronger magnetic field will also have a greater effect. The amount of magnetic flux interacting with a coil of wire is known as the **magnetic flux linkage**, and is simply the product of the number of turns of wire and the flux in that region:

flux linkage = $N\Phi$ measured in **weber-turns**

Remembering that $\Phi = BA$ means that we also have:

flux linkage = BAN

Worked example

Zora takes a wire and coils it into ten circular turns with a radius of 5 cm. She then passes it through a magnetic field with a strength of 20 mT. What is the flux linkage?

Area, $A = \pi \times (0.05)^2$

$= 7.85 \times 10^{-3} \, m^2$

Flux linkage = BAN

$= 0.02 \times 7.85 \times 10^{-3} \times 10$

$= 1.6 \times 10^{-3} \, Wb\text{-turns}$

As we have seen that $F = Bqv$, it is no surprise that the faster the relative motion between a magnetic field and a conductor, the greater the induced emf. Faraday investigated this and determined a law on the matter. Faraday's law of electromagnetic induction states that:

The magnitude of an induced emf is proportional to the rate of change of flux linkage.

Faraday's law and Lenz's law

fig. 2.3.14 Measuring the induced emf as a magnet falls through a coil of wire.

You can investigate Faraday's law using a magnet and a coil of wire connected to a voltage datalogger, as in fig. 2.3.14.

Lenz's law

If you drop a magnet down a copper tube, it falls more slowly than if you drop a similarly sized non-magnetic piece of metal through it (fig. 2.3.15). As copper is not a magnetic material, the friction forces should be identical on the two falling objects. This somewhat bizarre result is a product of **Lenz's law**.

fig. 2.3.15 Lenz's law slows a magnet falling down a copper tube.

Imagine the copper tube in fig. 2.3.15 as a series of coils of copper wire all stacked on top of each other. As the magnet falls through the tube, it will induce an emf in each copper circlet, which will cause a small current to flow around the tube.

This circling current will then generate an electromagnetic field, which will interact with the falling magnet. The direction of this newly created magnetic field will determine whether it slows the falling magnet or repels it faster down the tube. If the latter were the case, then the magnet would end up with more kinetic energy than the gravitational potential it had at the start. This is impossible, so the law of conservation of energy dictates Lenz's law:

The direction of an induced emf is such as to oppose the change creating it.

Hence, the emf in the tube acts to try and slow down the magnet, as the movement of the magnet is the change creating this emf.

Fleming's right hand rule

The direction of an induced emf can be found using Fleming's right hand rule (fig. 2.3.16). This is very similar to the left hand rule for the motor effect . The reason that the opposite hand is needed is a product of Lenz's law, in that the induced emf must be in the direction which opposes the change producing it.

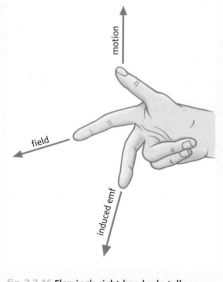

fig. 2.3.16 Fleming's right hand rule tells us the direction of an induced emf.

Calculating induced emfs

Putting Faraday's and Lenz's laws together gives us an expression for calculating an induced emf:

$$\varepsilon = \frac{-d(N\Phi)}{dt} \quad \text{or} \quad \varepsilon = \frac{-\Delta(N\Phi)}{\Delta t}$$

Faraday's law told us that the emf would be proportional to the rate of change of flux linkage. The minus sign in the equation comes from Lenz's law, to indicate the opposing direction.

Worked example

Zora takes her wire coil from the previous worked example and moves it from within the magnetic field to a place completely outside the field in 0.2 s. What emf is induced in her coil?

Flux linkage = 5×10^{-4} Wb-turns. This is completely removed in 0.2 s

$$\varepsilon = \frac{-d(N\Phi)}{dt} = \frac{-\Delta(N\Phi)}{\Delta t}$$

$$= \frac{-(-5 \times 10^{-4})}{0.2} = 2.5 \times 10^{-3} \text{ V}$$

Electromagnetic induction using an electromagnet

We have seen that the induction of emf is a result of the relative motion between a conductor, or coil, and the field due to a permanent magnet. The magnetic field which interacts with the coil could just as easily be produced electrically by another coil.

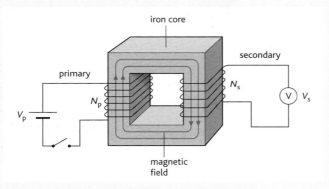

fig. 2.3.17 **Using an electromagnet to induce emf in a coil.**

In fig. 2.3.17 we have a pair of coils linked together by a soft iron core. Iron is extremely good at carrying magnetism, and in the setup shown, virtually all the magnetic field generated by the **primary coil** on the left would interact with the **secondary coil** on the right. When the primary switch is first closed, the primary coil suddenly produces a magnetic field which was not previously there. This means that a magnetic field is now within the secondary coil, which had not previously been there. This sudden change of flux linkage will generate an emf in the secondary coil. Once the electromagnetic field is stable there will no longer be any change in flux linkage over time, and so there will be no further induced emf in the secondary. The voltmeter needle would kick and then return to zero. If the primary circuit is switched off, the magnetic field it produces would suddenly disappear, and a brief emf would be

induced in the opposite direction to the switch-on voltage. The voltmeter needle would kick in the opposite direction and then return to zero again.

Worked example

The iron core in fig. 2.3.17 has a square cross-section with each side 4 cm. Suppose the primary produces a magnetic field with a strength of 0.5 T which takes 60 ms to generate, and to die away, when the primary circuit is switched on or off. The secondary coil has 120 turns. What emf would be induced in the secondary at the moments of switch-on and switch-off of the primary circuit?

$$\varepsilon = \frac{-d(N\Phi)}{dt}$$

$$= \frac{-\Delta(N\Phi)}{\Delta t}$$

$$= \frac{-\Delta(BAN)}{\Delta t}$$

$$= \frac{-(0.5 \times 0.04^2 \times 120)}{60 \times 10^{-3}} = -1.6 \text{ V}$$

At switch-off, the emf induced would be the same amount but in the opposite direction, so $\varepsilon = 1.6$ V.

Transformers

The circuit and situation described above is not really of much practical use, although it can be responsible for current surges in circuitry which can cause damage. The same principle is more usefully applied in the

transformer, in which an alternating current is supplied to the primary. As this current is constantly varying, the electromagnetic field produced by the primary coil is constantly varying. This means that there will be a constantly varying induced emf in the secondary. This emf will vary at the same rate as the a.c. supplied to the primary. It will also change constantly, depending on the varying rate of change of flux linkage. This comes from the strength of the magnetic field (which in turn depends on the number of turns on the primary coil) and the number of turns on the secondary coil. It turns out that the ratio of voltages between primary and secondary is identical to the ratio of the number of turns on these coils:

$$\frac{V_{primary}}{V_{secondary}} = \frac{N_{primary}}{N_{secondary}}$$

This is how the transformer can change voltage (fig. 2.3.18). More turns on the secondary gives a **step-up transformer**, in which the output voltage is higher than the input voltage. More turns on the primary gives a **step-down transformer**, in which the output voltage is lower than the input voltage.

fig. 2.3.18 **How a transformer can change voltage.**

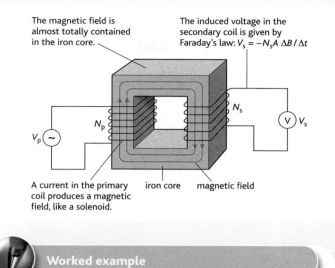

The magnetic field is almost totally contained in the iron core.

The induced voltage in the secondary coil is given by Faraday's law: $V_s = -N_s A \, \Delta B / \Delta t$

A current in the primary coil produces a magnetic field, like a solenoid.

iron core   magnetic field

Worked example

A local substation of the National Grid changes the voltage down from 11 kV to 415 V. If the primary coil in this transformer has 8000 turns, how many will be needed on the secondary to give the correct output voltage?

$$\frac{V_{primary}}{V_{secondary}} = \frac{N_{primary}}{N_{secondary}}$$

$$\frac{11 \times 10^3}{415} = \frac{8 \times 10^3}{N_{secondary}}$$

$$N_{secondary} = \frac{8 \times 10^3 \times 415}{11 \times 10^3} = 302 \text{ turns}$$

Questions

1   What is the flux linkage if a square coil with 10 cm sides and having 500 turns interacts with a magnetic field, $B = 0.33$ mT?

2   The graph shown in fig. 2.3.19 is a trace of induced emf against time as a magnet is dropped through a coil of wire.

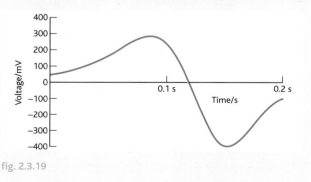

fig. 2.3.19

a   Describe and explain the trace obtained.

b   If the coil were connected in series to a light bulb, describe and explain how the current through the bulb would vary over time.

3   The coil from question 1 is turned through 90° within the 0.33 mT magnetic field, moving from a position perpendicular to the field, to a position parallel to the field. This action takes 12 ms. What is the induced emf in the coil? How would Lenz's law cause the **induced current** to affect the movement?

SC 4   A transformer for a toy train set converts the mains supply from 230 V down to 6 V to operate the model train. The transformer that makes this conversion has 160 turns on its secondary coil. How many primary turns does the transformer have?

fig. 2.3.20

Environmental concerns are causing an ever larger proportion of the population to be aware of the problems associated with the use of non-renewable supplies of energy. The mechanical power of the wind has long been harnessed by people, and for about 120 years this has also included generating electricity from the kinetic energy of the wind. Wind turbines can provide an excellent localised supply of electricity, especially in remote locations (fig. 2.3.20). Wind farms consisting of many turbines can be connected to the National Grid to assist with supply for a whole country. Britain is one of the best placed countries to harness wind power as our patterns of wind match very well with the greatest efficiency patterns: often windy but usually only at a moderate speed.

The first wind turbines

It is thought that the first wind-powered electricity generating system was built in 1888 by the American engineer Charles Brush to power his home in Cleveland, Ohio. Brush not only developed a very large wind turbine, but his system also incorporated a very sophisticated system of battery storage and regulation of voltage and current in variable wind conditions. It was both an electrical and an engineering masterpiece. A comprehensive article about Brush's setup was published in the magazine *Scientific American* on 20 December 1890 (fig. 2.3.21). Extracts of this article show that this early system still contained all the important elements of any wind electricity generation system:

The wheel, which is 56 feet in diameter, is secured to the shaft and is provided with 144 blades, which are twisted like those of screw propellers. The sail surface of the wheel is about 1,800 square feet, the length of the tail which turns the wheel towards the wind is 60 feet, and its width is 20 feet.

Today's wind turbines have rotor blades that are generally in the region of 40–50 m in diameter, whilst the very largest prototypes can be 80 m diameter. The 144 blades actually made Brush's wind turbine very heavy and inefficient. Modern designs have only two or three rotor blades.

The dynamo, which is one of Mr. Brush's own design ... makes fifty revolutions to one of the wheel. The speed of the dynamo at full load is 500 revolutions per minute, and its normal capacity at full load is 12,000 watts. The automatic switching devices are arranged so that the dynamo goes into effective action at 330 revolutions a minute, and an automatic regulator is provided which does not permit the electromotive force to run above 90 volts at any speed. The working circuit is arranged to automatically close at 75 volts and open at 70 volts.

At 12 kW, Brush built a very low power system which would have struggled to meet the demands of a modern home but, as his system was really only used for lighting his mansion, it was sufficient. Nowadays, wind turbines will usually generate 690V and have a power output of about 500 kW. Further research and development has led to the largest systems being able to produce up to 2.5 MW. Usually, of course, many wind turbines operate together to act as an equivalent to a power station.

Conductors extend underground from [the generator] to the dwelling house. ... In the basement of Mr. Brush's house there are 408 secondary battery cells arranged in twelve batteries of 34 cells each; these 12 batteries are charged and discharged in parallel; each cell has a capacity of 100 ampere hours. The jars which contain the elements of the battery are of glass, and each cell has its liquid covered with a layer of "mineral seal" oil, a quarter of an inch thick, which entirely prevents evaporation and spraying, and suppresses all odor.

The single biggest problem facing electricity generation using wind power is the randomly variable nature of the energy supply. As the wind changes with the weather, there needs to be smoothing or storage of electricity so that the electricity supply can be matched with consumer demands.

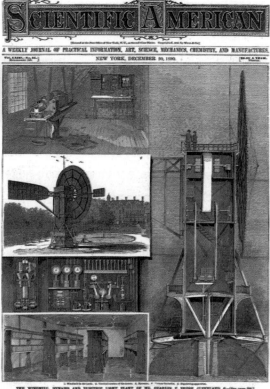

fig. 2.3.21 The front cover of Scientific American of
20 December 1890 showing Charles Brush's wind turbine and
electrical distribution system for his mansion.

 Questions

1   What was the diameter of Brush's wind turbine
    in metres?

2   If the brush system were operating at the highest
    allowed voltage (90 V) and producing 12 kW, what
    current would be delivered to each of the 12 parallel
    batteries of cells?

3   If a student were to build a model wind turbine to
    light an LED, list the main parts of the model that
    would be needed and what their function is – a
    diagram may help your explanation.

4   Explain the environmental importance of developing
    increased use of wind power electricity generation
    systems. In your answer, discuss the problems which
    will slow the pace of uptake of wind power as an
    alternative to non-renewable energy sources.

5   Carry out some research on the problem of variable
    wind power supply. Write a paragraph to explain how
    this problem is being overcome.

Build your own wind turbine

It is not difficult to make a model wind turbine that will
generate enough electricity to light an LED. A generator
(or dynamo) is exactly the same construction as a motor,
but if you spin the motor, electricity is delivered along
the wires, instead of the other way around. You could
use a model motor like that in fig. 2.3.5, connect some
homemade windmill blades and replace the battery pack
with an LED. If a hairdryer is used to blow your model
wind turbine it should provide enough energy to light the
LED. Alternatively, a vertical axis model can be made by
cutting a bottle in half vertically and then connecting the
two halves as shown in fig. 2.3.22, with magnets spinning
above coils at the bottom.

*Note that this practical activity is additional to those
suggested by the Edexcel specification.*

fig. 2.3.22 A simple home-made model wind turbine (vertical axis).

Examzone: Topic 2 Electric and magnetic fields

1 One practical arrangement for verifying Coulomb's law is to use a lightweight, negatively-charged, freely-suspended ball. It is repelled by the negative charge on a larger sphere that is held near it, on an insulated support. The small angle of deflection θ is then measured.

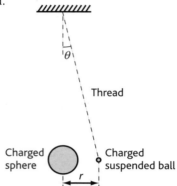

Thread

Charged sphere

Charged suspended ball

r

Draw a free-body force diagram for the suspended ball. (3)

The weight of the ball is W. Show that the force of repulsion F on the suspended ball is given by

$$F = W\tan\theta$$ (2)

A student takes several sets of readings by moving the larger sphere towards the suspended ball in order to increase the mutual force of repulsion between them. He measures the angle of deflection θ and the separation distance r in each case. He then calculates the magnitude of the force F.

Here are some of his results.

Force $F/10^{-3}$ N			142	568
Distance $r/10^{-3}$ m	36.0	27.0	18.0	9.0

Calculate the values that you would expect the student to have obtained for the missing forces, assuming that Coulomb's law was obeyed.

Write your answers in a copy of the table. (4)

Suggest why, in practice, it was necessary for the student to take measurements quickly using this arrangement. (1)

(Total 10 marks)

2 The diagram shows a high-speed alpha particle entering the space between two charged plates in a vacuum.

+2000 V

α particle

0 V

Add to a copy of the diagram the subsequent path of the alpha particle as it passes between the plates and well beyond them. (3)

The gap between the plates is 10 mm. Calculate the magnitude of the electric force on the alpha particle as it passes between the plates. (3)

(Total 6 marks)

3 The diagram shows two parallel plates with a potential difference of 3000 V applied across them. The plates are in a vacuum.

+3000 V

25 mm

0 V

On a copy of the diagram sketch the electric field pattern in the region between the plates. (2)

On the same diagram sketch and label two equipotential lines. (1)

The plates are 25 mm apart. Show that the force experienced by an electron just above the bottom plate is about 2×10^{-14} N. (3)

Copy and complete the graph to show how the force on the electron varies as the distance of the electron varies from the bottom plate to the top plate.

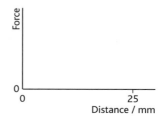

(2)

This force causes the electron to accelerate.

The electron is initially at rest in contact with the bottom plate when the potential difference is applied. Calculate its speed as it reaches the upper plate. **(3)**

(Total 11 marks)

4 Define capacitance. **(2)**

An uncharged capacitor of 200 μF is connected in series with a 470 kΩ resistor, a 1.50 V cell and a switch. Draw a circuit diagram of this arrangement. **(1)**

Calculate the maximum current that flows. **(2)**

Sketch a graph of voltage against charge for your capacitor as it charges. Indicate on the graph the energy stored when the capacitor is fully charged. **(4)**

Calculate the energy stored in the fully-charged capacitor. **(2)**

(Total 11 marks)

5 The diagram shows a graph of charge against voltage for a capacitor.

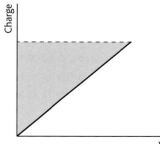

What quantity is represented by the slope of the graph? **(2)**

What quantity is represented by the shaded area? **(2)**

An electronic camera flash gun contains a capacitor of 100 μF which is charged to a voltage of 250 V. Show that the energy stored is 3.1 J. **(2)**

The capacitor is charged by an electronic circuit that is powered by a 1.5 V cell. The current drawn from the cell is 0.20 A. Calculate the power from the cell and from this the minimum time for the cell to recharge the capacitor. **(3)**

(Total 9 marks)

6 The magnitude of the force on a current-carrying conductor in a magnetic field is directly proportional to the magnitude of the current in the conductor. With the aid of a diagram describe how you could demonstrate this in a school laboratory. **(4)**

At a certain point on the Earth's surface the horizontal component of the Earth's magnetic field is 1.8×10^{-5} T. A straight piece of conducting wire 2.0 m long, of mass 1.5 g lies on a horizontal wooden bench in an east-west direction. When a very large current flows momentarily in the wire it is just sufficient to cause the wire to lift up off the surface of the bench.

State the direction of the current in the wire. **(1)**

Calculate the current. **(2)**

What other noticeable effect will this current produce? **(1)**

(Total 8 marks)

7 The diagram shows a rectangular coil PQRS which can rotate about an axis which is perpendicular to the magnetic field between two magnetic poles.

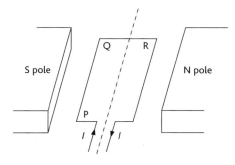

Explain why the coil begins to rotate when the direct current *I* is switched on. **(4)**

Add to a copy of the diagram an arrow showing the direction of the force on PQ. **(1)**

State *three* factors which would affect the magnitude of this force. **(3)**

A student notices that as the coil rotates faster the current in it reduces. Explain this observation. **(2)**

(Total 9 marks)

Topic 3 Particle physics

This topic covers atomic structure, particle accelerators and the standard quark–lepton model that is used to describe the behaviour of matter on a subatomic scale. The topic draws on physics which is still theoretical, and explains how scientists are currently experimenting to confirm these theories.

What are the theories?

The theories of the structure of matter at atomic and subatomic scales – albeit those which currently hold sway amongst the majority of physicists – are explained. The use of particle accelerators to investigate these ideas is outlined, together with explanations of the standard notation and commonly discussed reactions between these particles.

Einstein's famous equation accounting for interchange between matter and energy is used to calculate how some particles can be created, with a particular focus on the relationship between matter and antimatter.

What is the evidence?

Subatomic physics experiments tend not to be the stuff of the student laboratory, but some of these experiments are explained here. The topic covers the use of particle accelerators and detectors, explaining how the data is interpreted. Images from particle detectors give opportunities to practise interpreting this type of data.

The evidence for the theories underlying subatomic physics is still being generated and interpreted. You will gain a sense of the developmental nature of scientific enquiry from this topic, along with an idea of which elements of our models of the behaviour of matter are more reliably believable, and which remain hypothetical.

What are the implications?

Both the Large Hadron Collider and its soon-to-follow successor, known as Einstein's Telescope, have been designed to explore and confirm our current theoretical physics. The study of this topic brings us to the very boundaries of human knowledge, and may cause you to speculate beyond them. It may be that many ideas will be confirmed as correct, or it could be that the results of these accelerator experiments send science back to the drawing board.

The map opposite shows you the knowledge and skills you need to have by the end of this topic, and how they are linked together. The numbers refer to the sections in the Edexcel specification.

Chapter 3.1

use the terms nucleon number (mass number) and proton number (atomic number) (96)

describe how large-angle alpha particle scattering gives evidence for a nuclear atom (97)

recall that electrons are released in the process of thermionic emission and explain how they can be accelerated by electric and magnetic fields (98)

explain why high energies are required to see fine structure (part of 102)

use de Broglie's wave equation, $\lambda = \dfrac{h}{p}$ (108)

Chapter 3.2

explain the role of electric and magnetic fields in particle accelerators (linac and cyclotron) and detectors (general principles of ionisation and deflection only) (99)

explain why high energies are required to break particles into their constituents (part of 102)

recognise and use the expression $r = \dfrac{p}{BQ}$ for a charged particle in a magnetic field (100)

recall and use the fact that charge, energy and momentum are always conserved in interactions between particles and hence interpret records of particle tracks (101)

be aware of relativistic effects and that these need to be taken into account at speeds near that of light (use of relativistic equations not required) (105)

Chapter 3.3

recognise and use the expression $\Delta E = c^2 \Delta m$ in situations involving the creation and annihilation of matter and antimatter particles (103)

recall that in the standard quark–lepton model each particle has a corresponding antiparticle, that baryons (e.g. neutrons and protons) are made from three quarks, and mesons (e.g. pions) from a quark and an antiquark, and that the symmetry of the model predicted the top and bottom quark (106)

use the non-SI units MeV and GeV (energy) and $\dfrac{MeV}{c^2}$, $\dfrac{GeV}{c^2}$ (mass) and atomic mass unit u, and convert between these and SI units (104)

write and interpret equations using standard nuclear notation and standard particle symbols (e.g. π^+, e^-) (107)

3.1 Probing matter Spec 96, 97

A nuclear atom

HSW Atomic theories through history

People have long wondered about what the materials around us are fundamentally made of. There have been many philosophers and scientists, from Democritus in the fifth century BCE to Dalton in the early nineteenth century, who have suggested the idea of a tiny indivisible particle from which everything else is constructed. The basic model for one of these 'atoms' – which was published in a paper by Dalton in 1803 – is simply a hard solid sphere.

When Thomson discovered that tiny negatively charged bits (electrons) could be removed from an atom, leaving behind a positively charged ion, he produced the '**plum pudding model**'. This has the main body of the atom being composed of a nebulous positively charged material (the pudding 'dough') with electrons (the 'plums') randomly scattered through it. This model was successful at explaining the evidence available at that time. It was superseded in 1911 by Rutherford's model of the atom, which has a tiny positively charged nucleus carrying most of the mass of the atom, surrounded at some distance by the electrons, with most of the atom as empty space. Later in the twentieth century, Niels Bohr refined the nuclear model to have the electrons located around the nucleus in fixed orbits, following the emerging theory of quantised energy. Electrons could move from one fixed orbit to another depending on the energy they gained or lost, but other than these fixed jumps were stuck in an orbit. Bohr's model generated the commonly used analogy of the atom as being like a miniature solar system. This idea is not a perfect model as it is incorrect in many aspects, but most models have strengths and weaknesses. It is often necessary to use models in science and we must always be careful to work within the limitations of any model we use.

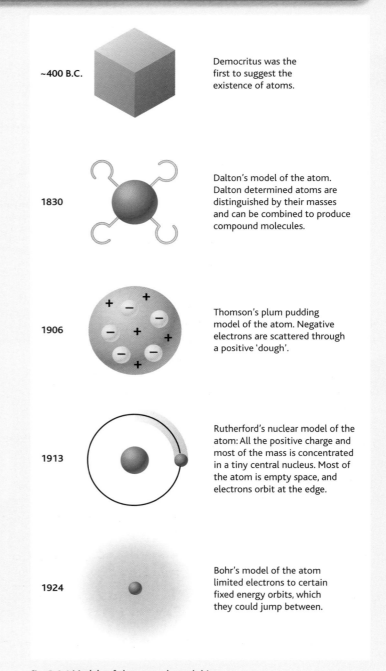

~400 B.C. — Democritus was the first to suggest the existence of atoms.

1830 — Dalton's model of the atom. Dalton determined atoms are distinguished by their masses and can be combined to produce compound molecules.

1906 — Thomson's plum pudding model of the atom. Negative electrons are scattered through a positive 'dough'.

1913 — Rutherford's nuclear model of the atom: All the positive charge and most of the mass is concentrated in a tiny central nucleus. Most of the atom is empty space, and electrons orbit at the edge.

1924 — Bohr's model of the atom limited electrons to certain fixed energy orbits, which they could jump between.

fig. 3.1.1 **Models of the atom through history.**

Alpha particle scattering

Between 1909 and 1911, Geiger and Marsden, students of Lord Rutherford at Manchester University, undertook an experiment in which they aimed an alpha particle source at an extremely thin gold foil (**fig. 3.1.2**).

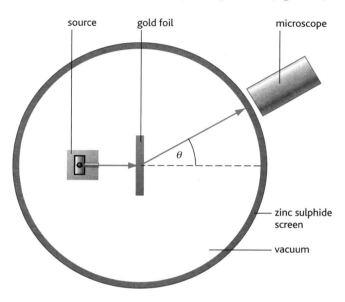

fig. 3.1.2 **Rutherford's alpha particle scattering apparatus.**

Their expectation was that all the alpha particles would pass through, possibly with a little deviation. The results generally followed this pattern – the vast majority passed straight through the foil. However, a few alpha particles had their trajectories deviated by quite large angles. Some were even repelled back the way they had come (**fig. 3.1.3**). Rutherford commented, 'It was almost as incredible as if you had fired a 15 inch [artillery] shell at a piece of tissue paper and it came back and hit you'. It was a shocking result based on the model of the atom

at that time. Having repeated the results hundreds of thousands of times, the only conclusion that Rutherford could reach was that to explain the results it was necessary to change the model of the atom. He developed a model with a small nucleus in the centre of the atom which contained all the positive charge and the vast majority of the mass of the atom (see **fig. 3.1.1** and **table 3.1.1**).

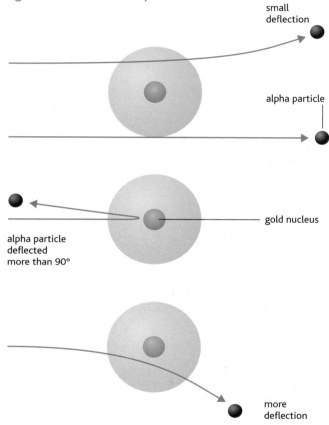

fig. 3.1.3 **Alpha particle paths in scattering from gold atoms.** Approximately 1 in 8000 was deflected through more than 90°. Momentum conservation dictates that this is only possible if scattering from something more massive than the alpha particle itself.

Angle of deflection/degrees	Evidence	Conclusion
0–10	Most alpha particles pass straight through with little deviation.	Most of the atom is empty space.
10–90	Some alpha particles deflected through a large angle.	All the atom's positive charge is concentrated in one place.
90–180	A few alpha particles are repelled back towards the source side of the foil.	Most of the mass, and all positive charge, is in a tiny, central nucleus.

table 3.1.1 **Evidence and conclusions from Rutherford's alpha particle scattering experiment.**

Chadwick's discovery of the neutron

Rutherford had determined that most of the atom's mass and all the positive charge was held in a very small nucleus in the centre, and that electrons were held in a position at the edge of the atom. The difference between the nuclear mass and the known number of protons in it caused a problem though. Nuclei were too massive for the number of protons they contained. Rutherford suggested that additional proton–electron pairs, bound together, formed the extra mass in the nucleus.

In 1930, Irene Joliot-Curie and her husband, Frederic, found that alpha particles striking beryllium caused it to give off an unknown radiation. Difficult to detect, this unknown, uncharged radiation could knock protons out of paraffin and these were detected by a Geiger–Müller tube.

The Joliot-Curies tried to explain the unknown radiation as gamma rays, but as these rays have no mass, this was a breach of the conservation of momentum. James Chadwick repeated the experiments (fig. 3.1.4) using other target materials as well as paraffin. By considering momentum transfer and conservation of kinetic energy in the collisions between the particles, Chadwick concluded that the beryllium radiation was a neutral particle which had a mass about 1% more than that of a proton. In 1932 he published his proposal for the existence of this new particle which he called a neutron, and in 1935 he was awarded the Nobel Prize for the discovery.

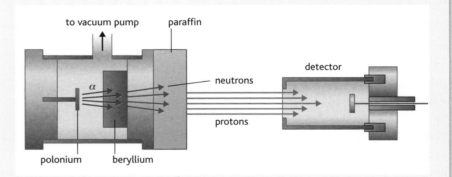

fig. 3.1.4 Chadwick's experiment to determine the existence of the neutron relied on conservation of momentum to work out the mass of this neutral particle.

Nuclear structure

As we have seen, the nucleus is made up from two particles: the proton and the neutron. Collectively these two particles, when in a nucleus, are known as **nucleons**. The number of protons in a nucleus determines which element the atom will be. The periodic table is a list of the elements ordered according to the number of protons in each atom's nucleus. This number is called the **proton number** or the **atomic number**. For small nuclei, up to about atomic number 20 (which is calcium), the number of neutrons in the nucleus is generally equal to the number of protons. There is some variation in the number of neutrons – atoms of the same element that have different numbers of neutrons are called **isotopes**.

Above atomic number 20, for the nucleus to be stable more neutrons than protons are generally needed. The neutrons help to bind the nucleus together as they exert a **strong nuclear force** on other nucleons, and they act as a space buffer between the mutually repelling positive charges of the protons. This buffering action means that as we progress through the periodic table to larger and larger nuclei, proportionately more and more neutrons are needed. By the time we reach the very biggest nuclei, there are as many as 50% more neutrons than protons.

To describe any given nucleus, it is necessary to specify how many protons and how many neutrons there are. Thus the chemical symbol written below refers to the isotope of radium which has 88 protons and 138 neutrons:

$$^{226}_{88}\text{Ra}$$

The number 226, called the **nucleon number** or the **mass number**, refers to the total number of nucleons – neutrons and protons – in a nucleus of this isotope. So to find the number of neutrons, we must subtract the atomic number from the mass number: $226 - 88 = 138$.

As radium must have 88 protons by definition, it is quite common not to write the 88. You might call this isotope 'radium-226', and this provides enough information to determine its proton number and **neutron number**.

HSW A quantum mechanical atom

In the 1920s, Werner Heisenberg altered the model of the atom which had electrons in orbits like planets in a solar system. His uncertainty principle states that we cannot know both the exact position and the velocity of anything at a given moment. His model of the atom has regions around the nucleus in which there is a high probability of finding an electron, and the shapes of these 'probability clouds' represent what we currently refer to as the electron 'orbitals' (**fig. 3.1.5**).

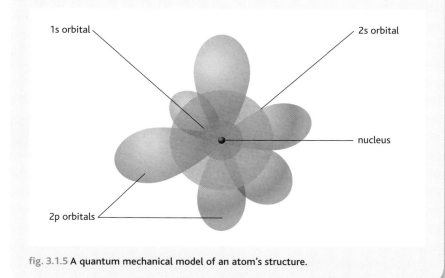

fig. 3.1.5 **A quantum mechanical model of an atom's structure.**

Questions

1 Use a periodic table to pick five elements at random. List them using standard symbols and then explain how many protons and neutrons each one has.

2 Suggest why it has taken so long for scientists to develop the current model of the atom.

3 Give two strengths and two weaknesses of the analogy that an atom is like a mini solar system.

4 Draw a flowchart which shows the stages of scientific discovery which slowly broke down our idea of an atom from a solid sphere to the current quantum mechanical model.

SC 5 Chadwick suggested that alpha particles colliding with beryllium produced neutrons according to:

$$^{4}_{2}\alpha + ^{A}_{B}\text{Be} \rightarrow ^{12}_{6}\text{C} + ^{1}_{0}\text{n}$$

What numbers are represented by A and B?

SC 6 A 4 MeV neutron collides head-on with a stationary hydrogen nucleus, and its kinetic energy is reduced to 1 MeV. What is the mass of the neutron? Mass of a proton = 1.6726×10^{-27} kg. (*Hint*: Remember $E_k = p^2/2m$.)

Electrons from atoms Spec 84, 86, 98, 108

Electron beams

Free conduction electrons in metals need a certain amount of energy if they are to escape from the surface of the metal structure. This energy can be supplied by a beam of photons, as seen in the **photoelectric effect**. The electrons can also gain enough energy simply through heating of the metal. The release of electrons from the surface of a metal as it is heated is known as **thermionic emission**.

If, on escaping, these electrons find themselves in an electric field, they will be accelerated by the field, moving in the positive direction. The kinetic energy they gain will depend on the pd, V, that they move through, according to the equation:

$$E_k = eV$$

where e is the charge on an electron.

Worked example

How fast would an electron be moving if it was accelerated from rest through a pd of 2500 V?

$$E_k = eV$$
$$= -1.6 \times 10^{-19} \times -2500$$
$$= 4 \times 10^{-16} \text{J}$$

(NB The pd is put into the equation as minus 2500 V because the electron accelerates in the opposite direction to the electric field lines. This then gives a positive answer for the energy.)

$$E_k = \tfrac{1}{2} mv^2$$
$$v = \sqrt{\frac{2E_k}{m}}$$
$$= \sqrt{\frac{2 \times 4 \times 10^{-16}}{9.11 \times 10^{-31}}}$$
$$v = 2.96 \times 10^7 \text{m s}^{-1}$$

Using thermionic emission to produce electrons, and applying an electric field to accelerate them, we can generate a beam of fast-moving electrons, traditionally known as a cathode ray. This beam of electrons will be deflected by a magnetic field. If a fast-moving electron hits a screen painted with a certain chemical, the screen will fluoresce – it will emit light. We saw this in operation in chapter 2.3 as a way in which to investigate the strength of the force on a charge moving in a magnetic field.

This is the principle by which cathode ray oscilloscopes (CROs) and old-style televisions operate. The electron beam in a CRO is moved left and right, and up and down, by passing the beam through an electric field which is generated by electric plates so its strength and direction can be altered. Thus the point on the screen which is targeted to emit light can be changed quickly and easily.

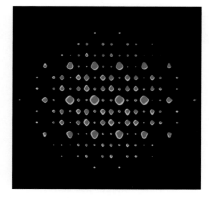

fig. 3.1.6 Electron diffraction patterns can explore the molecular structure of crystals.

An electron probe

Electron beams fired at a crystal will produce scattering patterns that can tell us about the structure of the crystal (fig. 3.1.6). Unlike the patterns found by Geiger and Marsden in their experiments with beams of alpha particles, it was shown in 1927 by Davisson and Germer that an electron beam produces a diffraction pattern. This provided the experimental evidence to prove a novel theory that had been suggested just three years earlier by the Belgian, Louis de Broglie. He was bemused that light could be shown to behave as a wave in some situations and as a particle in other circumstances. He hypothesised that this might also be the case for things which were traditionally considered to be particles. De Broglie proposed that the wavelength, λ, of a particle could be calculated from its momentum using the expression:

$$\lambda = \frac{h}{p}$$

where h is the Planck constant. So:

$$\lambda = \frac{h}{mv}$$

The Davisson–Germer experiment proved that the diffraction pattern obtained when a cathode ray hit a crystal could only be produced if the electrons in the beam had a wavelength that coincided with the de Broglie wavelength. As a consequence of this experimental confirmation, Louis de Broglie was awarded the 1929 Nobel Prize for Physics.

Worked example

What is the wavelength of an electron in a beam which has been accelerated through 2000 V?

$$E_k = eV$$
$$= -1.6 \times 10^{-19} \times -2000$$
$$= 3.2 \times 10^{-16} \text{J}$$
$$E_k = \tfrac{1}{2} mv^2$$
$$= 3.2 \times 10^{-16} \text{J}$$
$$\therefore v = \sqrt{\frac{2E_k}{m}}$$
$$= \sqrt{\frac{2 \times 3.2 \times 10^{-16}}{9.11 \times 10^{-31}}}$$
$$= 2.65 \times 10^7 \, \text{m s}^{-1}$$
$$\lambda = \frac{h}{mv}$$
$$= \frac{6.63 \times 10^{-34}}{9.11 \times 10^{-31} \times 2.65 \times 10^7}$$
$$= 2.75 \times 10^{-11} \text{m}$$

Observing electron diffraction

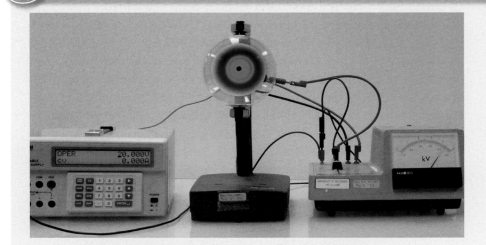

This is additional to the practicals suggested in the Edexcel specification.

You may have the equipment to observe electron diffraction. By measuring the radius of the circular pattern, for a certain accelerating voltage, you can perform a calculation to confirm de Broglie's hypothesis.

fig. 3.1.7 **Measuring electron diffraction occurring through a sliver of carbon.**

The idea of electrons acting as waves has allowed scientists to study the structure of crystals, along similar lines to X-ray crystallography. When waves pass through a gap which is about the same size as their wavelength, they are diffracted – they spread out. The degree of diffraction spreading depends on the ratio of the size of the gap to the wavelength of the wave. If a beam of electrons is aimed at a crystal, the gaps between atoms in the crystal can diffract the electron waves and produce a pattern on a screen. Measuring the pattern allows the spacings between the atoms in the crystal to be calculated.

Electron diffraction and alpha particle scattering both highlight the idea that we can study the structure of matter by probing it with beams of high-energy particles. The more detail – or smaller scale – the structure to be investigated, the higher energy the beam of particles needs to be. Accelerating larger and larger particles to higher and higher energies has been the aim of particle physicists since Thomson discovered the electron in 1897.

Questions

1 Calculate the de Broglie wavelengths for the following:

   a an electron travelling at 2% of the speed of light

   b an electron which has been accelerated through 1200 V

   c a proton with a momentum of $5 \times 10^{-21}\,\mathrm{kg\,m\,s^{-1}}$

   d you running at $5\,\mathrm{m\,s^{-1}}$.

2 Why would de Broglie not have been awarded the Nobel Prize before the Davisson–Germer experiment?

3 Calculate the speed that an electron would have to travel at if it were to be used to probe the structure of the nucleus. (It would need a de Broglie wavelength of about the size of the nucleus: $\lambda = 5 \times 10^{-15}\,\mathrm{m}$.)

4 Carry out some research to find out how the direction of the electron beam in a cathode ray oscilloscope can be changed in order to make any point on the screen light up. Show this in a diagram. Explain how such a CRO could be set up in a hospital to display the electrical impulses of a patient's heart.

3.2 Particle accelerators Spec 99, 100, 101, 105

fig. 3.2.1 **An early attempt at particle collision and detection!**

To investigate the internal substructure of particles, scientists collide them with other particles at very high speeds (very high energies). It is necessary to use high energy particles because at lower energies the particles just bounce off each other, keeping their internal secrets. If we can collide particles together hard enough they will break up, revealing their structure. In most cases additional particles are created from the energy of the collision. Sometimes these extra particles reveal or confirm other new physics.

The challenge for scientists has been to accelerate particles to sufficient speeds. Charged particles can be accelerated in straight lines using a potential difference, and their direction changed along a curved path by a magnetic field.

Linear accelerators

One of the simplest systems for producing high energy particles for particle collisions is to accelerate a beam of charged particles along a straight path. However, this is limited by the maximum achievable potential difference. To overcome this problem, the particles are accelerated in stages (**fig. 3.2.2**). They are repeatedly accelerated through the maximum pd, building the particle energies to very high values. Using this principle the 3.2 kilometre Stanford Linear Accelerator in the US can accelerate electrons to an energy of 25 GeV, meaning that they have effectively passed through a potential difference of 25 billion volts.

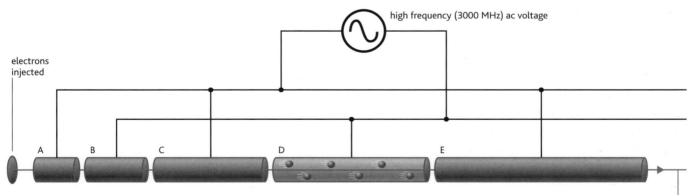

fig. 3.2.2 **The structure of a linear accelerator.**

If the particles to be accelerated in the **linear accelerator** are electrons, they are generated by an electrostatic machine (like a van der Graaff generator) and introduced into the machine (**fig. 3.2.2**). The electrons are attracted towards tube A by making its metal cylinder positive. Once inside the cylinder, the electrons move in a straight line, as the electrode is equally attracting in all directions. The alternating voltage supply is made to change as the electrons pass the middle of tube A, so it becomes negative. This repels the electrons out of the end of tube A and on towards tube B, which now has a positive potential. They accelerate towards it, and the whole process repeats as they pass through tube B and are then

accelerated on towards tube C. This carries on until the electrons reach the end of the line, at which point they emerge to collide with a target.

In order to keep accelerating particles that are moving faster and faster, the acceleration tubes must be made longer and longer as the particles travel through each successive tube at a higher speed, whilst the time between potential difference flips is fixed as the alternating voltage has a uniform frequency of a few gigahertz (often referred to as radio frequency). The limit on the use of this kind of accelerator is how long you can afford to build it, remembering that the whole thing must be in a vacuum so that the particles do not collide with air atoms.

HSW Was Einstein right?

One of Einstein's claims in his theory of special relativity is that nothing can accelerate beyond the speed of light. This means that particles in accelerators must be faced with a problem when they are already travelling close to the speed of light and then pass through a pd which should accelerate them beyond it. In 1964, William Bertozzi demonstrated that, at very high speeds, particles deviate from the equation $\frac{1}{2}mv^2 = qV$ and do indeed never accelerate beyond the speed of light.

By measuring the actual speed of electrons accelerated from a van der Graaff generator, and then determining their

actual kinetic energy by colliding them with a target and measuring the heat generated, Bertozzi was able to show that the energy imparted by the accelerating pd started to become more than the amount expected from $\frac{1}{2}mv^2$.

This demonstration showed that whilst the kinetic energy and momentum of particles can continue to increase without limit, their speed does not. This can only happen if the mass of a particle increases with its speed. This mass increase becomes significant at speeds approaching light speed – known as 'relativistic speeds'.

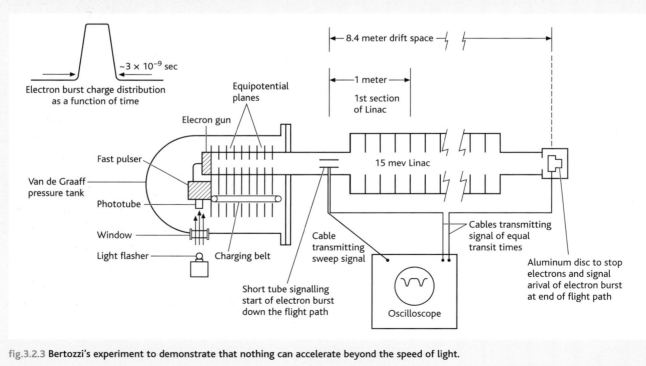

fig.3.2.3 **Bertozzi's experiment to demonstrate that nothing can accelerate beyond the speed of light.**

Accelerating particles in circles

Struggling to produce ever longer linear accelerators, scientists wanted to coil their accelerators up into a circle so that the particles could be accelerated in an electric field repeatedly in a smaller space. To do this, we use the fact that charged particles moving across a magnetic field will feel a centripetal force, and so will move in a circular path. We can work out the radius of this circular path, and thus construct a circular accelerator of the right dimensions.

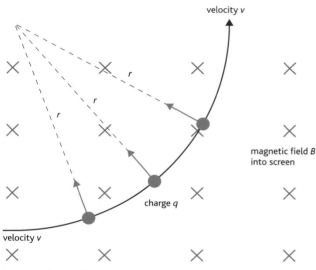

fig. 3.2.4 **The circular trajectory of a charged particle moving across a magnetic field. Note that field lines can be shown coming out of a page by drawing a dot, and those going into a page (like the magnetic field here) can be shown by drawing a cross.**

We have previously seen the equation for the force on a charged particle moving across a magnetic field (chapter 2.3):

$$F = Bqv$$

This force acts at right angles to the velocity, v, meaning that the particle will follow a circular path. Recall that the equation for the centripetal force on anything moving in a circle is:

$$F = \frac{mv^2}{r}$$

We can therefore equate the expressions:

$$Bqv = \frac{mv^2}{r}$$

Dividing out the velocity from each side and re-arranging to find an expression for the radius of the circle gives:

$$r = \frac{mv}{Bq}$$
or $r = \frac{p}{Bq}$

This means that for a given magnetic field, the radius of the path of a charged particle is proportional to its momentum. At slow speeds, the radius is proportional to velocity (or the square root of the kinetic energy), but as these experiments generally send particles at speeds approaching the speed of light, relativistic effects need to be accounted for. In particular, at these very high speeds the particle's mass increases, which would also alter its momentum. The overall result is that a particle increasing in speed would travel along an outwardly spiralling path.

The cyclotron

In 1930, Lawrence developed the first cyclotron, a circular accelerator which could give protons about 1 MeV of energy.

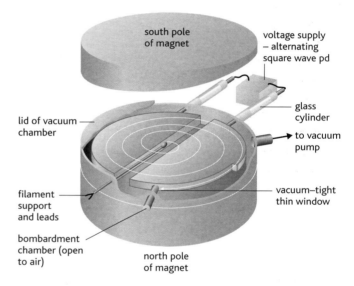

fig. 3.2.5 **The structure of a cyclotron.**

In a cyclotron, there are two 'dee'-shaped electrodes, and the particles are accelerated in the electric field in the gap between them. Whilst inside the dees, the particle will travel along a semicircular path under the influence of the magnetic field, before being accelerated across the gap again; then another semicircle, another acceleration across the gap, and so on. As each acceleration increases the momentum of the particle, the radius of its path increases, and so it steadily spirals outwards until it emerges from an exit hole and hits the target placed in a bombardment chamber in its path.

Cyclotron frequency

In order to maintain the accelerations at exactly the correct instant, the pd needs to switch direction at exactly the moment the particle exits from one dee to move across the gap between them. This means the voltage supply has to follow a square wave pattern where it flips polarity instantaneously.

The frequency of these polarity switches only depends on the particle being used and the strength of the magnetic field applied:

$$f = \frac{1}{T} \qquad T = \frac{2\pi r}{v}$$

During one complete period of the alternating voltage the particle will pass through both dees, thus completing a full circle at that radius.

But:

$$r = \frac{mv}{Bq}$$

$$T = \frac{2\pi mv}{Bqv} = \frac{2\pi m}{Bq}$$

$$f = \frac{Bq}{2\pi m}$$

Thus the frequency needed is independent of the radius, meaning that a constant frequency can be used and the particle will complete each semicircle through a dee in the same time. That is until the speed becomes so great that the mass changes through relativistic effects!

The synchrotron

Once the relativistic effects of mass increase are included in the equation for cyclotron frequency, it becomes:

$$f = \frac{Bq}{2\pi m} \times \sqrt{1 - \frac{v^2}{c^2}}$$

As the frequency of the applied accelerating potential difference now depends on the velocity of the particles, this means that to use a cyclotron to generate high energy particle beams, it needs very clever circuitry to produce accurately timed polarity switches. The technology to do this was first developed in 1945 and the 'synchrocyclotron' can accelerate particles to as much as 700 MeV.

With the development of varying frequency for the accelerating pd, the next logical step was to vary the strength of the magnetic field using an electromagnet. This means that the radius of the particle beam's path can be kept constant by simply increasing the magnetic field strength in line with the increasing momentum. A single ring accelerator like this is called a **synchrotron**.

Alternate accelerating tubes and bending magnets can generate very high energy particle beams. The Tevatron, at Fermilab near Chicago, can give particles 1 TeV of energy (tera = 10^{12}). Alternatively, these rings can be used to store charged particles by making them circulate endlessly at a constant energy. This is a particularly important use when trying to store antimatter, which will annihilate if it comes into contact with normal matter.

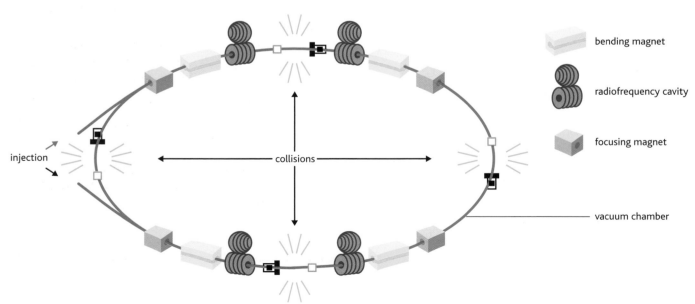

bending magnet

radiofrequency cavity

focusing magnet

vacuum chamber

injection

collisions

fig. 3.2.6 The Large-Electron-Positron Collider at CERN, near Geneva, is a 27 km synchrotron.

HSW Ninovium – scientists sometimes cheat too

In 1999, the Lawrence Berkeley Laboratory in California published a paper claiming that they had produced an isotope of an element with atomic number 118. The paper claimed they had succeeded in observing a chain of alpha decays following their collision of 449 MeV krypton-86 ions into a target of lead-206. The radioactive decay sequence was indicative of having started from element 118 – initially named 'ninovium' after the Bulgarian team leader Victor Ninov. No other lab in the world was able to reproduce the results, and after a two year inquiry, it was determined that Ninov had falsified the results. The Berkeley Lab retracted the paper, and Victor Ninov, who has continually maintained his innocence, was fired.

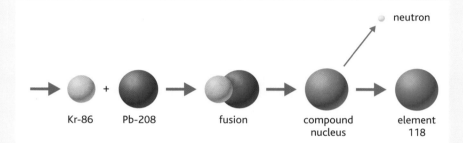

fig. 3.2.7 The fusion reaction which was claimed to produce element 118.

In 2006, an accelerator facility in Dubna, Russia, working jointly with an American group from the Lawrence Livermore National Laboratory, claimed to have fused calcium-48 and californium-249 to produce the as yet unnamed element 118 with a mass number of 294.

The team used a particle accelerator to bombard Cf-249 with high energy ions of Ca-48. With the previous problems surrounding this heavy element 118, the research team were very careful about the accuracy of their data, but it may be some time before the results are reproduced by an independent corroborating experiment – californium is rare and highly radioactive. Mark Stoyer, a nuclear chemist at Lawrence Livermore National Laboratory, who was part of the research team, said, 'We saw something interesting, and the way we've interpreted it, it's element 118. But you need someone else to duplicate it. A fundamental tenet of science is reproducibility.'

Questions

1 Why do the electrodes in a linear accelerator get progressively longer?

2 Lawrence's second cyclotron, built with the assistance of Stanley Livingstone, was 25 cm in diameter and accelerated protons to 1 MeV.

   a Calculate the speed of these protons.

   b Calculate the momentum of these protons.

   c Calculate the magnetic field strength Lawrence used in this cyclotron, assuming that the protons move in a circle around the very edge of the machine.

   d Calculate the frequency of the voltage that Lawrence and Stanley had to apply to achieve this proton acceleration.

3 The Large Hadron Collider is a giant circular accelerator near Geneva in Switzerland. The LHC website provides some facts about it:

   • the circular ring has a circumference of 27 km
   • each proton goes around over 11 000 times a second
   • each proton has 7×10^{12} eV of kinetic energy.

   a Calculate the speed of these protons.

   b Calculate $\frac{1}{2}mv^2$ for these protons using $m_p = 1.67 \times 10^{-27}$ kg.

   c How does your answer to b compare with the 7 TeV of kinetic energy the protons are given through pd acceleration?

   d Explain this difference.

Particle detection Spec 99, 101

Principles of detection

Both school laboratory electron diffraction and Geiger and Marsden's alpha scattering experiment rely on observing the light given off from a fluorescent screen when it is hit by a particle. In order to obtain accurate enough data to reinvent the structure of the atom, Geiger and Marsden spent two years sitting in a darkened room, for eight hours at a time, counting the flashes of light they saw through a microscope. Geiger found this so frustrating that he jointly invented the Geiger–Müller(GM) tube to detect particles which could then be counted electrically.

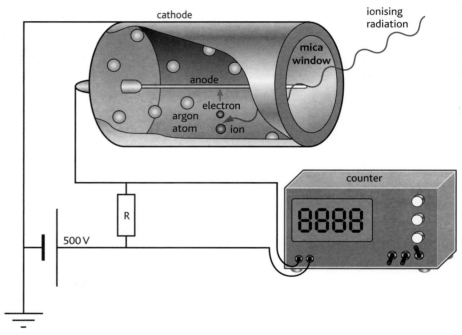

fig. 3.2.8 The internal workings of a Geiger–Müller detector.

The GM tube works on the fundamental principle that is common to most particle detectors – ionisation. As the particle to be detected passes through the tube, it ionises atoms of a gas (typically argon) which fills the tube. The ions and electrons produced are accelerated by an electric field between electrodes in the tube and then discharged when they reach the electrodes. This produces a pulse of electricity which is counted by a counter connected to the tube. Many different types of detector have been invented by particle physicists, but the majority detect ionisation caused by the particles to be detected.

Analysing detections

Particle-counting detectors have their uses, but they can't commonly distinguish between different types of particles, a characteristic that is becoming increasingly important in detectors. Modern particle physics experiments are carried out using such high energies that they can produce hundreds of different types of particles. Unless the detectors used in these experiments can identify properties of the particles, like their energy, charge or mass, the experimental results will be useless. On page 66 we saw how the mass spectrometer deflects an ion using a magnetic field. The ion can then be identified by the amount of deflection, since this is dependent on the mass and charge of the ion, and the strength and direction of the magnetic field used.

fig. 3.2.9 a A hydrogen bubble chamber, and b an image of particle tracks it can detect.

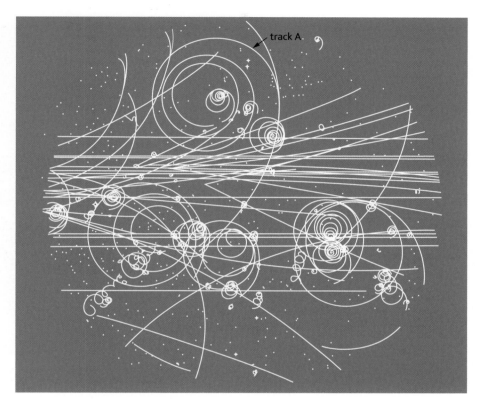

track A.

Particle physics experiments took a major leap forward with the invention of the bubble chamber detector. As Professor Siegbahn of the Swedish Academy of Sciences commented when presenting the 1960 Nobel Prize in Physics:

> Dr. Glaser, your invention of the 'bubble chamber' has opened up a new world for nuclear science. We can now observe with our own eyes all the strange processes which occur when high-energy beams from [particle accelerators] are directed into your chamber.

Professor Siegbahn went on to explain that the bubble chamber acts like a combination of jet-plane vapour trails and the bubbles that suddenly appear when you open a bottle of fizzy drink. Superheated liquid hydrogen bubbles into gas form at any point where ions are generated within it. These bubbles can be observed within the liquid and thus the trails show the paths of moving particles. As the example picture in **fig. 3.2.9b** shows, particles can be tracked as they progress through the bubble chamber, and those affected by the magnetic field across it follow curved paths. As in the mass spectrometer, the radius of curvature of the tracks will tell us the mass and charge of the particles. In addition, the picture allows us to analyse interactions as they happened, as the tracks sometimes end abruptly or have sharp changes in direction when they collide. In some cases, particle tracks appear to start from nothing. These show instances where particles have been created.

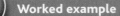

Worked example

Look at track A in **fig. 3.2.9b**. If the magnetic field in the bubble chamber went at right angles to this picture and into the page, would the particle shown by track A be an electron or a positron (positively charged anti-electron)?

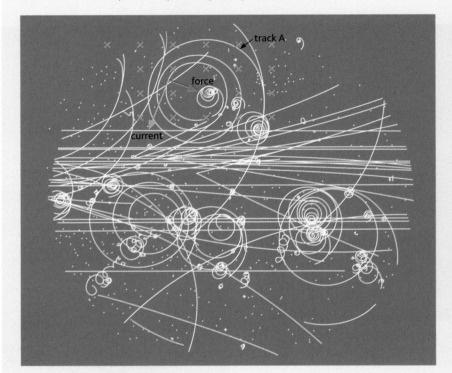

fig. 3.2.10 **Fleming's left hand rule can be used to find the charge on the particle of track A.**

Using Fleming's left hand rule, with the index finger pointing into the page (magnetic field), the centripetal force shown by the thumb leaves the middle finger, indicating a current flowing, along the spiral from the centre outwards. However, the particle would be slowing down as it loses kinetic energy by ionising other particles in its path. The radius of curvature for these tracks is proportional to the velocity of the particle, so deceleration would cause the particle to spiral inwards. This means the particle must be travelling in the same direction along the track as the flow of conventional current as defined in Fleming's left hand rule, so the particle must be positive – a positron.

Questions

1 Explain why ionisation is important in the operation of the Geiger–Müller tube.

2 In **fig. 3.2.11** the red and yellow tracks show the creation of an electron and positron. Identify which track is the electron. The magnetic field goes into the page.

3 The photo in **fig. 3.2.12** was taken by Carl Anderson and published in Physical Review in March 1933 as evidence for a positively charged particle with the mass of an electron. He had discovered the positron.

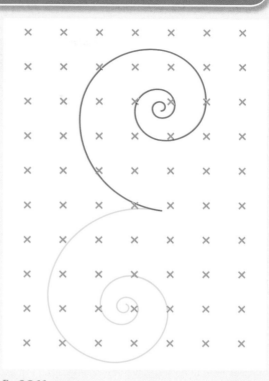

fig. 3.2.11

The dark grey bar across the middle of the picture is a lead absorber which removes about two thirds of the particle's energy. Explain how you can tell that the particle is moving upwards in the picture.

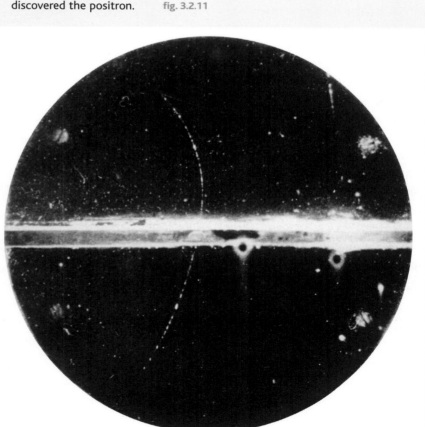

fig. 3.2.12 Anderson's positron track in the thin curving grey line.

The Large Hadron Collider Spec 99, 100, 101, 102

HSW The Large Hadron Collider

fig 3.2.13 Inside the Large Hadron Collider.

At the Conseil Européen pour la Recherche Nucléaire (CERN), or European Council for Nuclear Research, they have been planning and constructing the biggest machine in the history of planet Earth. This is the Large Hadron Collider – a gigantic synchrotron over 8 km in diameter, built 100 metres underground on the border between Switzerland and France. On 10 September 2008 it was switched on (after a couple of years of delays), at a total cost of just under four billion Euros, with staff from 111 nations involved in its building and operation. It is the largest experiment ever undertaken. Running at 1.9 K the LHC will be the coldest place in the Solar System when running (excluding colder man-made experiments).

Four smashing experiments

The machine is designed to collide protons into each other at energies of 14 TeV (14×10^{12} eV), travelling at 99.9999991% of the speed of light. These conditions emulate those occurring in the Universe 1 billionth of a second after the Big Bang. LHC scientists are hoping that this will then produce particles and interactions not seen since the Big Bang.

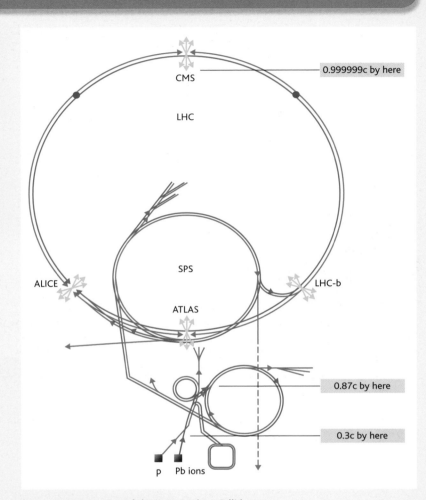

fig. 3.2.14 An overview of the Large Hadron Collider.

At such high energies, the beams of protons counter-rotating around the 27 km ring will cross each other's paths 30 million times every second, resulting in 600 million collisions per second. There are four critical experiments in the LHC, each named by an acronym: CMS, LHCb, ATLAS, and ALICE. Each of these experiments has an incredibly complex detector built in a cavern around the accelerator and one of the beam-crossing points is at the centre of each detector. Each experiment is aimed at detecting particular products from the collisions; each is searching for specific undiscovered but theoretical particles.

The detectors include strong magnetic fields and will track the movements of particles through the space that the detector occupies. As mass–energy and momentum are always conserved in particle interactions, along with charge, the records of particle tracks can be interpreted to identify the particles in the detector and any reactions that they undergo.

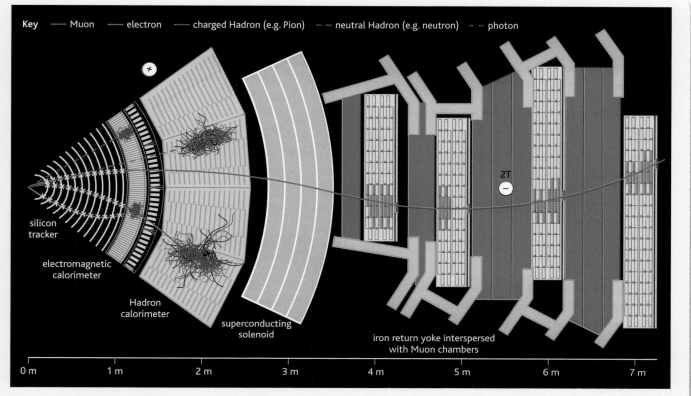

Key ——— Muon ——— electron ——— charged Hadron (e.g. Pion) – – – neutral Hadron (e.g. neutron) - - - photon

silicon tracker

electromagnetic calorimeter

Hadron calorimeter

superconducting solenoid

2T

iron return yoke interspersed with Muon chambers

0 m   1 m   2 m   3 m   4 m   5 m   6 m   7 m

fig. 3.2.15 **Particle detection in the Compact Muon Solenoid**

CMS – the Compact Muon Solenoid

If the Large Hadron Collider achieves the exciting discoveries it has been designed for, they may well come from this detector. There are several hypotheses in different areas of theoretical physics which may gain confirmation evidence from the LHC. Some of these sound a little bizarre. For example, it is hoped that the CMS will observe mini black holes, dark matter, supersymmetric particles, gravitons and the Higgs boson.

The CMS is set up with various detecting chambers for different types of particle and has 100 million individual detectors organised in a 3D barrel containing as much iron as the Eiffel Tower. By monitoring the tracks of particles their charges and masses can be determined. The energies and momenta can also be measured, and all this information analysed together can identify all the particles and reactions in each collision.

LHCb – Large Hadron Collider beauty experiment

This detector will be watching out for the decays of both the bottom quark (sometimes called beauty) and the charm quark by looking for mesons containing these. This is particularly aimed at working out why our Universe contains mostly matter and very little antimatter, when theoretically the two should appear in equal amounts.

A Large Ion Collider Experiment

Although ALICE will initially observe the proton–proton collisions that the LHC will start with, this detector is particularly intended to study the collisions of heavy ions, such as lead, accelerated to almost the speed of light. It is hoped that these collisions will create a quark–gluon plasma which has been predicted by quantum mechanics theory.

ATLAS

The ATLAS detector is 45 m long and 25 m high. Among the possible discoveries are the origin of mass, extra dimensions of space, microscopic black holes, and evidence for dark matter particles in the universe. Originally, ATLAS was an acronym for A Toroidal Lhc ApparatuS, but this has now largely been dropped and it is simply the name of the experiment.

What must a detector be capable of doing?

In developing the Large Hadron Collider experiment, the scientists had to work out what they needed the detectors to do. The following nine points are listed on the ATLAS website as their intentions as to the abilities of the detector.

1 *Measure* the directions, momenta, and signs of charged particles.

2 *Measure* the energy carried by electrons and photons in each direction from the collision.

3 *Measure* the energy carried by hadrons (protons, pions, neutrons, etc.) in each direction.

4 *Identify* which charged particles from the collision, if any, are electrons.

5 *Identify* which charged particles from the collision, if any, are muons.

6 *Identify* whether some of the charged particles originate at points a few millimetres from the collision point rather than at the collision point itself (signalling a particle's decay a few millimetres from the collision point).

7 *Infer* (through momentum conservation) the presence of undetectable neutral particles such as neutrinos.

8 Have the *capability* of processing the above information fast enough to permit flagging about 10–100 potentially interesting events per second out of the billion collisions per second that occur, and recording the measured information.

9 The detector must also be *capable* of long and reliable operation in a very hostile radiation environment.

Data analysis

It has been estimated that the amount of data resulting from the LHC experiments will be approximately 10% of that produced through all human activities across the world. To analyse the raw data from the incredibly complex detectors, a system of computer analysis called the Grid will be used. This enables hundreds of computers across the world to be linked together via the internet in order that their combined computing power can be used to study the experimental results and search out any which indicate the new discoveries it is hoped the LHC will produce. Of every 10 billion collision results, we expect only about 10–100 will be 'interesting' reactions. The ones that show things we already know need to be quickly filtered out of the data so that computing power is not wasted.

Questions

1 How can the curvature of a particle track tell us about its charge and mass?

2 How could momentum conservation 'infer the presence of undetectable neutral particles such as neutrinos'?

3 Why would we need four separate detector machines to undertake the various different particle searches that scientists are intending?

4 Do you think the cost of the LHC is justified? Explain your reasons for your answer.

3.3 Particle interactions Spec 103, 104

Creation

'In the beginning, God created the Heaven and the Earth'. This is the first line of the Christian holy book, the Bible. The creation story of the indigenous people of Australia claims that everything was created from the dreams of their distant ancestors. Hinduism has several accounts of creation, one being that everything was magically created by Brahma, under the instruction of Vishnu, who had just been awakened from dreaming by the primordial sound. Some native Americans hold to the idea that 'Earthmaker wished for the Earth and it was formed'.

The implication from most creation stories is that, from nothing, the material of the Earth was brought into being by an unexplained entity. Some scientists take such apparently supernatural whimsy as strong evidence that religion is fanciful nonsense. However, one of Einstein's most important theories suggests exactly this. Matter and energy are regularly interchanged according to his well-known equation, $E = mc^2$. In this equation, multiplying the mass of an object by the square of the speed of light gives the equivalent amount of energy (see also p.135). Given a suitable quantity of energy, such as that in a gamma ray photon, particles can spontaneously appear and the energy disappears from existence (**fig. 3.3.1**). This is so commonplace in the Universe that it should not surprise us. The reason it does is that these events only happen on a subatomic scale, so we cannot detect them without complex machinery.

fig. 3.3.1 Matter can appear out of nowhere, as if by magic. It is converted from energy according to $\Delta E = c^2 \Delta m$.

Worked example

A gamma ray photon converts into an electron and a **positron** (an anti-electron which has an identical mass to the electron). Calculate the frequency of the gamma photon.

$$\Delta E = c^2 \times \Delta m$$
$$= (3 \times 10^8)^2 \times 9.11 \times 10^{-31}$$
$$= 8.2 \times 10^{-14} \text{ J}$$

This is the amount of energy needed to produce an electron or a positron so, to produce both, the energy of the photon must be double this: 16.4×10^{-14} J.

$$E = hf$$
$$\therefore \ f = \frac{E}{h}$$
$$= \frac{16.4 \times 10^{-14}}{6.63 \times 10^{-34}}$$
$$= 2.47 \times 10^{20} \text{ Hz}$$

This reaction is known as electron–positron **pair production**.

Annihilation

Just as matter can appear spontaneously through a conversion from energy, so energy can appear through the disappearance of mass. This is the source of energy in nuclear fission and fusion. In both reactions, the sum of the masses of all matter involved before the reaction is greater than the sum of all mass afterwards. This mass difference is converted into energy (see chapter 5.2). In a nuclear power station we extract this energy as heat and use it to drive turbines to generate electricity.

If a particle and its antiparticle meet, they will spontaneously vanish from existence to be replaced by the equivalent energy: we call this interaction **annihilation**. This reaction was supposedly the main power source driving the starship *Enterprise* in the science fiction series *Star Trek* (**fig. 3.3.2**). It is not commonly suggested that annihilation reactors could be used as a power source on Earth, as **antimatter** exists so rarely. Also, if we could find a supply of antimatter, it would annihilate on contact with any matter, which would most likely be before it reached the reaction chamber we had set up to extract the energy for conversion into electricity.

fig. 3.3.2 The fictional starship *Enterprise* was said to be powered by a matter/antimatter annihilation reaction.

HSW Electronvolt units

We have seen the **electronvolt** (eV) as a unit for very small amounts of energy. Remember that one electronvolt is the amount of energy gained by an electron when it is accelerated through a potential difference of one volt. This is equivalent to 1.6×10^{-19} joules, so it is a very small amount of energy, even in particle physics terms. It is common for particles to have energies of millions or even billions of electronvolts. For this reason we often use MeV and GeV as units of energy in particle interactions.

Similarly, the atomic mass unit, u, is not an SI unit but is commonly used in particle interactions as it is often easier to get to grips with. $1\,u = 1.66 \times 10^{-27}\,kg$. As we know that energy and mass are connected by the equation $\Delta E = c^2 \Delta m$, we can also have mass units which are measures of E/c^2, such as MeV/c^2 and GeV/c^2. $1\,u$ of mass is equivalent to about 931.5 MeV.

Worked example

Calculate the mass in kilograms of $1\,MeV/c^2$.

$$1\,MeV = 1 \times 10^6 \times 1.6 \times 10^{-19}$$
$$= 1.6 \times 10^{-13}\,J$$

In SI units, $c = 3 \times 10^8\,m\,s^{-1}$.

$$1\,MeV/c^2 = \frac{1.6 \times 10^{-13}}{(3 \times 10^8)^2}$$
$$= 1.78 \times 10^{-30}\,kg.$$

This is about twice the mass of an electron.

None of the particle interactions described here can occur if they violate any of various conservation rules. In any interaction:

- momentum is conserved
- mass/energy is conserved
- charge is conserved.

There are other rules that must be obeyed, but these three are critical as all particles involved may have some of each property.

Questions

1 A positron with kinetic energy 2.2 MeV collides with an electron at rest, and they annihilate each other.

   a Calculate the average energy of the two gamma photons produced as a result of the annihilation.

   b Calculate the frequency of the these gamma photons.

2 In 1977, in an accelerator at Fermilab, the upsilon particle was discovered. Its mass was determined as 9.46 GeV/c^2 . What is the mass of the upsilon particle in kilograms?

3 A gamma ray photon travelling through space spontaneously converts into an electron and a positron.

   a Explain why the two new particles must move in opposite directions to each other.

   b A scientist observes a similar event in a detector and the incoming photon had a frequency of 4.89×10^{20} Hz. She sees the tracks of the electron and positron from the reaction are 160° apart and hypothesises that a third particle must be produced. Calculate the mass of this third particle in MeV/c^2.

4 Figure 3.3.3 shows the track in a hydrogen bubble chamber which has been bombarded with antiprotons.

   One antiproton hits a proton in the chamber. The resulting tracks show the tracks of various pairs of particles (π^+/π^-, e^+/e^-) which are created in the collision.

fig. 3.3.3

   a Identify the incoming antiproton track.

   b How did you identify the incoming antiproton? What does this tell you about its kinetic energy compared to the resulting particles?

   c How does the picture illustrate the conservation of matter/energy?

   d Identify a π^+/π^- pair and an e^+/e^- pair. How do you know that the tracks show you a pair of identical but opposite particles.

   e How does the picture illustrate conservation of charge?

   f How can you distinguish between the pion pair and the electron pair?

   g How does the picture illustrate the conservation of momentum in two dimensions?

The bricks of matter Spec 106, 107

Twelve fundamental particles

After a century in which scientists rapidly discovered many subatomic particles, they have developed a theory for how these come together to build up the materials we see around us. This theory is known as the **standard model**. As the idea of the atom as indivisible was swept aside by Rutherford and Thomson, so the idea of the proton and neutron as fundamental has also been overturned. We have probed inside these two nucleons and discovered that each is constructed from smaller particles known as **quarks**. The electron has so far survived as being considered fundamental. However, it has two partners – particles of a similar type – each with a neutrino associated with it, forming a group of six fundamental particles known as **leptons**.

Scientists like to see the Universe as balanced, or symmetrical, and we have now found that quarks are also a group of six, although only the lightest two are found in protons and neutrons. The heavier quarks are found in more exotic particles. The two groups are distinct because quarks can undergo interactions via the **strong nuclear force** (see page 106) whereas leptons do not feel the strong force. It is the strong nuclear force that binds nucleons together. In each group of six there are three pairs with a similar order of magnitude for mass, and these are known as the three generations of matter.

Generation	Name	Symbol	Charge	Mass (MeV/c^2)
I	Electron	e^-	−1	0.511
I	Electron neutrino	v_e	0	0 ($<2.2 \times 10^{-6}$)
II	Muon	μ	−1	106
II	Muon neutrino	v_μ	0	0 (<0.17)
III	Tau	τ	−1	1780
III	Tau neutrino	v_τ	0	0 (<20)

table 3.3.1 The family of leptons. These do not feel the strong nuclear force.

Generation	Name	Symbol	Charge	Mass (GeV/c^2)
I	Up	u	+2/3	0.003
I	Down	d	−1/3	0.006
II	Strange	s	−1/3	0.1
II	Charm	c	+2/3	1.3
III	Bottom	b	−1/3	4.3
III	Top	t	+2/3	175

table 3.3.2 The family of quarks. These are subject to the strong nuclear force.

Only the first three quarks were known (up, down, strange) from the early part of the twentieth century, and charm was discovered in 1974. The symmetry of the standard model indicated to scientists that there were other particles they had never observed which should exist – bottom and top quarks. Experiments were carried out to find these and the accelerator experiments at Fermilab discovered bottom in 1977 and top in 1995.

Current particle theory holds that all matter in the Universe is constructed from combinations of some of these 12 particles, and no others. Each of the 12 particles listed in **tables 3.3.1** and **3.3.2**. also has an antiparticle. The antiparticles have the same mass but all their other properties are opposite to those of the normal matter particle. The symbol for an **antiparticle** is the same as for the normal particle, but with a bar above the symbol. For example, the charge on an anti-down quark is $+\frac{1}{3}$ and its symbol is $\bar{d}$. In a few cases, the antiparticle is a different particle in its own right and the bar may not be used. The positron (anti-electron) does not use a bar, but is written as e^+.

The Higgs boson

One of the great hopes for CERN's Large Hadron Collider (LHC) experiment is that it will discover the Higgs boson. First suggested by Peter Higgs in 1964, this very massive particle (its exact mass is not certain, but lies between the mass of an iron nucleus and that of uranium) is the means by which particles get mass. The Higgs mechanism is considered to be a bit like frictional drag on particles caused by a field called the Higgs field. Thus, an electron suffers less of this drag from the Higgs field than a proton, and so it has less mass. Remember that one of the key points about mass is that it gives objects inertia – the reluctance to change velocity – hence the idea of the frictional drag effect. This is only a model though – the Higgs mechanism is not easy to describe in everyday terms.

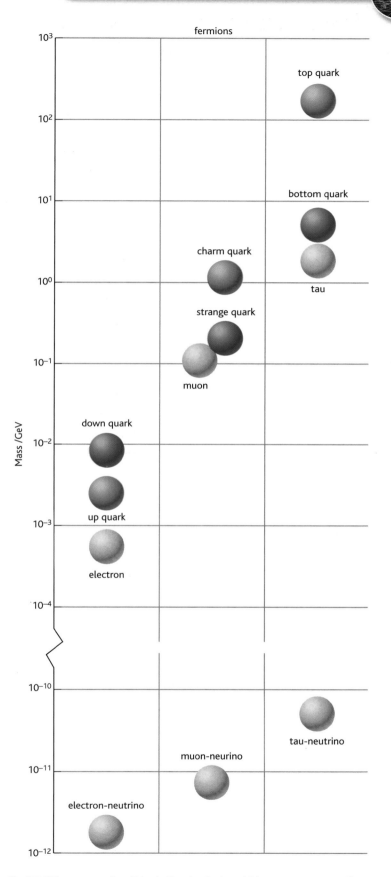

fig. 3.3.4 **The masses of particles in the standard model increase over generations.**

Questions

1 An anti-electron is called a positron. Why is it usually written with the symbol e^+?

2 What is the difference between:

   a a quark and a lepton?

   b a quark and an anti-quark?

   c an electron and a muon?

3 Having discovered up, down, strange, charm and bottom quarks, why did scientists undertake similar experiments using higher and higher energies?

4 The properties of top quark that they discovered are shown in table 3.3.2. What properties would an anti-top quark have?

5 Look at fig. 3.3.4 and consider the three generations of neutrino, compared with the other fundamental particles in the standard model.

   a Why are the masses of the neutrinos surprising?

   b How do the masses of the different neutrinos follow the same trends as the other particles in the three generations?

Particle reactions Spec 106, 107

Baryons

If three quarks are combined together, the resulting particle is a **baryon** (**fig. 3.3.5**). Protons and neutrons are baryons. A proton consists of two up quarks and a down quark, while a neutron is two down quarks combined with an up quark. Other baryons are more obscure and have very short lives, as they decay through a strong nuclear force reaction which makes them highly unstable. Yet other baryons, like the sigma, omega and lambda particles, decay via the weak nuclear force and are longer lived, with lives as long as 10^{-10} seconds!

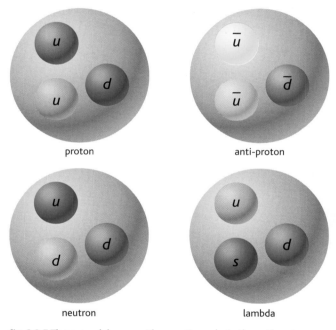

fig. 3.3.5 Three-quark baryons. Three anti-quarks in the anti-proton make it an **anti-baryon**.

Mesons

If a quark and an anti-quark are combined together, the resulting particle is known as a **meson** (**fig. 3.3.6**). The **pion** and the kaon are the most common examples of mesons. A π^+ meson ($u\overline{d}$) is made from an up quark (u) combined with an anti-down ($\overline{d}$) quark.

If a meson is a combination of a quark and its anti-quark, then the meson's charge must be zero. This is the case for the J/ψ particle, which was first discovered in 1974 by two independent researchers at separate laboratories. Its slow decay (with a lifetime of 8×10^{-19} s) did not fit the pattern generated by up, down and strange quarks and it is thought to be a charm/anti-charm combination ($c\overline{c}$). The two independent discoverers of this, Richter and Ting, shared the 1976 Nobel Prize for their discovery of the fourth quark.

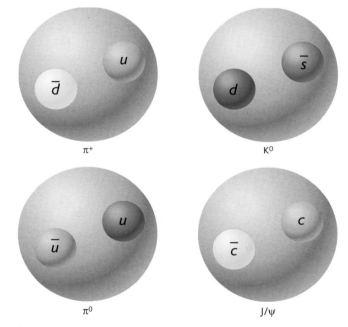

fig. 3.3.6 Mesons are formed from quark/anti-quark combinations.

Hadrons

Quarks can interact via the strong nuclear force. Thus baryons and mesons can interact via the strong nuclear force. Any particle which feels the strong force is called a **hadron**. So, baryons and mesons are both hadrons. Leptons do not feel the strong force and so are in a separate class of particle from the hadrons.

Reactions conserve properties

In order for any particle reaction to occur, the overall reaction must conserve various properties of the particles involved. The combination of mass/energy must be equal before and after the reaction. Momentum and charge must also be conserved. Momentum and mass/energy are difficult to confirm. A reaction can overcome any apparent mass difference by having the particles begin or end with more kinetic energy to make up the difference. This is essentially how accelerator collision experiments can create large mass particles: particles with high kinetic energies can have the energy converted into mass to generate a host of particles with less energy. Reactions also have similar flexibility to ensure momentum conservation, but we can quickly see if charge is conserved by looking at a reaction's equation. Consider two common nuclear reactions, **alpha decay** and **beta-minus decay**:

alpha decay: $^{235}_{92}\text{U} \rightarrow {}^{231}_{90}\text{Th} + {}^{4}_{2}\alpha$

charge: $+92 \rightarrow +90 + +2$ ✔

beta-minus decay: $^{14}_{6}\text{C} \rightarrow {}^{14}_{7}\text{N} + {}^{0}_{-1}\beta + {}^{0}_{0}\bar{\nu}_e$

charge: $+6 \rightarrow +7 + -1 + 0$ ✔

Alpha decay

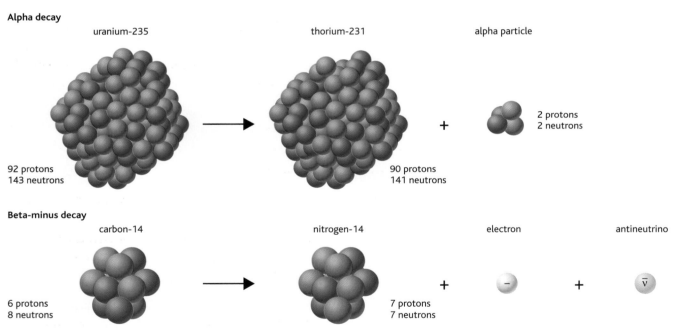

uranium-235

thorium-231

alpha particle

2 protons
2 neutrons

92 protons
143 neutrons

90 protons
141 neutrons

Beta-minus decay

carbon-14

nitrogen-14

electron

antineutrino

6 protons
8 neutrons

7 protons
7 neutrons

fig. 3.3.7 Alpha and beta decay conserve mass/energy and charge.

The reaction for beta-minus decay led to the development of the theory that neutrinos and antineutrinos exist. They are massless and have no charge, so are almost impossible to detect. If the same nuclear change were producing the same single particle every time, then for mass/energy to be conserved, the beta particles would have to have the same energy every time. This is what is found for alpha particles. However, scientists found that beta particles from nuclei of the same isotope have a range of kinetic energies. This suggested that another particle was flying away with some kinetic energy so that the total kinetic energy produced was always the same.

Worked example

For each of these reactions, confirm whether or not they can occur through conservation of charge.

a **Beta-plus decay:**

$$^{13}_{7}\text{N} \rightarrow {}^{13}_{6}\text{C} + {}^{0}_{+1}\beta + {}^{0}_{0}\nu_e$$

Answer: $+7 \rightarrow +6 + 1 + 0$ ✔

This reaction is permitted as it conserves charge. It would also need to conserve mass/energy and momentum.

b **Positive pion decay:**

$$\pi^+ \rightarrow \mu^- + {}^{0}_{0}\nu_\mu$$

Answer: $+1 \rightarrow -1 + 0$ ✘

This reaction is not permitted as it does not conserve charge.

(NB: In fact, a positive pion decays into an anti-muon, μ^+, and a muon neutrino with a lifetime of some 26 nanoseconds.)

Questions

1 What is the difference in the quark composition of a proton and a neutron? Explain what you think happens to the quarks when a neutron undergoes beta-minus decay.

2 What is the difference between:

   a a meson and a baryon?

   b a hadron and a lepton?

3 For each of these reactions, confirm whether or not they can occur through conservation of charge.

   a Phosphorus beta-plus decay, in which the phosphorus isotope is converted into a sulphur isotope and emits a positron and an electron neutrino:

$$^{32}_{15}\text{P} \rightarrow {}^{32}_{16}\text{S} + {}^{0}_{+1}\beta^+ + {}^{0}_{0}\nu_e$$

   b Neutral pion decay, in which a neutral pion becomes an electron, a positron and a gamma photon:

$$\pi^0 \rightarrow e^- + e^+ + \gamma$$

More on the standard model

Baryon and lepton numbers

For a reaction to be possible, the lepton number and baryon number must be conserved. This provides another means of checking on the possibility of a reaction occurring. Each quark has a **baryon number, B**, of $+\frac{1}{3}$ and so a baryon has a value of $B = +1$. Each lepton has a **lepton number, L**, of $+1$. Antiparticles have the opposite number. As mesons are quark/anti-quark combinations, their total baryon number is zero ($+\frac{1}{3} + -\frac{1}{3} = 0$).

Particle	Symbol	Charge	Lepton number, L	Baryon number, B	Antiparticle	Symbol	Charge	Lepton number, L	Baryon number, B
Electron	e^-	−1	1	0	Positron	e^+	+1	−1	0
Electron neutrino	ν_e	0	1	0	Anti-electron neutrino	$\bar{\nu}_e$	0	−1	0
Muon	μ	−1	1	0	Anti-muon	$\bar{\mu}$	+1	−1	0
Muon neutrino	ν_μ	0	1	0	Anti-muon neutrino	$\bar{\nu}_\mu$	0	−1	0
Tau	τ	−1	1	0	Anti-tau	$\bar{\tau}$	+1	−1	0
Tau neutrino	ν_τ	0	1	0	Anti-tau neutrino	$\bar{\nu}_\tau$	0	−1	0

Table 3.3.3 **Leptons and anti-leptons and their particle properties.**

Particle	Symbol	Charge	Lepton number, L	Baryon number, B	Antiparticle	Symbol	Charge	Lepton number, L	Baryon number, B
Proton	p	+1	0	+1	Anti-proton	$\bar{p}$	+1	0	−1
Neutron	n	0	0	+1	Anti-neutron	$\bar{n}$	0	0	−1
Neutral pion	π^0	0	0	0	Neutral pion	π^0	0	0	0
Pi-plus	π^+	+1	0	0	Anti-pi-plus	$\bar{\pi}^+$	0	0	0
Down quark	d	$-\frac{1}{3}$	0	$+\frac{1}{3}$	Anti-down	$\bar{d}$	$+\frac{1}{3}$	0	$-\frac{1}{3}$
Xi-minus	Ξ^{-1}	−1	0	+1	Xi-plus	Ξ^{+1}	+1	0	−1

Table 3.3.4 **Various particles and their properties.**

Reactions conserve all properties

Particle reactions can only occur if they conserve baryon and lepton numbers overall. This means the total for each property must be the same before and after any reaction, or else it cannot occur. Let us revisit alpha and beta decay and check on conservation of these numbers.

Alpha decay: $\quad\quad {}^{235}_{92}U \rightarrow {}^{231}_{90}Th + {}^{4}_{2}\alpha$

charge: $\quad\quad\quad +92 \rightarrow +90 + 2$ ✔

baryon number: $\quad +235 \rightarrow +231 + 4$ ✔

lepton number: $\quad\quad 0 \rightarrow 0 + 0$ ✔

Beta-minus decay: $\quad {}^{14}_{6}C \rightarrow {}^{14}_{7}N + {}^{0}_{-1}\beta + {}^{0}_{0}\bar{\nu}_e$

charge: $\quad\quad\quad +6 \rightarrow +7 -1 + 0$ ✔

baryon number: $\quad +14 \rightarrow +14 + 0 + 0$ ✔

lepton number: $\quad\quad 0 \rightarrow 0 +1 + -1$ ✔

If we isolate the individual neutron decay reaction in beta-minus decay, we can check again:

Beta-minus decay: $\quad {}^{1}_{0}n \rightarrow {}^{1}_{1}p + {}^{0}_{-1}\beta + {}^{0}_{0}\bar{\nu}_e$

charge: $\quad\quad\quad 0 \rightarrow + 1 -1 + 0$ ✔

baryon number: $\quad +1 \rightarrow + 1 + 0 + 0$ ✔

lepton number: $\quad\quad 0 \rightarrow 0 + 1 + -1$ ✔

Here we again see that this reaction must have an anti-lepton on the right hand side to balance the electron, and thus we have further evidence for the suggestion that an antineutrino is produced.

If we zoom in further and isolate the individual quark decay reaction in beta-minus decay, we can check again:

Beta-minus decay: $\quad d \rightarrow u + {}^{0}_{-1}\beta + {}^{0}_{0}\bar{\nu}_e$

charge: $\quad\quad\quad -\frac{1}{3} \rightarrow +\frac{2}{3} + -1 + 0$ ✔

baryon number: $\quad +\frac{1}{3} \rightarrow +\frac{1}{3} + 0 + 0$ ✔

lepton number: $\quad\quad 0 \rightarrow 0 + 1 + -1$ ✔

Again, everything is conserved.

Strangeness

The strange quark adds an additional property to reactions, which must also be conserved. This is called **strangeness**, **S**. Each strange quark has a strangeness of $+1$, each anti-strange quark has $S = -1$, and all other particles have zero strangeness.

Worked example

The lambda particle is a baryon and consists of one each of up, down and strange quarks (uds). It commonly decays via the strong force into a proton (uud) and a negative pion (which is $d\bar{u}$). True or false?

Proposed decay: $\quad {}^{1}_{0}\Lambda \rightarrow {}^{1}_{1}p + {}^{0}_{-1}\pi$

charge: $\quad\quad\quad\quad 0 \rightarrow +1 + -1$ ✔

baryon number: $\quad +1 \rightarrow +1 + 0$ ✔

lepton number: $\quad\quad 0 \rightarrow 0 + 0$ ✔

strangeness: $\quad\quad +1 \rightarrow 0 + 0$ ✘

This reaction is not permitted in nature as it does not conserve strangeness.

The four forces of the apocalypse

There are four other particles that we have not yet mentioned here, because they are not matter particles. These are known together as **exchange bosons**. The matter particles interact by the four forces of nature. These are **gravity**, the **electromagnetic force**, the **strong nuclear force** and the **weak nuclear force**. Each force acts on particles which have a certain property, such as mass in the case of gravity, or electric charge for the electromagnetic force. The process by which these forces act has been modelled by scientists as an exchange of other particles – the exchange bosons. For example, for a proton and an electron to attract each other's opposite charge, they pass photons backwards and forwards between each other.

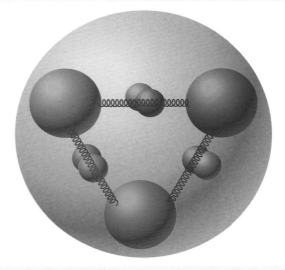

fig. 3.3.8 Gluons – themselves made from quark pairs – are exchanged between quarks to hold the quarks together. In this example, the three quarks form a proton.

This may sound bizarre, but it has been shown experimentally to be an appropriate model for the electromagnetic, strong and weak forces. In the case of gravity, the so-called graviton has been theoretically invented to complete the model, but gravitons are yet to be discovered. Many experiments are currently being carried out to try and detect gravitons.

Force	Exchange boson	Boson symbol	Boson charge	Boson mass (GeV/c^2)
Electromagnetic	Photon	γ	0	0
Weak nuclear	W or Z boson	W$^-$	−1	80.4
		W$^+$	+1	80.4
		Z^0	0	91.2
Strong nuclear	Gluon	g	0	0
Gravity	Graviton	Undetermined		

Table 3.3.5 The four forces of nature and their exchange bosons.

Whilst gravity is the force we experience most obviously, it is the one scientists know about in the least detail. The electromagnetic force is well understood, and the exchange of photons to make it work has also led to an understanding of the generation of photons such as light. The weak nuclear force is also fairly well understood, as the W and Z bosons predicted by theory have since been detected in accelerator experiments in which protons are crashed together. This is particularly strong science, as the existence of the weak nuclear force bosons had been theoretically predicted and then they were detected in later experiments. Many particle decays where other particles are formed, such as beta decay for example, occur via a weak nuclear force interaction.

Questions

1 Beta-plus decay is similar to the better known beta-minus decay. In beta-plus decay, a proton is converted into a neutron, with the emission of a positron and an electron neutrino. Write the fundamental reaction for beta-plus decay and confirm that it is permitted by the conservation rules you have seen.

2 One theoretical physicist at CERN has proposed that the LHC may see a neutron decay reaction in which a lambda particle (up, down, strange baryon) and a kaon (down/anti-strange meson) are produced.

   Proposed reaction 1: $^1_0n \rightarrow ^1_0\Lambda + ^0_0K$

   A second theoretical physicist imagines that the reaction might produce two kaons and also produce a positron and an antineutrino.

   Proposed reaction 2: $^1_0n \rightarrow ^1_0\Lambda + 2^0_0K + ^0_1e + ^0_0\overline{\nu}_e$

   Work out which reaction is possible.

Extension questions

3 What is an exchange boson?

4 How do you know that the W^+ boson cannot be its own antiparticle?

5 Describe what happens to make a proton repel another proton.

6 Why would discovery of the Higgs boson take us a step closer to understanding how gravity works?

Examzone: Topic 3 Particle physics

1 The theory of relativity established that all forms of energy possess mass and, conversely, that material particles are a form of energy. If enough energy is concentrated, new particles of matter will appear. Thus, the violent collision of two protons, for example, can produce more protons. Whenever matter is created this way in the laboratory it is always accompanied by an equivalent quantity of antimatter. Each lepton and quark possesses an antiparticle in which all the physical properties except mass are reversed. If an antiparticle encounters its mirror particle they annihilate each other, usually in the form of gamma radiation.

[Adapted from Paul Davies: *The particles and forces of nature*, in Revised NAS Physics, Longman 1986.]

a The collision between two protons is described as being a violent collision. Explain why the collision must be a violent one in order to produce more protons. **(2)**

b Whenever matter is created *"it is always accompanied by an equivalent quantity of antimatter"*.

What conservation laws does this statement imply? **(3)**

c An electron encounters a positron. The rest mass of an electron and that of a positron is $0.00055\,u$.

Describe the outcome of the encounter.

Support your description with relevant calculations. **(4)**

(Total 9 marks)

2 a The equation for β^- decay can be written as:

$$n \rightarrow p + \beta^- + \bar{\nu}$$

i) For each particle, either give its quark composition or state whether it is a fundamental particle. **(2)**

ii) Write a similar equation for β^+ decay. **(2)**

b A hydrogen atom consists of one proton and one electron. For each particle underline all the words that could be used to make a correct statement.

A proton is a {baryon / meson / lepton / hadron}

An electron is a {baryon / meson / lepton / hadron} **(2)**

c In 1995 scientists at CERN created atoms of antihydrogen.

i) Name the particles that make up antihydrogen. **(1)**

ii) Describe these particles in terms of charge and quark structure where relevant. **(2)**

iii) State the charge of an atom of antihydrogen. **(1)**

iv) Explain why it is not possible to store atoms of antihydrogen. **(2)**

(Total 12 marks)

3 The following strong interaction has been observed.

$$K^- + p \rightarrow n + X$$

The K^- is a strange meson of quark composition $\bar{u}s$.

The u quark has a charge of $+2/3$.

The d quark has a charge of $-1/3$.

Deduce the charge of the strange quark. **(1)**

Use the appropriate conservation law to decide whether particle X is positive, negative or neutral. **(2)**

Is particle X a baryon or a meson? Show how you obtained your answer. **(2)**

State the quark composition of X. Justify your answer. **(3)**

(Total 8 marks)

4 State one similarity and two differences between alpha and beta particles. **(3)**

(Total 3 marks)

5 The Ω^- (omega minus), a particle with strangeness -3, was identified in 1964 in an experiment involving an interaction between a K^- meson of strangeness -1 and a proton.

$$K^- + p \rightarrow \Omega^- + K^+ + K^0$$

Is the Ω^- particle a baryon or a meson? Give *two* reasons for your answer. **(2)**

Using the information in the table, deduce the quark composition of all particles in the equation.

Quark	Charge	Strangeness
u	+2/3	0
d	−1/3	0
s	−1/3	−1

(4)

(Total 6 marks)

6 Neutrons, like electrons, are often used to study crystal structure. A suitable de Broglie wavelength for the neutrons would be about 1 nm.

Explain why the neutrons must have a de Broglie wavelength of this order of magnitude. **(2)**

Given the mass of a neutron as 1.67×10^{-27} kg, calculate the kinetic energy of a neutron which has a de Broglie wavelength of 1.20 nm. **(3)**

What is meant by **wave–particle duality**? Illustrate your answer with the example of neutrons. You may be awarded a mark for the clarity of your answer. **(4)**

(Total 9 marks)

Topic 4 Thermal energy

This topic covers areas in which heat and temperature effects can be measured. The movements of particles are explained by the kinetic theory and this in turn leads to explanations of many aspects of heat-related physics. In particular, physical laws relating to the properties of gases, and how much things heat up, will be explored in detail.

What are the theories?

The concepts of temperature, internal energy, specific heat capacity and ideal gases are explained in detail. You will look at what we actually mean by the word 'temperature' and compare different temperature scales in order to see how to define it in an absolute way.

The gas laws can be understood as relationships between two properties of a gas in which all other variables are controlled, and we will see that these can then be combined to give a more general law – the equation of state for an ideal gas.

What is the evidence?

The equations presented in these topics can generally be examined quite easily in the school or college laboratory. You may have the opportunity to measure the specific heat capacity for a material. Or you may be able to discover for yourself one of the gas property relationships which have been used by scientists and engineers since the earliest reliable experiments were done on this subject approximately 300 years ago.

What are the implications?

This area of physics is often taken a little for granted. However, the CERN scientists struggling to maintain the Large Hadron Collider's superconducting magnets at −272 °C know how important the slightest change in a material's temperature can be. Similarly, the transport of fuels in pressurised gaseous form is one of the latest developments in the world's use of energy resources, and relies on calculations made using the gas laws.

The map opposite shows you the knowledge and skills you need to have by the end of this topic, and how they are linked together. The numbers refer to the sections in the Edexcel specification.

Chapter 4.1

explain the concept of internal energy as the random distribution of potential and kinetic energy amongst molecules (110)

recognise and use the expression $\Delta E = mc\Delta\theta$ (109)

recognise and use the expression $\frac{1}{2}m\langle c^2\rangle = \frac{3}{2}kT$ (112)

explain the concept of absolute zero and how the average kinetic energy of molecules is related to the absolute temperature (111)

use the expression $pV = NkT$ as the equation of state for an ideal gas (113)

4.1 Thermal physics Spec 109, 110, 111, 112

Heat and temperature

Temperature

Heating an object causes its temperature to rise. This seems a very obvious statement, based on our everyday experience, but what is really happening when we heat an object, and what do we mean by 'temperature'?

To understand the concept of temperature, we need to think about materials in terms of the particles from which they are made. According to the **kinetic theory**, when energy is supplied to an object, the particles in that object take up the energy as kinetic energy, and move faster. In solids, this motion is usually in the form of vibrations. If we are considering a gas, we imagine the molecules whizzing around their container at a greater speed. It is this kinetic energy that determines the temperature. If the average kinetic energy of the molecules of a substance increases, then it is at a higher temperature (**fig. 4.1.1**).

It is important to remember that internal kinetic energy on the scale of the particles that make up an object is separate from the idea of overall movement of the object. For example, as a cricket ball flies through the air, it has kinetic energy due to its overall movement. In addition to this, its molecules will be vibrating within it, and it is this internal energy that determines the temperature.

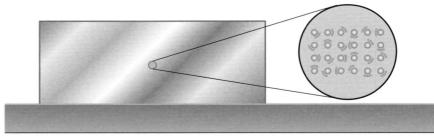

fig 4.1.1 A stationary piece of metal has no kinetic energy. But all its atoms are vibrating all the time. Although overall these tiny velocities must sum to zero (or else it would be moving), their kinetic energies are the object's heat energy.

HSW The 'molecule'

You may previously have learned in chemistry that a molecule is a combination of atoms. However, this term can also be used to refer more generally to any small particle. In kinetic theory, scientists use the word 'molecule' in this way to describe any particle, even when they know that it is an atom. For example, when we refer to helium gas particles moving faster when heated, we should refer to them as helium molecules, even though we know that helium usually forms a monatomic gas.

HSW Absolute zero

Taking energy away from the molecules of a substance causes its temperature to become lower. If you imagine a situation in which energy is continuously being taken away from a collection of molecules, then there will come a moment when all the internal kinetic energy has been removed from the substance. The molecules will no longer be moving at all. At this point, the temperature is said to be **absolute zero**.

Different scales of temperature have historically placed zero in arbitrary places compared with the average internal kinetic energy of the molecules (**table 4.1.1**). For example, Anders Celsius chose the freezing point of water as the zero on his temperature scale, but Daniel Gabriel Fahrenheit placed zero at 32 degrees below the freezing point of water (in the expectation that there would never be a temperature colder than this to measure!). On these scales, absolute zero is at −273.15° C and −459.66° F. In 1848, Lord Kelvin defined an absolute temperature scale which started with zero at absolute zero (**fig. 4.1.2**). For convenience, he made the gaps in his scale identical to those on the Celsius scale. This is known as the Kelvin scale of temperature, or sometimes as **absolute temperature**. As the units begin from a definite zero and go up in proportion to the amount of energy added to the molecules of the substance being measured, the temperatures on this scale are not compared to something else (like the freezing point of water). This is why the term absolute temperature is used, and why we do not use the word or symbol for 'degrees' when quoting values on the Kelvin scale. For example, the temperature at which lead becomes superconducting is 7.19 kelvin, or 7.19 K. The Scottish engineer William Rankine proposed a similar absolute temperature scale with degrees separated by the same amount as in the Fahrenheit scale. The Rankine scale is now obsolete.

fig. 4.1.2 **William Thomson, made Baron Kelvin of Largs in 1892, was one of Britain's most prolific and important scientists. Lord Kelvin is now buried next to Isaac Newton in Westminster Abbey.**

Temperature scale	Celsius	Fahrenheit	Kelvin	Rankine
Symbol	°C	°F	K	R
Boiling point of water (at 1 atm = 101 325 Pa)	100	212	373.15	671.67
Freezing point of water (at 1 atm = 101 325 Pa)	0	32	273.15	491.67
Absolute zero	−273.15	−459.67	0	0

table 4.1.1 **Various scales of temperature compared.**

Heat transfer

We have seen that the temperature of a substance depends on the kinetic energy of the molecules within it. As the molecules move, they collide with one another, and during these collisions there is an exchange of energy.

Imagine that one end of a long metal rod is being heated. In the hotter parts of the metal, the molecules are moving more quickly and there are more frequent collisions. In the cooler parts of the metal, further from the heat source, the molecules are moving more slowly. When a molecule with more energy collides with one with less, they share the energy more evenly, with the faster one slowing down and the slower one speeding up. The effect of these collisions is that the increase in the internal kinetic energy caused by heating becomes distributed throughout a substance, with the heat being passed from hotter areas to colder ones.

Specific heat capacity

Transferring the same amount of heat energy to two different objects will increase their internal energy by the same amount. However, this will not necessarily cause the same rise in temperature in both. The effect that transferred heat energy has on the temperature of an object depends on three things:

1 the amount of heat energy transferred

2 the mass of the object

3 the specific heat capacity of the material from which the object is made.

How much the temperature rises is dependent upon the nature of a material, and is given by a property known as its **specific heat capacity**, c. This is defined as the amount of energy needed to raise the temperature of 1 kg of a particular substance by 1 K. Different materials have different specific heat capacities because their molecular structures are different and so their molecules will be affected to different degrees by additional heat energy.

For a certain amount of energy, ΔE, transferred to a material, the change in temperature $\Delta\theta$ is related to the mass of material, m, and the specific heat capacity, c, by the expression:

$$\Delta E = mc\Delta\theta$$

With each quantity measured in SI units, this means that the specific heat capacity has units of $J\,kg^{-1}\,K^{-1}$. The *change* in temperature, $\Delta\theta$, is the same whether measured in Celsius or Kelvin, as the intervals are the same on both scales.

Worked examples

How long will a 2 kW kettle take to raise the temperature of 800 grams of water from 20° C to 100° C? The specific heat capacity of water is 4200 J kg^{-1} K^{-1}.

$$\Delta\theta = 100 - 20 = 80\,°C = 80\,K$$

$$\Delta E = mc\,\Delta\theta = 0.8 \times 4200 \times 80 = 268\,800\,J$$

$$t = \frac{E}{P} = \frac{268\,800}{2\,000} = 134\,s$$

So the kettle takes 2 minutes and 14 seconds to heat this water to boiling temperature. We assume that no energy is wasted in heating the surroundings.

Measuring specific heat capacity

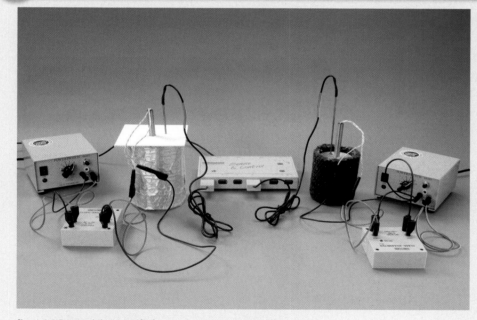

fig. 4.1.3 **Determining specific heat capacity experimentally.**

It is quite straightforward to measure the specific heat capacity of most materials (some values are given in **table 4.1.2**). Providing you can measure the heat energy put in to a known mass of the material, and insulate the material well enough that virtually all this heat goes towards raising its temperature, then a close measurement can be made (**fig. 4.1.3**). To gain very accurate measurements requires significantly more complex insulation. The inaccuracy in the rough experiment can usually be kept to under 5% with careful experimentation.

Substance	Specific heat capacity/ J kg^{-1}K^{-1}	Substance	Specific heat capacity/ J kg^{-1}K^{-1}
Water	4200	Marble	860
Ice	2100	Iron/Steel	450
Steam	2010	Copper	390
Wood	1670	Silver	240
Air (50 °C)	1050	Mercury	140
Aluminium	900		

table 4.1.2 **Some typical specific heat capacities.**

Internal energy

The average kinetic energy of the molecules in a material give it its temperature. However, as well as having kinetic energy, each molecule will have some potential energy by virtue of its position within the structure of the material, or in relation to other molecules in the substance. This potential energy is due to the bonds between molecules. If we sum the kinetic and potential energies of all the molecules within a given mass of a substance, we have measured its **internal energy**.

It is important to note that the molecules do not all have the same amount of kinetic and potential energies. The internal energy is randomly distributed across all the molecules according to the **Maxwell–Boltzmann distribution**.

The Maxwell–Boltzmann distribution

If we identify the individual velocity of each molecule in a particular sample, the values will range from a few moving very slowly to a few moving very fast, with the majority moving at close to the average speed. As they all have the same mass, the kinetic energies are directly dependent on the speeds. If we plot the kinetic energy against the number of molecules that have that energy, we obtain a curved graph called the Maxwell–Boltzmann distribution (**fig. 4.1.4**).

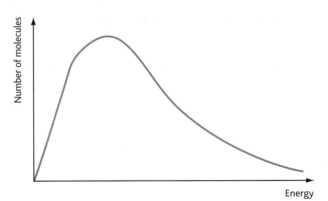

fig. 4.1.4 The Maxwell–Boltzmann distribution of the energies of a collection of molecules, at one particular temperature.

The characteristic shape of the graph in **fig. 4.1.4** shows that:

- there are no molecules with zero energy
- only a few molecules have high energies
- there is no maximum value for the energy a molecule can have.

A Maxwell–Boltzmann distribution graph is for one specific temperature. As the temperature changes, so the graph changes. The peak on the graph moves towards higher energies (and therefore higher speeds) as the temperature increases.

There are two different average speeds of particles in a material which are of interest to physicists. One is the most probable speed of the particles, which corresponds to the peak of the Maxwell–Boltzmann distribution graph. The second and more useful average is the **root-mean-square speed**, which has the symbol $\sqrt{<c^2>}$. This is the speed associated with the average kinetic energy, $\frac{1}{2}m<c^2>$, where c is the speed of the particle and m is its mass. The root-mean-square speed, often abbreviated to r.m.s. speed, is found by squaring the individual speeds of a set of molecules, finding the mean of the squares, and then taking the square root (see the Worked example).

Worked example

Find the r.m.s. speed of the five molecules of atmospheric nitrogen shown in **fig. 4.1.5**.

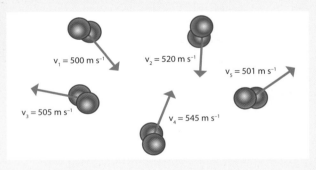

fig. 4.1.5

First, find the square of each value:

$$v_1^2 = 250\,000 \qquad v_2^2 = 270\,400 \qquad v_3^2 = 255\,025 \; v_4^2$$
$$= 297\,025 \qquad v_5^2 = 251\,001$$

The average of the square values is:

$$<c^2> = \frac{v_1^2 + v_2^2 + v_3^2 + v_4^2 + v_5^2}{5}$$

$$= \frac{250\,000 + 270\,400 + 255\,025 + 297\,025 + 251\,001}{5}$$

$$= \frac{1\,323\,451}{5}$$

$$= 264\,690.2$$

Finally, take the square root to get the r.m.s. speed:

$$\sqrt{<c^2>} = \sqrt{264\,690.2} = 514\,\text{m s}^{-1}$$

Molecular kinetic energy

The average kinetic energy of any molecule in a gaseous sample is proportional to the absolute temperature of the gas. This relationship can be expressed in symbols as:

$$\tfrac{1}{2} m <c^2> = \tfrac{3}{2} kT$$

where k is the Boltzmann constant, $1.38 \times 10^{-23}\,\text{JK}^{-1}$. Here the temperature, T, must be in kelvin.

From this equation relating kinetic energy and absolute temperature, we can see that zero on the absolute scale of temperature must indicate a situation where the molecules are stationary. Their mass cannot change, so for their kinetic energy to be zero at absolute zero, their r.m.s. speed must decrease to zero.

Worked example

What is the r.m.s. speed of helium molecules in a child's balloon at 20° C?

(Atomic mass of helium, $m = 6.68 \times 10^{-27}$ kg.)

$T = 20 + 273 = 293\,\text{K}$

$\tfrac{1}{2} m <c^2> = \tfrac{3}{2} kT$

$= \tfrac{3}{2} \times 1.38 \times 10^{-23} \times 293$

$= 6.0651 \times 10^{-21}\,\text{J}$

$<c^2> = \dfrac{\tfrac{3}{2}kT}{\tfrac{1}{2}m}$

$= \dfrac{6.0651 \times 10^{-21}}{\tfrac{1}{2}(6.68 \times 10^{-27})}$

$= 1\,820\,000$

r.m.s speed $= \sqrt{<c^2>}$

$= \sqrt{1\,820\,000}$

$= 1350\,\text{ms}^{-1}$

The r.m.s. speed of a helium molecule at 20° C is 1350 ms^{-1}.

Questions

1 $\Delta E = mc\,\Delta\theta$

Re-arrange this equation to make the change in temperature the subject. Explain why the change in temperature would depend on the other quantities in your equation.

2 How long would a 2 kW heater take to raise the temperature of 800 grams of mercury from 20° C to the boiling temperature of mercury, which is 357° C? What assumption have you made?

3 In a school experiment, 2 kg of methyl alcohol, in an insulated beaker, is heated using an immersion heater connected to a joulemeter. The joulemeter registers 51 000 J for an increase in temperature of the liquid from 18° C to 28° C. What is the specific heat capacity of methyl alcohol?

4 What is the r.m.s. speed for a group of hydrogen molecules with the following speeds?
$v_1 = 530\,\text{ms}^{-1}$ $v_2 = 520\,\text{ms}^{-1}$ $v_3 = 525\,\text{ms}^{-1}$
$v_4 = 540\,\text{ms}^{-1}$ $v_5 = 512\,\text{ms}^{-1}$

5 Estimate the r.m.s. speed of molecules in the air in your lab.

6 A 500 g ball of copper at 75° C is cooled by dropping it into 300 g of water at 20° C. Assuming no heat is lost, what will be the equilibrium temperature?

7 What would be represented by the area underneath the Maxwell–Boltzmann curve?

Kinetic theory of gases Spec 110, 112, 113

Boyle's law

Over the last 400 years, scientists investigating the physics of gases have determined a number of laws governing their behaviour. The first of these was discovered by Robert Boyle, an Irish physicist working at Oxford University. **Boyle's law** states that:

> **For a constant mass of gas at a constant temperature, the pressure exerted by the gas is inversely proportional to the volume it occupies.**

If you imagine lying on an air mattress, after you sink slightly, it provides a force to hold you up. Your body squashes the volume of the mattress, making it smaller. This increases the pressure exerted by the gas inside, until the force applied by the gas pressure equals your weight. This is Boyle's law in action.

Demonstrating Boyle's law

fig. 4.1.6 Apparatus to demonstrate Boyle's law.

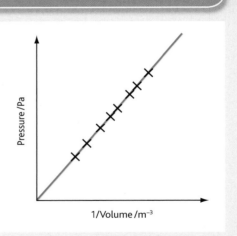

fig. 4.1.7 **Graph of data from Boyle's law experiment.**

Boyle's law can be demonstrated using the apparatus shown in **fig. 4.1.6**. Measurements of the length of air trapped in the vertical glass column represent the volume of the gas, and the pressure is measured using the barometer. A graph of pressure against 1/volume will give a straight best-fit line, indicating that:

$$p \propto \frac{1}{V}$$

Charles's law

About a 140 years after Boyle published his law, the French scientist Joseph Louis Gay-Lussac published two further gas laws. One was based on unpublished data from experiments undertaken by Jacques Charles. **Charles's law** states that:

> **For a constant mass of gas at a constant pressure, the volume occupied by the gas is proportional to its absolute temperature.**

This law can be shown in symbols as:

$$V \propto T$$

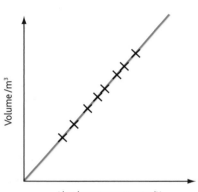

fig 4.1.8 **Graph of data from Charles's law experiment.**

The pressure law

Gay-Lussac's other gas law sometimes bears his name, and is sometimes simply referred to as the **pressure law**:

> **For a constant mass of gas at a constant volume, the pressure exerted by the gas is proportional to its absolute temperature.**

The pressure law law can be shown in symbols as:

$$p \propto T$$

Demonstrating the pressure law

fig. 4.1.9 **Apparatus to demonstrate the pressure law. The temperature and pressure readings could be taken by electronic sensors and the data logged by an attached computer.**

The pressure law can be demonstrated using the apparatus shown in **fig.4.1.9**. Measurements of the gas pressure and temperature can be data-logged to produce a graph of pressure against absolute temperature. This will give a straight best-fit line going through the origin (**fig. 4.1.10**), indicating that:

$$p \propto T$$

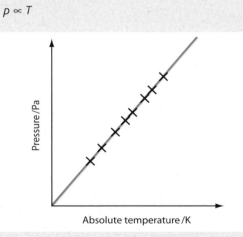

fig. 4.1.10 **Graph of data from pressure law experiment.**

Ideal gases

The three gas laws were worked out from graphs of experimental results which showed distinct, straight best-fit lines, allowing scientists to claim them as empirical laws (laws worked out from experimental data). However, if very accurate experiments are undertaken with a variety of different gases, we find that the laws are not perfectly accurate. For example, Charles's law suggests that if we reduce the temperature to zero kelvin, the gas would have zero volume – it would disappear. This does not happen, as the gas volume cannot reduce to less than the combined volume of its molecules.

The three gas laws are idealised, and would work perfectly if we could find a gas which did not suffer from the real world difficulties that real gases have. An **ideal gas** would have the following properties:

1   The molecules have zero size.

2   The molecules are identical.

3   The molecules collide with each other and the walls of their containers without any loss of energy, in collisions which take zero time.

4   The molecules exert no forces on each other, except during collisions.

5   There are enough molecules so that statistics can be applied.

Assuming an ideal gas, we can combine the three gas laws to produce a single equation relating the pressure, volume, temperature and amount of a gas:

$$pV = NkT$$

where N is the number of molecules of the gas and k is the Boltzmann constant. The temperature must be absolute temperature in kelvin.

This is known as the **equation of state** for an ideal gas, expressed in terms of the number of molecules present.

To make this more useful in practice, where we are dealing with very large numbers of molecules, we replace the Boltzmann constant and the number N to obtain:

$$pV = nRT$$

where n is the number of moles of the gas; and R is the Universal gas constant, $R = 8.31 \, \mathrm{J \, kg^{-1} \, mol^{-1}}$.

HSW The mole

The mole (abbreviated to mol) is an SI unit used to measure the amount of a substance. One mole of a substance is defined to consist of the Avogadro number of molecules of that substance. N_A is the symbol for the Avogadro number, 6.02×10^{23}.

For 1 mole of an ideal gas ($n = 1$):

$$pV = RT$$

Comparing this with the equation of state:

$$N_A \times k = R$$

$$6.02 \times 10^{23} \times 1.38 \times 10^{-23} = 8.31$$

Worked example

What would be the pressure in a child's helium balloon, at 20° C, if it is a sphere of radius 20 cm, containing three moles of helium gas?

Use $pV = NkT$

$$V = \tfrac{4}{3}\pi r^3 = \tfrac{4}{3}\pi \times (0.2)^3 = 3.35 \times 10^{-2}\,m^{-3}$$

$$N = 3 \times N_A$$

$$= 3 \times 6.02 \times 10^{23}$$

$$= 18.06 \times 10^{23}$$

$$p = \frac{NkT}{V}$$

$$= \frac{18.06 \times 10^{23} \times 1.38 \times 10^{-23} \times 293}{3.35 \times 10^{-2}}$$

$$= 217\,914\,Pa$$

$$= 218\,000\,Pa \quad (3\ s.f.)$$

Or use $pV = nRT$

$$p = \frac{nRT}{V}$$

$$= \frac{3 \times 8.31 \times 293}{3.35 \times 10^{-2}}$$

$$= 217\,914\,Pa$$

$$= 218\,000\,Pa \quad (3\ s.f.)$$

Questions

1 a Draw a labelled diagram of the apparatus you would use to verify that the pressure exerted by a fixed mass of gas at constant volume is directly proportional to its kelvin temperature.

   b State the readings you would take. Explain how you would use your measurements to verify this relationship between pressure and temperature. You may be awarded a mark for the clarity of your answer.

   c State one precaution that you would take in order to ensure accurate results.

2 Explain why a sample of air will not behave exactly as an ideal gas.

3 Assuming air to be an ideal gas, calculate the amount of air left in a scuba diver's tank if it has a volume of 12 litres and, when in 15° C water, the pressure is $2 \times 10^7\,Pa$.

4 Devise an experiment to verify Charles's law. Using a diagram, explain the measurements that would be made, how you would keep the control variables constant, and how your results could be analysed to show that you had 'proven' Charles's law.

Examzone: Topic 4 Thermal energy

1 A car of weight 12 000 N is stationary on a horizontal road. The four wheels of the car are fitted with air-filled (pneumatic) tyres. The pressure of the air in each tyre is $3.0 \times 10^5 \, \text{N m}^{-2}$.

Estimate the area of contact between each tyre and the road surface. **(2)**

The rubber in the tyres is repeatedly stretched and relaxed when the car is in motion but the overall volume of the tyres remains constant. During a journey the temperature of the air in the tyres rises from 10 °C to 30 °C. Calculate the pressure of the air at 30 °C.
(3)

Sketch a graph to show how the area of contact between a tyre and the road varies with the pressure of the air. **(3)**

(Total 8 marks)

2 You are asked to measure the specific heat capacity of aluminium using a cylindrical block of aluminium that has been drilled out to hold an electrical heater and a thermometer.

Draw a diagram of the apparatus, including the electrical circuit, which you would use. **(3)**

List the measurements you would take. **(4)**

Explain how you would use these measurements to find the specific heat capacity of aluminium. State any assumptions you have made. **(3)**

(Total 10 marks)

3 A sauna is a room in which there is a stove containing very hot bricks of basalt over which water is poured.

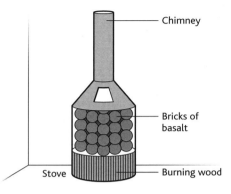

Before use the basalt is tested for resistance to cracking by first heating the bricks to 750 °C and then dropping them into cold water.

Each brick has a mass of 1.4 kg and an initial temperature of 22 °C. Each receives 860 kJ of energy from the burning wood. Show that the specific heat capacity of basalt is approximately $850 \, \text{J kg}^{-1} \text{K}^{-1}$.
(3)

(Total 3 marks)

4 A small electrical heater, operating at a constant power, was used to heat 64 g of water in a thin plastic cup. The mass of the cup was negligible. The temperature of the water was recorded at regular intervals for 30 minutes and a graph drawn of temperature against time.

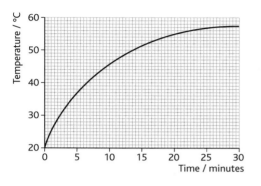

a **i)** Use the graph to determine the initial rate of temperature rise of the water. (2)

   ii) The specific heat capacity of water is 4200 J kg^{-1} K^{-1}. Determine the rate at which energy was supplied to the water by the heater. (3)

b After 26 minutes the rate of temperature rise became very small. Explain why. (2)

c The experiment was repeated using the same mass of water in a thick ceramic mug. The initial temperature of the water was the same and the water was heated for the same length of time.

   i) Copy the axes above and add a possible graph of temperature against time for the water in the mug. (2)

   ii) Explain your reasoning for your graph. (2)

(Total 11 marks)

Topic 5 Nuclear decay

This topic combines two related areas from the Edexcel specification. The first is an exploration of radioactive decay processes, and their applications in society. The section on nuclear fission and fusion processes delves into the processes which power stars.

What are the theories?

Naturally radioactive materials release energy from nuclear processes which are relatively straightforward and well understood. By using these energy-releasing materials, mankind has developed some elegant solutions to otherwise tricky problems. However, the mechanisms themselves cannot be controlled, and this leads to the potential for great environmental problems.

The energy released from stars comes in such amazingly large quantities that before the theory of nuclear fusion, scientists were at a loss to explain their existence. Here we will learn about nuclear fusion, and how to calculate the energy available from it.

What is the evidence?

There are many experimental verifications of the nature of radioactivity, from the first tentative suggestions by the (Nobel prize-winning) Curie family members to our current well-founded and complete model of the phenomena we can observe.

Whilst scientists can verify the action of nuclear fusion, we are a long way from producing a controlled fusion reaction that can be harnessed as a long-term high-yield power source. Our observations of stars have, thus far, served to confirm the theoretical calculations about nuclear fusion, but it is an inherently difficult area of experimental study.

What are the implications?

A controllable fusion reaction is one of several grails of modern science. With the ever-increasing global demand for energy and the ever-decreasing supply of non-renewable fuels, an energy supply that can run on the hydrogen from electrolysing water would indeed be a remarkable discovery.

The far less 'green' use of radioactive materials and fission-based nuclear power stations will generate disposal problems in the environment which will need clever solutions if we are to avoid ecological disasters. The huge concentrated release of energy from nuclear processes can lead to widespread and wide-ranging problems, quite apart from the continuing enormous threat to life on Earth posed by nuclear weapons.

The map opposite shows you the knowledge and skills you need to have by the end of this topic, and how they are linked together. The numbers refer to the sections in the Edexcel specification.

Chapter 5.1

show an awareness of the existence and origin of background radiation, past and present (114)

recognise nuclear radiations (alpha, beta and gamma) from their penetrating power and ionising ability (115)

describe the spontaneous and random nature of nuclear decay (116)

discuss the applications of radioactive materials, including environmental and ethical issues (118)

determine the half-lives of radioactive isotopes graphically and use the expressions for radioactive decay:
$$\frac{dN}{dt} = -\lambda N, \lambda = \frac{\ln 2}{t_{1/2}} \text{ and } N = N_0 e^{-\lambda t} \text{ (117)}$$

Chapter 5.2

explain the concept of nuclear binding energy, and recognise and use the expression $\Delta E = c^2 \Delta m$ and use the non SI atomic mass unit (u) in calculations of nuclear mass (including mass deficit) and energy (136)

describe the processes of nuclear fusion and fission (137)

explain the mechanism of nuclear fusion and the need for high densities of matter and high temperatures to bring it about and maintain it (138)

▶ To Topic 7 (136, 137, 138)

5.1 Nuclear decay Spec 114, 115

Nuclear radiation

Background radiation

Human beings can survive small doses of nuclear radiation relatively unscathed. This has been important in our evolution, as the natural environment exposes us to low levels of radiation from both natural and man-made sources. This is called **background radiation** (fig. 5.1.1). In the UK it averages to about one radioactive particle every two seconds in any given place. If we measure background radiation using a Geiger–Müller tube, the number of counts per second usually ranges from 0.5 to 30. Radiation levels are often reported in counts per second, and this unit is called the **becquerel** (**Bq**) after Henri Becquerel, the French physicist credited with the discovery of spontaneous radiation in 1896.

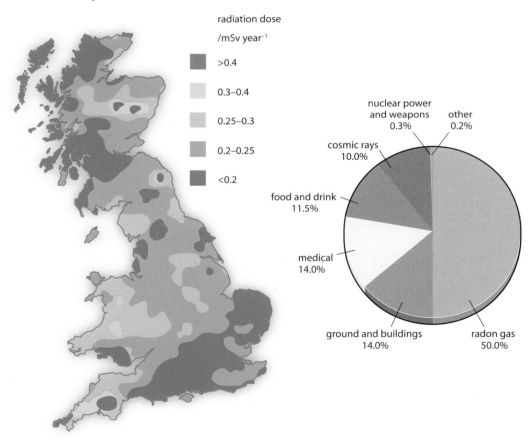

fig. 5.1.1 The environment continually exposes us to low levels of nuclear radiation. a Levels of background radiation dose in the UK (the radiation dose is measured in mSv, which takes into account the energy of the radiation); b sources of background radiation.

The actual exposure to nuclear radiations that any individual will receive from their environment will depend on where they are and for how long, as different environmental factors contribute to the local level of background radiation. On Earth, approximately half of the background radiation is from naturally radioactive gases in the atmosphere, particularly radon. Radon is produced in the decay of uranium ore present in certain rocks (especially granite) and thus is more prevalent in certain parts of the world than others. In Cornwall in the UK, some houses are fitted with radon detectors and special ventilation systems to flush out excess radon gas from the household atmosphere.

Measuring background radiation

It is easy to determine the average background radiation in your area using a Geiger–Müller tube and counter. As radioactive decay is a random and spontaneous process, the activity in your lab must be measured over a long period of time (30 minutes or more) and then an average calculated. Otherwise, you may find that the measurement is, by chance, particularly high or particularly low and thus does not truly indicate the average over time. For example, if the G-M tube and counter are set to counting for two hours, and the final count is then divided by 7200 (seconds), this will give a good approximation to the average over time as the count time is long compared with the typical average count of about 0.5 Bq.

Worked example

In a school experiment, Richard measured the background radiation using a G-M tube and counter for half an hour. The final reading was 747 counts. What is the average background radiation?

time $= 30 \times 60 = 1800\,s$

activity $= \dfrac{747}{1800} = 0.415\,Bq$

The background count will skew the results of investigations into nuclear radiations. Whenever such an investigation is undertaken, the background radiation must also be measured separately and then deducted from each count measured in the main part of the investigation.

Types of nuclear radiation

Many nuclei are slightly unstable and there is a small probability that, in any given time interval, they may **decay**. This means that a nucleon may change from one type to another, or the composition or energy state of the nucleus as a whole may change.

The three main types of nuclear radiation are called **alpha** (α), **beta** (β) and **gamma** (γ) radiation. Each one comes about through a different process within the nucleus, each one is composed of different particles, and each one has different properties.

Penetrating power of alpha, beta and gamma radiation

Before attempting this investigation, make sure you know the safety precautions you must follow when using radioactive materials.

You can investigate the penetrating power of alpha, beta and gamma radiation using a Geiger–Müller tube to detect them. Between the source and G-M tube, place absorber sheets which progressively increase in density, and measure the average count rate. This investigation is often simulated using computer software. This removes all risk of exposure to radiological hazards (see below).

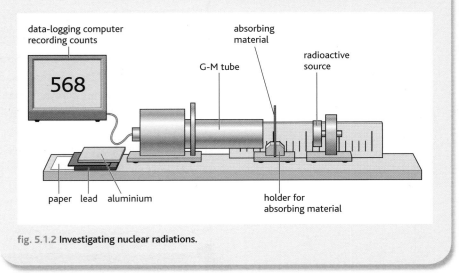

fig. 5.1.2 **Investigating nuclear radiations.**

When a nuclear decay occurs, the radiation particle emitted will leave the nucleus with a certain amount of kinetic energy. As the particle travels, it will ionise particles in its path, losing a small amount of that kinetic energy at each ionisation. When all the kinetic energy is transferred, the radiation particle stops and is absorbed by the substance it is in at that moment. Alpha particles are composed of two protons and two neutrons, the same as a helium nucleus. This is a relatively large particle with a significant positive charge (+2e), so it is highly ionising. As it ionises so much, it quickly loses its kinetic energy and is easily absorbed. A few centimetres travel in air is enough to absorb alpha particles, and they are completely blocked by paper and skin.

A beta particle is an electron emitted at high speed from the nucleus when a neutron decays into a proton. With its single negative charge and much smaller size, the beta particle is much less ionising than an alpha particle, and thus can penetrate much further. Several metres of air, or a thin sheet of aluminium, are needed to absorb beta particles.

Gamma rays are high energy, high frequency, electromagnetic radiation. These photons have no charge and no mass and so will rarely interact with particles in their path, which means they are the least ionising nuclear radiation. They are never completely absorbed, although their energy can be significantly reduced by several centimetres of lead, or several metres of concrete. If the energy is reduced to a safe level, gamma rays are often said to have been absorbed.

HSW Dangers from nuclear radiations

Ionising radiations can interact with the particles which make up human cells. There may be so much ionisation that the cells die as a result. Where there is less ionisation, the molecules of DNA in the cells may change slightly. These DNA mutations can cause cells to have an increased tendency to become cancerous. As the different types of nuclear radiation ionise to different extents, the hazard to humans is different for each type. The hazard levels are given in **table 5.1.1.**

Type of radiation	Inside body	Outside body
Alpha, α	Highly ionising – very dangerous, radiation poisoning and cancer possible.	Absorbed by surface layer of dead skin cells – no danger.
Beta, β	Moderate ionisation and danger, exposure should be minimised.	Moderate ionisation and danger, close exposure should be minimised.
Gamma, γ	Minimal ionisation – cancer danger from long-term exposure.	Minimal ionisation – cancer danger from long-term exposure.

table. 5.1.1 **Hazards from nuclear radiations.**

Questions

1 Create a table summarising everything you know about alpha, beta and gamma radiations.

2 In preparation for an experiment using a radioactive sample, Xian measured the radioactivity in her laboratory without the sample present. In one hour, her Geiger–Müller tube measured 1645 counts. What was the background count in becquerel?

3 Why is it theoretically safe to hold a sample which only emits alpha radiation? Why should you still never do so?

4 Why does the UK government's Health Protection Agency list 'living in Cornwall' as one of the most (radiologically) hazardous activities that the public can undertake?

5 It is thought that some soil could be contaminated with a radioisotope. You have a sample of this soil. Design an experiment to find what types of radiation are emitted.

Rate of radioactive decay Spec 116, 117

Probability and decay

Since radioactive decay is a spontaneous and random process, any radioactive nucleus may decay at any moment. For each second that it exists, there is a certain probability that the nucleus will decay. This probability is called the **decay constant**, λ. But just like guessing which number will come up next in a lottery, it is not possible to predict when any given nucleus will decay. The likelihood that a particular nucleus will decay is not affected by factors outside the nucleus, such as temperature or pressure, or by the behaviour of neighbouring nuclei – each nucleus acts entirely independently.

If we have a large sample of the nuclei, the probability of decay will determine the fraction of these nuclei that will decay each second. Naturally, if the sample is larger, then the number that decay in a second will be greater. So the number decaying per second, called the **activity**, A (or dN/dt), is proportional to the number of nuclei in the sample, N. Mathematically, this is expressed as:

$$A = -\lambda N$$
$$\frac{dN}{dt} = -\lambda N$$

The minus sign in this formula occurs because the number of nuclei in the sample, N, decreases with time. In practice we ignore the negative sign when using the formula.

Worked examples

The decay constant for carbon-14 is $\lambda = 3.84 \times 10^{-12}\,s^{-1}$. What is the activity of a sample of 100 billion atoms of carbon-14?

$$\frac{dN}{dt} = -\lambda N$$
$$\frac{dN}{dt} = -(3.84 \times 10^{-12}) \times (100 \times 10^{9}) = 0.384\,Bq$$

The formula for the rate of decay of nuclei in a sample is a differential equation. We have previously met this type of equation when studying the discharge of a capacitor. The equation $dN/dt = -\lambda N$ can be solved to give a formula for the number of nuclei remaining in a sample, N, after a fixed time, t:

$$N = N_0 e^{-\lambda t}$$

where N_0 is the initial number of nuclei within a sample and λ is the decay constant.

Worked examples

If our sample of 100 billion carbon-14 atoms were left for 300 years, how many carbon-14 atoms would remain?

time, $t = 300 \times 365 \times 24 \times 60 \times 60 = 9.46 \times 10^9 \, \text{s}$

$$N = N_0 e^{-\lambda t}$$

$$\lambda t = (3.84 \times 10^{-12}) \times (9.46 \times 10^9)$$

$$= 0.0363$$

$$N = (100 \times 10^9) \times e^{-0.0363}$$

$$= 9.64 \times 10^{10} \text{ atoms}$$

Half-life

As we have seen, the activity of a radioactive sample decreases over time as the radioactive nuclei decay. While the activity of a sample depends on the number of nuclei present, the rate at which the activity decreases depends only on the particular isotope. A measure of this rate of decrease of activity is the **half-life**, $t_{1/2}$. This is the time taken for half of the atoms of that nuclide within a sample to decay.

Mathematically, the half-life can be found by putting $N = \frac{1}{2} N_0$ into the decay equation:

$$N = N_0 e^{-\lambda t}$$

$$\frac{N_0}{2} = N_0 e^{-\lambda t_{1/2}}$$

$$\frac{1}{2} = e^{-\lambda t_{1/2}}$$

$$\ln\left(\frac{1}{2}\right) = -\lambda t_{1/2}$$

$$-\ln 2 = -\lambda t_{1/2}$$

$$t_{1/2} = \frac{\ln 2}{\lambda}$$

Rearranging, this also gives us:

$$\lambda = \frac{\ln 2}{t_{1/2}}$$

Worked examples

What is the half-life of carbon-14?

$$\lambda = 3.84 \times 10^{-12} \, \text{s}^{-1}$$

$$t_{1/2} = \frac{\ln 2}{\lambda}$$

$$t_{1/2} = \frac{\ln 2}{3.84 \times 10^{-12}}$$

$$t_{1/2} = 1.81 \times 10^{11} \, \text{s} = 5720 \, \text{years}$$

Measuring radioactive decay

fig. 5.1.3 **Measuring the half-life of protactinium.**

fig. 5.1.4 **Measuring the half-life of dice.**

You may have the equipment to measure the half-life for a radioactive sample, as shown in **fig. 5.1.3**. If you do not, a simulation in which dice represent the radioactive nuclei can demonstrate the exponential decay of a sample (**fig. 5.1.4**).

Half-life graphs

An experiment to determine the half-life of a substance will usually measure its activity over time. As activity is proportional to the number of nuclei present, when the activity is plotted against time, the shape of the curve is exponential decay (**fig. 5.1.5**). The activity, A, follows the equation:

$$A = A_0 e^{-\lambda t}$$

We can use the graph of activity against time to determine the half-life of the substance by finding the time taken for the activity to halve.

To find the half-life from such a graph, find a useful start point on the curve. In the example shown in **fig.5.1.5**, this could be the start point where the activity is 800 Bq. As the half-life is defined as the time taken for the activity to fall to half of its original value, we use the graph to find the time taken for the count to drop to 400 Bq, which is 70 seconds. Doing this a second time, from a count rate of 400 Bq to a count rate of 200 Bq, gives a time of 80 seconds. Notice that the time interval is not identical each time. This is due to the random nature of radioactive decay, plus experimental

and graphing errors. The best-fit curve will be a matter of the drawer's judgement. Thus, to get the best answer for the half-life, we must undertake the analysis on the graph several times in different parts of the graph and average the results. From the two half-lives shown in **fig. 5.1.5**, the average half-life for protactinium would be 75 seconds.

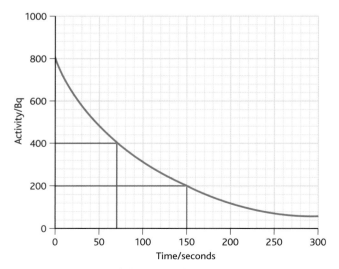

fig. 5.1.5 **Determining half-life graphically.**

Questions

1 Calculate the decay constants for the following isotopes which are commonly used in school laboratories:

a radium-226: half-life = 1602 years
b strontium-90: half-life = 28.8 years
c cobalt-60: half-life = 5.3 years.

2 If the cellar in a house in Cornwall contains 6.5 billion atoms of radon-220 gas, with a decay constant $\lambda = 0.0126\,\mathrm{s}^{-1}$, how many radon gas atoms will there be one minute later?

3 Technetium-99 is a gamma emitter which is often used as a medical tracer to monitor lymph node activity. Use the graph of experimental results shown in **fig. 5.1.6** to work out the half-life of technetium-99.

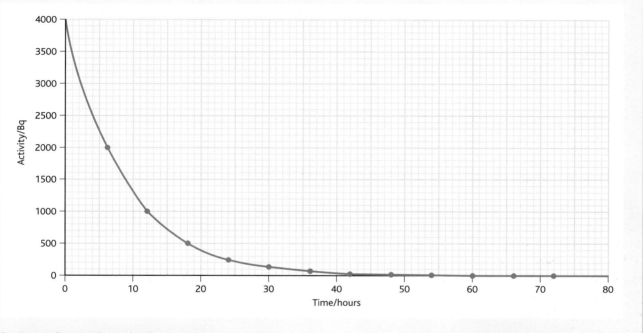

fig. 5.1.6 **Radioactive decay of technetium-99m.**

4 Explain why a radioactive isotope with a very small decay constant will have a long half-life.

5.2 Nuclear fission and fusion Spec 136, 137, 138

Energy–mass equivalence

Particle	Mass / atomic mass units (u)	Mass / SI units (kg)
Proton	1.007 276	1.672623×10^{-27}
Neutron	1.008 665	1.674929×10^{-27}
Electron	0.000 548 58	9.109390×10^{-31}

table 5.2.1 **Masses of subatomic particles.**

We have previously seen that a nucleon has a mass which is approximately equal to 1 unified atomic mass unit, u ($= 1.66 \times 10^{-27}$ kg). The exact masses of a proton, a neutron and an electron are given in **table 5.2.1**.

We might expect that if we know the constituent parts of any nucleus, we can calculate its mass by finding the total mass of its nucleons. However, in practice we find that the actual, measured mass of a nucleus is always less than the total mass of its constituent nucleons. This difference is called the **mass deficit**, or sometimes the **mass defect**.

Worked example

Fig. 5.2.1 shows how to calculate the mass deficit for carbon-12.

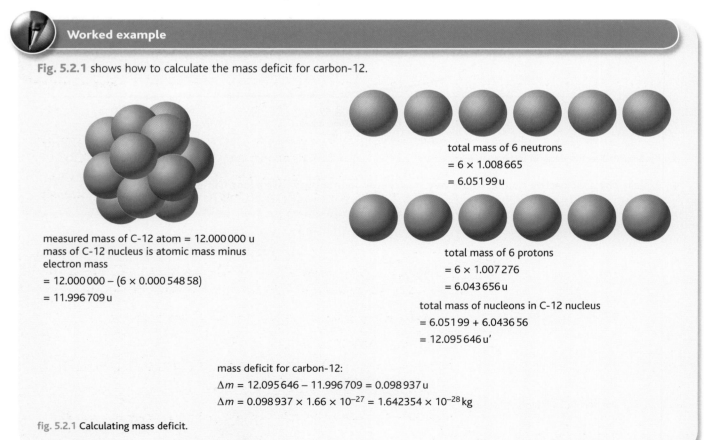

measured mass of C-12 atom = 12.000 000 u
mass of C-12 nucleus is atomic mass minus electron mass

= 12.000 000 − (6 × 0.000 548 58)

= 11.996 709 u

total mass of 6 neutrons
= 6 × 1.008 665
= 6.051 99 u

total mass of 6 protons
= 6 × 1.007 276
= 6.043 656 u

total mass of nucleons in C-12 nucleus
= 6.051 99 + 6.043 656
= 12.095 646 u'

mass deficit for carbon-12:
$\Delta m = 12.095646 - 11.996709 = 0.098937$ u
$\Delta m = 0.098937 \times 1.66 \times 10^{-27} = 1.642354 \times 10^{-28}$ kg

fig. 5.2.1 **Calculating mass deficit.**

Nuclear binding energy

The mass deficit comes about because a small amount of the mass of the nucleons is converted into the energy needed to hold the nucleus together. This is called **binding energy**. It is calculated using Einstein's mass–energy relationship:

$$\Delta E = c^2 \Delta m$$

where c is the speed of light.

There are two common systems of units for calculating binding energy. If you have calculated the mass deficit in kilograms (SI units) then using $c = 3.00 \times 10^8\,\mathrm{m\,s^{-1}}$ will give the binding energy in joules. Alternatively, if you have calculated the mass deficit in atomic mass units, then you convert this into binding energy in mega-electronvolts (MeV) using:

$$1\,\mathrm{u} = 931.5\,\mathrm{MeV}$$

Worked example: The binding energy for carbon-12

Calculate the binding energy for a carbon-12 nucleus in both joules and electronvolts.

Working in kilograms, from **fig. 5.2.1**:

$$\Delta m = 1.642\,354 \times 10^{-28}\,\mathrm{kg}$$

$$\Delta E = c^2 \Delta m$$

$$= (3 \times 10^8)^2 \times (1.642\,354 \times 10^{-28})$$

$$= 1.478 \times 10^{-11}\,\mathrm{J}$$

Converting to electronvolts:

$$\Delta E = \frac{1.478 \times 10^{-11}}{1.6 \times 10^{-19}}$$

$$= 9.226 \times 10^7\,\mathrm{eV}$$

$$= 92.3\,\mathrm{MeV}$$

Alternatively, working in atomic mass units, from **fig. 5.2.1**:

$$\Delta m = 0.098\,937\,\mathrm{u}$$

$$\Delta E = 931.5 \times \Delta m$$

$$= 931.5 \times 0.098\,937$$

$$= 92.2\,\mathrm{MeV}$$

Note that in calculations of both mass deficit and binding energy, you need to use as many significant figures as possible, only rounding off at the very end of the calculation. The difference in our two answers here has come from rounding off the speed of light and the charge on an electron, and the mass in kilograms of $1\,\mathrm{u}$.

Binding energy per nucleon

How much energy would be needed to remove one nucleon from a nucleus? To work this out we need to know both the binding energy of a nucleus, and the number of nucleons within it. This gives us the binding energy per nucleon in a nucleus, in MeV, and from this we can determine how strongly different nuclei are held together.

Worked example

Does helium-4 or carbon-12 have the higher binding energy per nucleon?

The binding energy of helium-4 is 28.3 MeV, and it contains 4 nucleons.

$$\text{binding energy per nucleon} = \frac{28.3}{4} = 7.08\,\mathrm{MeV}$$

The binding energy for carbon-12 is 92.2 MeV, and it contains 12 nucleons.

$$\text{binding energy per nucleon} = \frac{92.2}{12} = 7.68\,\mathrm{MeV}$$

So, carbon-12 nuclei are more tightly bound together than those of helium-4.

Drawing a graph of binding energy per nucleon against mass number for the nuclei gives us a useful means of comparing how tightly different nuclides are bound together.

Looking at **fig. 5.2.2**, you will see that the isotope with the highest binding energy per nucleon is iron-56 at 8.8 MeV per nucleon. Any nuclear reaction which increases the binding energy per nucleon will give out energy.

The graph shows us that small nuclides can combine together to make larger nuclei (up to Fe-56) with a greater binding energy per nucleon. This process is called nuclear **fusion**. Similarly, larger nuclei can break up into smaller pieces which have a greater binding energy per nucleon. Reactions like this are called nuclear **fission**. Both of these types of nuclear reaction will give out energy, and could be used as power sources.

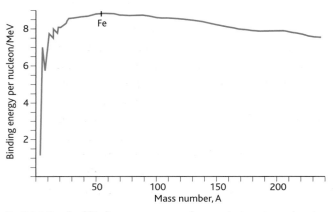

fig. 5.2.2 Graph of binding energy per nucleon against mass number, A.

Nuclear fusion

If we take some light nuclei and force them to join together, the mass of the new, heavier, nucleus will be less than the mass of the constituent parts, as some mass is converted into energy. However, not all of this energy is used as binding energy for the new larger nucleus, so energy will be released from this reaction. The binding energy per nucleon afterwards is higher than at the start. This is the process of nuclear fusion and is what provides the energy to make stars shine (**fig. 5.2.3**).

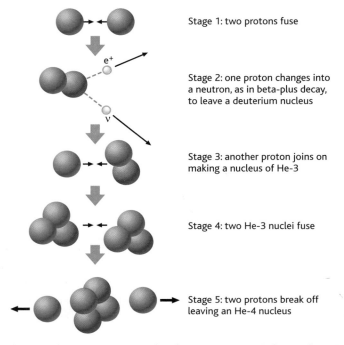

Stage 1: two protons fuse

Stage 2: one proton changes into a neutron, as in beta-plus decay, to leave a deuterium nucleus

Stage 3: another proton joins on making a nucleus of He-3

Stage 4: two He-3 nuclei fuse

Stage 5: two protons break off leaving an He-4 nucleus

fig. 5.2.3 The proton–proton nuclear fusion reaction, typical in small cool stars like our Sun, where the core temperature is about 15×10^6 K.

Worked example

The proton–proton chain nuclear fusion reaction effectively takes four protons and converts them into a helium-4 nucleus and two positrons (which have the same mass as electrons). Calculate the energy released in this reaction.

The measured atomic mass of ^{4}He is 4.002 602 u.

Mass of 4 protons = 4 × 1.007 276 u

$\qquad$ = 4.029 104 u

Mass of ^{4}He nucleus + 2 positrons

$\qquad$ = (4.002 602 − 2 × 0.000 548 58) u + 2 × 0.000 548 58 u

$\qquad$ = 4.002 602 u

Mass deficit $\qquad$ = 4.029 104 u − 4.002 602 u

$\qquad$ = 0.0265 u

$\qquad$ = 24.7 MeV (3 s.f.)

These reactions occurring in enormous numbers provide the energy which causes the Sun to emit heat and light in all directions in great quantities.

Converting hydrogen into helium with the release of energy would appear to be a fantastic way of supplying our planet's energy needs. The seas are full of hydrogen in water molecules, and the helium produced would be an inert gas which could simply be allowed to float off into the upper atmosphere. However, scientists have not yet successfully maintained a controlled nuclear fusion reaction. The problem lies in forcing two positively charged, mutually repelling, protons to fuse together. The kinetic energy they need to have to collide forcefully enough to overcome this electrostatic repulsion requires temperatures of many million kelvin. Moreover, to ensure enough colliding protons for the reaction to be sustained requires a very high density of them.

HSW The Joint European Torus

The Joint European Torus (JET) experiment in Oxfordshire is a research facility which investigated sustained nuclear fusion reactions (**fig. 5.2.4**). The eventual aim is to develop the technology to build nuclear fusion power stations. However, after 25 extremely expensive years of tests on confining and controlling 'burning plasmas', the main JET experiment has been retired. The equipment is now being used to provide developmental support for the ITER project (International Thermonuclear Experimental Reactor), which is JET's successor. This is a truly international project, whereas JET was a European funded experiment. The costs were becoming too much for the European Union to bear alone, and although the ITER will be sited in France, the money for it is also coming from six other large nations (India, China, Russia, USA, Korea and Japan).

fig. 5.2.4 The JET experiment to investigate the possibility of nuclear fusion being used to provide the energy for electricity generation.

Nuclear fission

We have seen that nuclear fusion is not yet an option for electricity generation as we have not been able to create the high densities and temperatures needed to sustain a fusion reaction. However, another process which releases binding energy from nuclei is called nuclear fission. In this process a large nucleus breaks up into two smaller nuclei, with the release of some neutrons and energy (**fig. 5.2.5**).

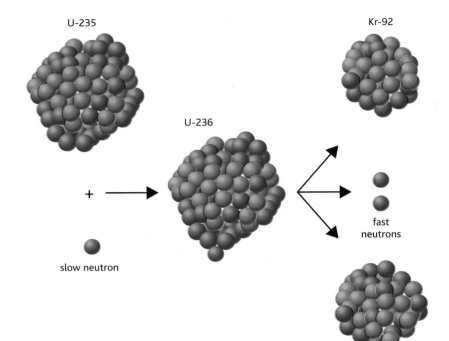

fig. 5.2.5 **Nuclear fission of uranium-235.**

Worked examples

1 Although there are a variety of possible products from nuclear fission reactions, the amount of energy released in each one is roughly similar at about 200 MeV.

Calculate the energy released in the following fission reaction:

$$^{235}U + n \rightarrow {}^{141}Ba + {}^{92}Kr + 3n + energy$$

(Data: mass of U-235 = 235.0439 u; mass of Ba-141 = 140.9144 u; mass of Kr-92 = 91.9262 u.)

Mass difference:

$$\Delta m = 235.0439 + 1.008665 - 140.9144 \\ - 91.9262 - (3 \times 1.008665)$$

$$= 0.1860\,u$$

Energy released:

$$E = 0.1860 \times 931.5$$

$$= 173\,MeV$$

$$= 2.77 \times 10^{-11}\,J$$

This is the energy per fission. If one mole of these were to occur, using 235 g of U-235, then the total energy produced would be:

$$E = 6.02 \times 10^{23} \times 2.77 \times 10^{-11}$$

$$= 1.67 \times 10^{13}\,J$$

However, U-235 is a small proportion ($\approx$ 0.7%) of all the uranium found, and thus a larger amount of uranium fuel would be needed in order to provide enough U-235 atoms to produce this much energy.

2 What are the changes in binding energy per nucleon in the above reaction?

(Data: binding energy of U-235 = 1786 MeV; binding energy of Ba-141 = 1170 MeV; binding energy of Kr-92 = 782 MeV.)

Find the binding energies per nucleon:

U-235: $\dfrac{1786}{235} = 7.6\,MeV$

Ba-141: $\dfrac{1170}{141} = 8.3\,MeV$

Kr-92: $\dfrac{782}{92} = 8.5\,MeV$

So the two fission products each have a higher binding energy per nucleon than the original uranium nuclide.

HSW Nuclear bombs

In controlled nuclear fission reactions the neutrons are slowed to speeds needed to sustain fission using a **moderator**. However, some nuclear fission reactions, such as those using plutonium, will progress by reacting with high speed neutrons, meaning that a moderator is not required. If such a reaction were allowed to run uncontrolled, it would produce energy continuously, at an ever-increasing rate, until all the fuel were used up. This is the essential concept behind the design of atomic bombs. A lump of plutonium-239 about the size of a cricket ball can completely react in less than a microsecond, releasing the energy equivalent of 20 kilotonnes of TNT, about 90×10^{12} J.

This type of bomb was dropped on the city of Nagasaki in Japan during World War II (**fig. 5.2.6**). It killed 40 000 people immediately and a similar number had died from after effects by the end of 1945. The atomic bombings in Japan were so devastating that the country surrendered to the Allies just six days after the Nagasaki bomb, and continues to have a government constitution which does not allow Japan to ever hold nuclear weapons.

fig. 5.2.6 A Fat Man plutonium fission bomb.

Questions

1 Use the data in table 5.2.1 to work out how much energy could be produced if a proton, neutron and electron were each completely converted into energy.

2 The atomic mass unit used to be different in Physics and Chemistry until the system was unified in the 1960s. Previously, it was based on the mass of an atom of oxygen-16 in Physics, which is 15.994915 u. Using the modern values, calculate the binding energy of a nucleus of oxygen-16.

3 Inside large mass stars, fusion of elements heavier than in the proton–proton cycle can occur. At about 10^8 K, helium-4 nuclei will fuse into carbon-12 nuclei according to the equation:

$$^4He^{2+} + {}^4He^{2+} + {}^4He^{2+} \rightarrow {}^{12}C^{6+}$$

a Calculate the energy released in this reaction.

b How does the binding energy per nucleon change in the reaction?

c What is the average kinetic energy and r.m.s. speed of the helium nuclei in the star?

4 Complete the following nuclear fission reaction to determine X:

$$^{235}U + n \rightarrow {}^X Rb + {}^{139}Cs + 2n + energy$$

5 Calculate the amount of fission energy, in joules, that can be generated from 2 kg of uranium fuel, if the U-235 represents 0.7% of the metal, and every fission reaction produces 200 MeV.

6 Calculate the energy released in one fission in the following reaction:

$$^{235}U + n \rightarrow {}^{94}Zr + {}^{139}Te + 3n + energy$$

(Data: mass of Zr-94 = 93.9063 u; mass of Te-139 = 138.9347 u.)

7 Explain, in terms of binding energy per nucleon, why nuclear fusion and nuclear fission can release energy.

Nuclear power stations Spec 115, 116, 118, 137

fig. 5.2.7 Sizewell B nuclear reactor power station, Suffolk, UK.

Nuclear reactors

The most common nuclear fission reaction used in power stations is that of uranium-235 (fig. 5.2.7). If a nucleus of this uranium isotope is hit by a slow moving neutron, often called a **thermal neutron**, it may absorb the neutron to form U-236, which is unstable and quickly breaks up. The products of this disintegration will be two medium-sized (and radioactive) nuclei with roughly half the nucleons each, plus a number of high speed neutrons. The actual composition of the two main products varies – the vast majority of these fissions will produce heavier daughter nuclei with mass numbers in the range 130–150, whilst the lighter product usually has a mass number in the range 85–105.

There is a difference in the amount of binding energy in the U-236 and the daughter products. This is given off as the kinetic energy of the various particles and harnessed by the nuclear reactor to drive an electricity-generating system (fig. 5.2.8). A moderator, such as water or graphite, is used to slow down the emitted neutrons, so that they arrive at the next uranium **fuel rod** at the slow speed needed to allow them to be absorbed by further U-235 nuclei to cause further fissions and continue the reaction (fig. 5.2.9). As each reaction requires only one neutron but produces two or three, this **chain reaction** could run out of control, as is the case in an atom bomb. To control the reaction in a nuclear reactor, **control rods** typically made of cadmium or boron absorb excess neutrons. These control rods are lowered into the reactor on an electromagnetic support. If there is a failure in the control rods system, gravity will pull them completely down into the reactor core, where they will absorb all neutrons and shut down the reaction.

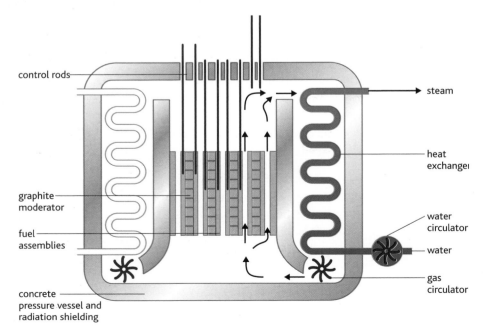

fig. 5.2.8 Advanced Gas Cooled Reactor – a typical nuclear reactor design in the UK.

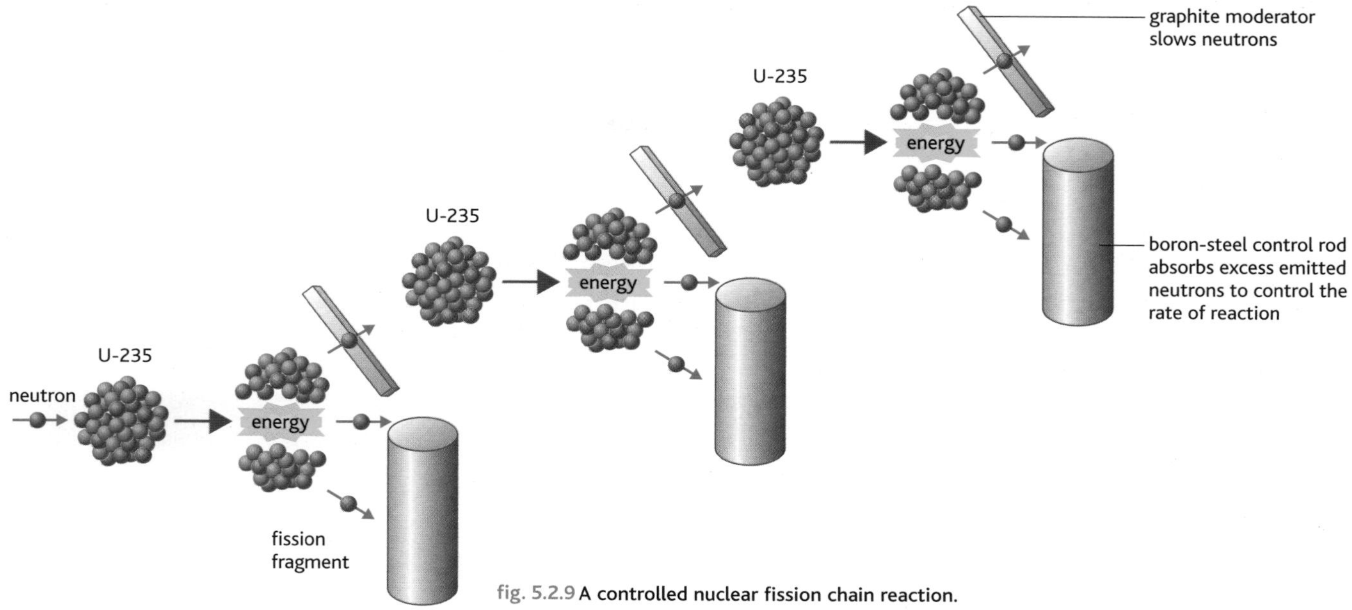

fig. 5.2.9 A controlled nuclear fission chain reaction.

An alternative non-renewable energy

Radioactive materials which can supply energy through a controlled nuclear fission reaction are not uncommon in the Earth's crust – uranium is about 500 times more abundant than gold. And in order to supply a standard size power station, such fuels are only needed in very small quantities. 3 kg of uranium-235 per day will run a 1000 MW nuclear power station. Compare this with the 9000 tonnes of coal per day which would be needed in a coal-fired power station of the same output. Indeed, a million tonnes of uranium-235 could supply the energy equivalent to all the fossil fuels on Earth. There is estimated to be about seven times that quantity of uranium available. However, it is principally located in only a handful of countries, with Australia, Canada, Kazakhstan, South Africa and Brazil having over 70% of global reserves (table 5.2.2). This raises some serious issues about the security of fuel supply for countries that choose to use nuclear power.

Country	Uranium reserves/tonnes
Australia	460 000
Canada	426 000
Kazakhstan	254 000
South Africa	186 000
Brazil	112 000
Namibia	110 000
Uzbekistan	109 000
USA	102 000
Niger	94 000
Russia	75 000

fig. 5.2.2 Uranium reserves of the top ten countries, which hold 96% of the world's known reserves (considered as those that could be mined for less than US$80 per kilogram).

Recent global increased interest in nuclear power has caused the potential longevity of reserves to be called into question. Considering only the reserves that could be mined for less than US$40 a kilogram suggests that reserves could run out in as little as 20 years. As the market price has increased recently, this allows less-easily mined ores to become more viable, and the time estimates improve. However, should there be any unexpected supply problem (for example, the McArthur River mine in the US, which produces 11% of world supply, was flooded in 2004, which took it out of action for three months), the precarious balance between supply and demand would be highlighted.

HSW How does society choose to use nuclear power?

The first generation of nuclear power stations in the UK were built and run by the government. Many of them have now been sold to private energy companies, and politicians are currently keen to have all future nuclear installations built and run privately. There is a legitimate economic argument that this will increase efficiency within the operation, and in the end this should make the electricity cheaper for the consumer, even after allowing for the company's profits.

In recent years, public opinion in the UK, along with the viewpoint of British industry (as represented by the Confederation of British Industries (CBI)) and that of MPs, have all moved towards a more positive stance on nuclear power.

The Health and Safety Executive has a department covering nuclear installations and they implement various acts of parliament governing the required safety procedures in such power stations.

Nuclear disasters

All industries have a risk of accidents occurring, and the potential hazards must be balanced by the likelihood of their occurrence, and the checks put in place to minimise this likelihood or limit the potential damage. In the nuclear industry the hazards are extreme, so the probability of accidents must be seriously minimised.

Nuclear power poses the greatest potential hazard to health and safety, as a major incident can destroy an entire landscape. In 1986, a reactor explosion at Chernobyl in the Ukraine released about 5% of the reactor core material into the atmosphere (**fig. 5.2.10**). Up to 2004, there had been 56 fatalities which could be directly attributed to this disaster, 28 of these occurring within a few weeks from acute radiation exposure. Large areas of Russia, Ukraine and Belarus were contaminated, and 336 000 people have been resettled elsewhere. There will be an ongoing (small) increased incidence of cancer amongst the 'liquidators' – the half million people from all over the Soviet Union who worked on the clean-up operation in the two years after the explosion. However, the World Health Organisation, International Atomic Energy Agency and United Nations have all undertaken investigations and their reports on the region's population are in agreement that the actual harmful effects have been considerably overestimated.

fig. 5.2.10 Chernobyl nuclear reactor number 4 exploded on 26 April 1986.

The most harmful isotopes released decayed quite quickly, leaving the area with a background radiation which is at present about 50% higher than normal. There were four reactors at Chernobyl, and the other three continued to operate for many years afterwards. Reactor number 4 was encased in a concrete shield very soon afterwards, and this is to be enhanced by a more permanent shelter in 2011.

Nuclear power legacies

Nuclear fission of uranium produces a variety of daughter products which are also radioactive, with varying half-lives. This spent fuel is the most dangerous of the radioactive wastes generated in the process. The material of the reactor core's construction will also become slightly radioactive during the course of its lifetime, mostly through exposure to free neutrons which can be absorbed by a nucleus, turning it into an unstable, radioactive isotope.

This means that the production of radioactive waste from a nuclear power station occurs throughout its lifetime and then the decommissioning process at the end of the useful lifetime will generate about the same amount of waste again (table 5.2.3). The projected cost for decommissioning all of the nuclear power stations in Britain is over £70 billion.

Waste level	Types of material	Sources	Volume percentage of global waste / %	Activity percentage of global waste / %	Treatment
High	Heavy metals, fuel rods	Spent fuel, fuel reprocessing products	3	95	Cooled in a water pool for 1–20 years, then buried in a deep underground repository
Intermediate	Resins, chemical sludges, reactor components	Reactor decommissioning	7	4	Solidified in concrete or bitumen and buried
Low	Paper, rags, tools, clothing, filters	Hospitals, laboratories, industry	90	1	Incinerated and buried

table 5.2.3 Radioactive waste levels and their treatments.

Questions

1 List all the factors that should be taken into consideration when deciding whether or not to build new nuclear power stations.

2 Carry out some research to find out about the methods for disposing of high, medium and low level radioactive wastes.

3 Explain why a mechanical system using levers moved by hand would be inappropriate for use to lower the control rods into a nuclear reactor.

4 Write a short editorial piece for a local newspaper, outlining your views about nuclear power generation in Britain, and the implications for your local area.

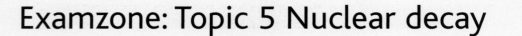

Examzone: Topic 5 Nuclear decay

1 Name two sources of natural background radiation. (2)

Caesium-137 is a by-product of nuclear fission within a nuclear reactor. Copy and complete the two boxes in the nuclear equation below which describes the production of $^{137}_{55}\text{Cs}$.

$$^{235}_{92}\text{U} + {}^{1}_{0}\text{n} \longrightarrow {}^{137}_{55}\text{Cs} + \boxed{^{95}\text{Rb}} + \boxed{{}^{1}_{0}\text{n}}$$

(2)

The half-life of caesium-137 is 30 years. When the fuel rods are removed from a nuclear reactor core, the total activity of the caesium-137 is 5.8×10^{15} Bq. After how many years will this activity have fallen to 1.6×10^{6} Bq? (4)

Comment on the problems of storage of the fuel rods over this time period. (2)

(Total 10 marks)

2 Radon-220 (also know as thoron) is a radioactive gas which decays by α emission to polonium $^{216}_{84}$. The half-life of this decay is approximately 1 minute.

Describe an experiment you could perform in a school laboratory to determine the half-life of an α emitter of half-life approximately 1 minute. (5)

A sample of milk is contaminated with a very small quantity of strontium-90. This isotope decays by β^- emission with a half-life of approximately 28 years.

Give two reasons why it would be very difficult to use this contaminated sample of milk to obtain an accurate value for the half-life of strontium-90. (2)

(Total 7 marks)

3 The graph shows the decay of a radioactive nuclide.

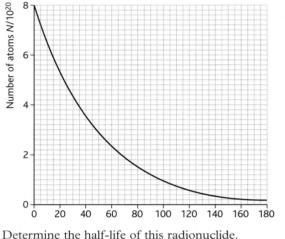

Determine the half-life of this radionuclide. (2)

Use your value of half-life to calculate the decay constant λ of this radionuclide. (1)

Use the graph to determine the rate of decay dN/dt when $N = 3.0 \times 10^{20}$. (3)

Use your value of the rate of decay to calculate the decay constant λ of this radionuclide. (2)

Explain which method of determining the decay constant you consider to be more reliable. (1)

(Total 9 marks)

4 Alpha particle radiation has a short range in matter. With reference to the effect of alpha particles on atoms, explain why they only travel a short distance. **(2)**

A worker in the nuclear industry accidentally swallows some liquid that emits alpha particles.

The Plant Manager tells him not to worry as the swallowed liquid will be excreted within a day.

However, the health physicist investigating the accident is still anxious to determine the half-life of the radioisotope involved. Explain the significance of the radioactive half-life for the health of the worker. **(2)**

(Total 4 marks)

5 A graph of binding energy per nucleon against nucleon (mass) number is shown.

On a copy of the graph, label the approximate positions of the elements, deuterium D (an isotope of hydrogen), uranium U and iron Fe.

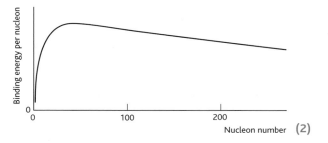

(2)

What is meant by the term *binding energy*?

With reference to the graph, state and explain which of the elements mentioned above would be likely to undergo nuclear fission. **(5)**

(Total 7 marks)

6 A physics student asked a large group of children to stand up and perform a simple experiment to model radioactive decay. Each child flipped a coin. Those who flipped a "head" sat down.

The children left standing again flipped a coin and those who flipped a "head" sat down.

This process was repeated twice more.

There were initially 192 children standing. Copy the axes below and plot the expected graph of the results. Add a scale to the *y*-axis.

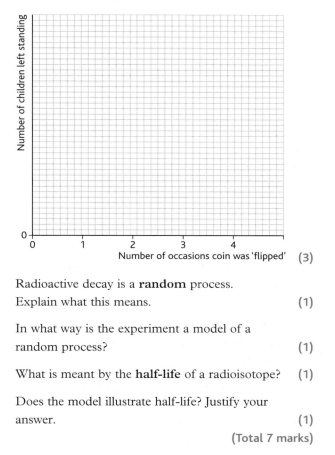

(3)

Radioactive decay is a **random** process. Explain what this means. **(1)**

In what way is the experiment a model of a random process? **(1)**

What is meant by the **half-life** of a radioisotope? **(1)**

Does the model illustrate half-life? Justify your answer. **(1)**

(Total 7 marks)

Topic 6   Oscillations

Above absolute zero, everything will be made of vibrating particles. A general treatment of the underlying theory behind oscillations, particularly simple harmonic oscillations, is introduced in this topic. This becomes more detailed as we consider how vibrations can be caused or altered once started.

What are the theories?

The causes of oscillations and the results of driving oscillations in different ways, and in different real situations, are presented. You will learn how to describe and measure oscillations and, following on from this, how to carry out calculations on various aspects of an oscillating system. As with everything in physics, these ideas are all founded upon a transfer of energy, and you will see how oscillations change energy from one form to another and, ultimately, conserve it.

What is the evidence?

The equations presented in these topics can generally be examined very accurately and in some detail using straightforward experiments. For example, you may use the oscillations of a simple pendulum to measure the acceleration due to gravity. This is one of the most accurate experiments you can undertake, and results can often be within 0.5% of the accepted value.

Vibration as a means to transfer energy is one of the most important areas of scientific study. All the other Physics topics you will study at Advanced Level depend on oscillations at one point or another. From the rotations of galaxies, to the vibrations of electrons within atoms, to the movements of electromagnetic waves, the fundamentals described in this section have been experimentally confirmed across many scientific disciplines.

What are the implications?

It is no great surprise then that this area of Physics can have implications in all others. From the design of children's toys to the study of the cosmos, the ramifications of systems oscillating are immensely important. We will look at how to make a quieter washing machine, how to build an earthquake-resistant skyscraper, and how to walk over a bridge without breaking it.

The map opposite shows you the knowledge and skills you need to have by the end of this topic, and how they are linked together. The numbers refer to the sections in the Edexcel specification.

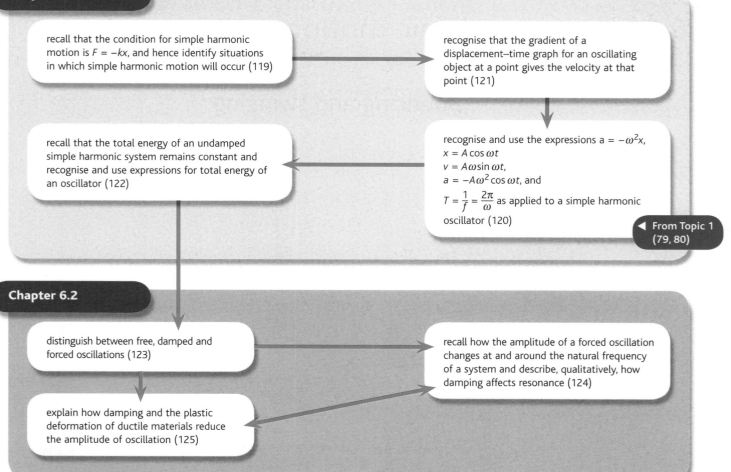

Chapter 6.1

recall that the condition for simple harmonic motion is $F = -kx$, and hence identify situations in which simple harmonic motion will occur (119)

recognise that the gradient of a displacement–time graph for an oscillating object at a point gives the velocity at that point (121)

recall that the total energy of an undamped simple harmonic system remains constant and recognise and use expressions for total energy of an oscillator (122)

recognise and use the expressions $a = -\omega^2 x$,
$x = A \cos \omega t$
$v = A\omega \sin \omega t$,
$a = -A\omega^2 \cos \omega t$, and
$T = \frac{1}{f} = \frac{2\pi}{\omega}$ as applied to a simple harmonic oscillator (120)

◄ From Topic 1 (79, 80)

Chapter 6.2

distinguish between free, damped and forced oscillations (123)

recall how the amplitude of a forced oscillation changes at and around the natural frequency of a system and describe, qualitatively, how damping affects resonance (124)

explain how damping and the plastic deformation of ductile materials reduce the amplitude of oscillation (125)

6.1 Simple harmonic motion

Bouncing and swinging

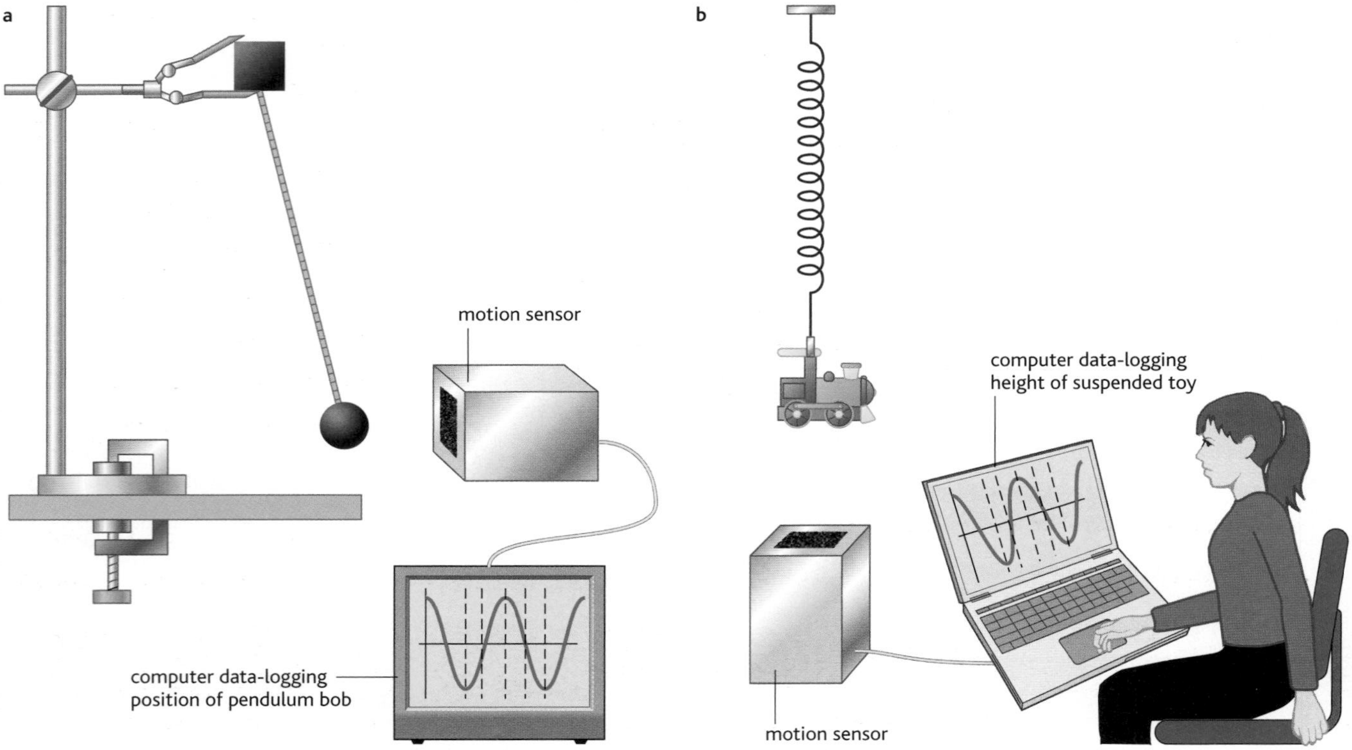

fig. 6.1.1 Why does a pendulum swing in the way that it does? How quickly does a bouncing spring toy move?

There are many things around us which **oscillate** (**fig. 6.1.1**). This means they undertake continuously repeated movements. Some oscillating systems move in a way that is relatively easy to understand. A child's swing, for example, goes backwards and forwards through the same positions over and over again. If left to swing freely, it will always take the same time to complete one full swing. This is known as its time **period**, T. The motion of the swing is described as **simple harmonic motion** (**SHM**).

When a system is moving in SHM, a force, known as a **restoring force**, is trying to return the object to its centre position. This force is proportional to the distance from that centre position. This is described mathematically as:

$$F = -kx$$

where k is a constant that depends on the particular oscillating system.

You will notice that this is the same equation as for Hooke's law, and the oscillation of a mass attached to a spring must, by definition, be an example of SHM.

Worked example

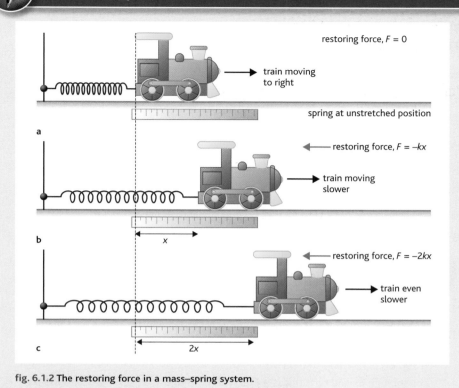

restoring force, $F = 0$

train moving to right

spring at unstretched position

a

restoring force, $F = -kx$

train moving slower

b x

restoring force, $F = -2kx$

train even slower

c $2x$

fig. 6.1.2 The restoring force in a mass–spring system.

a A 500 g toy train is attached to a pole by a spring, with a spring constant of $100\,\text{N}\,\text{m}^{-1}$, and made to oscillate horizontally. What force will act on the train when it is at its maximum displacement position of 8 cm from equilibrium?

$$F = -kx = -(100) \times (0.08) = -8\,\text{N}$$

A force of 8 N will act on the train, trying to pull it back towards the equilibrium position.

b What is the train's acceleration at this position?

From Newton's second law:
$$a = \frac{F}{m} = \frac{-8}{0.5} = -16\,\text{m}\,\text{s}^{-2}$$

Pendulum dynamics

Using the setup shown in **fig. 6.1.1a**, it is easy to find out a lot of detail about the oscillation of a pendulum. An ultrasonic position sensor can take hundreds of readings every second to produce an extremely detailed displacement–time graph for the pendulum bob. The ultrasonic data-logging sensor can also measure the velocity at each reading by making a calculation of the change in position divided by the time between readings. This will allow a velocity–time graph to be drawn. However, you should remember from simple mechanics that the gradient of a displacement–time graph at any point gives the velocity at that moment. Thus the velocity–time graph could be generated mathematically from the distance–time graph.

To make the pendulum oscillate, hold it to one side at its maximum displacement and release it. This maximum displacement from the equilibrium position is the **amplitude**, A, of the swing. The pendulum will always be stationary, i.e. have zero velocity, at this displacement, and at the equivalent displacement at the other side of the swing. As it swings from one stationary position to the other, it

accelerates to a maximum velocity and then slows down again to a stop. This all happens symmetrically, with the maximum velocity occurring in the middle at zero displacement. As the restoring force is proportional to the displacement, the acceleration is a maximum when the displacement is maximum, and zero when the displacement is zero in the middle.

You may notice that the amplitude reduces slightly over time, but this should not affect the time period for your pendulum. If the period is independent of the amplitude, such oscillations are known as **isochronous**. Legend has it that Galileo was just 17 when, watching a hanging lantern in the cathedral in Pisa, he observed that a pendulum's time period is independent of the size of the oscillations. In fact, the period for a pendulum is given by the expression:

$$T = 2\pi\sqrt{\frac{l}{g}}$$

Thus the period is only dependent on the length, l, of the pendulum string, and the force of gravity on the planet on which it has been set up!

Angular velocity and motion in a circle

For objects moving in a circle (**fig. 6.1.3**), the relationship between angular velocity, ω, angular displacement, θ, and time, t, is:

$$\omega = \frac{\theta}{t}$$

In **chapter 1.2** we also met the relationships for period, T, frequency, f and angular velocity, ω for circular motion:

$$T = \frac{1}{f}$$

$$T = \frac{2\pi}{\omega}$$

Therefore for an object moving in a circle:

$$\omega = 2\pi f$$

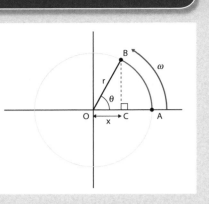

fig. 6.1.3 Relationships in circular motion.

HSW Angular velocity and SHM

The movement of a particle oscillating with SHM follows a similar pattern to that of circular motion, and so the equations for angular velocity, displacement, frequency and time period are equally valid for simple harmonic motion.

In **fig. 6.1.3,** consider the horizontal displacement of the object from the vertical axis through O, and how this changes with time as the object moves around the circle. When the object is at position A, this projected distance x is equal to the radius of the circle, r, but at position B this distance is shown by OC. This distance can be calculated from:

$$x = r\cos\theta$$

As the object moves around the circle, its angular displacement changes according to its angular velocity, $\omega = \theta/t$. Rearranging this as $\theta = \omega t$, the displacement can be rewritten as:

$$x = r\cos(\omega t)$$

The motion of all simple harmonic oscillators can be described by an equation of this form. The displacement of a pendulum bob over time is also governed by this equation. Indeed, all simple harmonic oscillators can be described by sine or cosine functions which give their displacement, velocity and acceleration over time.

For a pendulum bob swinging, the radius of the circle is replaced by the amplitude A of the pendulum's swing. The expression for displacement becomes:

$$x = A\cos\omega t$$

The relationships

$$T = \frac{1}{f}$$

$$T = \frac{2\pi}{\omega}$$

and therefore

$$\omega = 2\pi f$$

are all valid for use with SHM as well as for circular motion. So, for an object performing SHM, we can determine its angular velocity, despite the fact that it may not actually be moving in a circle. Its motion is the *projection* of motion in a circle.

Worked example

The pendulum which operates a grandfather clock is released from its maximum displacement, which is 10 cm from the centre of its swing. It swings completely through one cycle every two seconds. What is its angular velocity, and where will it be after 8.2 seconds?

$A = 10\,\text{cm} = 0.1\,\text{m}$ $T = 2\,\text{s}$

$$\omega = \frac{2\pi}{T}$$

$$= \frac{2\pi}{2}$$

$$= 3.14\,\text{rad}\,\text{s}^{-1}$$

Releasing from maximum displacement means the displacement is given by:

$$x = A\cos\omega t$$

$$x = 0.1\cos(3.14 \times 8.2) = 0.1\cos(25.75) = 0.1 \times 0.815 = 0.082\,\text{m}$$

Questions

1 a Draw three free-body diagrams showing the forces acting on the toy in **fig. 6.1.1b**. The diagrams should show the situations when the toy is at its equilibrium position, and when it is above and below the equilibrium position.

  b Why might the motion of this toy not follow simple harmonic motion?

2 a If the lantern Galileo observed in Pisa cathedral had a mass of 5 kg hanging on a chain 4.4 m long, what would its time period have been?

  b What would the angular velocity be for this lantern pendulum?

  c Galileo used his own heartbeat as a stopwatch when measuring the time period. How could he have reduced any experimental error in the time measurement?

3 Draw sketch graphs of the following in relation to the swinging of a pendulum:

  a displacement against time
  b force against time
  c acceleration against time
  d velocity against time
  e kinetic energy against time
  f potential energy against time
  g total energy against time.

You may need to think carefully about the motion in order to work out some of these.

4 What is the angular velocity of a child's swing which completes 42 swings every minute?

5 a What is meant by *simple harmonic motion*?

  b Calculate the length of a simple pendulum with a period of 2.0 s.

The graph in **fig. 6.1.4** shows the variation of displacement with time for a particle moving with simple harmonic motion.

  c What is the amplitude of the oscillation?

  d Estimate the speed of the particle at the point labelled Z.

  e Draw a graph of the variation of velocity, *v*, with time for this particle over the same period of time. Add a scale to the velocity axis.

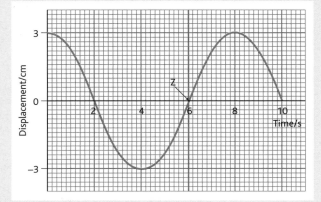

fig. 6.1.4

SHM mathematics Spec 120, 122

For an object to be moving with SHM the restoring force must, by definition, be proportional to the displacement, $F = -kx$. As we can describe the position using $x = A\cos\omega t$, this gives the equation for the force over time as:

$$F = -kA\cos\omega t$$

Not all SHM oscillations involve a spring, so here k refers to some constant relevant to the oscillator setup. From Newton's second law, we can also show that:

$$ma = -kx$$

so

$$a = \frac{-k}{m}x$$

$$= \frac{-k}{m}A\cos\omega t$$

From this we can see that acceleration and displacement in SHM have the same form, but the acceleration acts in the *opposite* direction to the displacement. When the displacement is zero, so is the acceleration, and when x is at its maximum displacement, the acceleration is also at its maximum value (**fig. 6.1.5**).

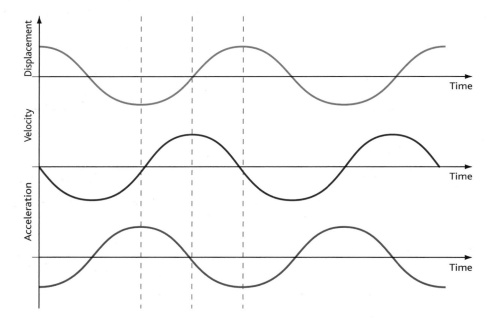

fig. 6.1.5 The changes in position, velocity and acceleration over time for a simple harmonic oscillator. The displacement can be described using either sine or cosine (depending upon whether the oscillations are taken to start from the centre or at amplitude). Velocity and acceleration are then also sine or cosine as appropriate.

We can calculate the velocity of an oscillator at any moment from the gradient of the displacement–time graph (**fig. 6.1.5**). For a function $x = \sin\theta$, the derivative function, dx/dt, which tells us the gradient at each point, is $\frac{dx}{dt} = \cos\theta$. For $x = \cos\theta$, the derivative function is $\frac{dx}{dt} = -\sin\theta$.

If $x = A\cos\omega t$, then the change in displacement with time is given by:

$$\frac{dx}{dt} = v = -A\omega\sin\omega t$$

The change in velocity with time is then:

$$\frac{dv}{dt} = \frac{d^2x}{dt^2} = a = -A\omega^2\cos\omega t$$

or

$$a = -\omega^2 x$$

So if we know the mass of the oscillating object, and the angular velocity of the oscillation, we can work out the restoring force constant k in any SHM.

$$a = \frac{-k}{m}x = -\omega^2 x$$

$$k = \omega^2 m$$

Worked example

A science museum has a giant demonstration tuning fork. The end of each prong vibrates in simple harmonic motion with a time period of 1.20 s and starts vibrating from an amplitude of 80.0 cm. Calculate the displacement, velocity and acceleration of a prong after 5.00 seconds.

$A = 0.800\,\text{m} \quad T = 1.20\,\text{s}$

$\omega = \dfrac{2\pi}{T}$

$\quad = 5.24\,\text{rad s}^{-1}$

$x = A\cos\omega t$

$\quad = 0.8 \times \cos(5.24 \times 5.00)$

$\quad = 0.386\,\text{m}$

$v = -A\omega\sin\omega t$

$\quad = -0.8 \times 5.24 \times \sin(5.24 \times 5.00)$

$\quad = -3.67\,\text{m s}^{-1}$

$a = -A\omega^2\cos\omega t$

$\quad = -\omega^2 x$

$\quad = -(5.24)^2 \times (0.386)$

$\quad = -10.6\,\text{m s}^{-2}$

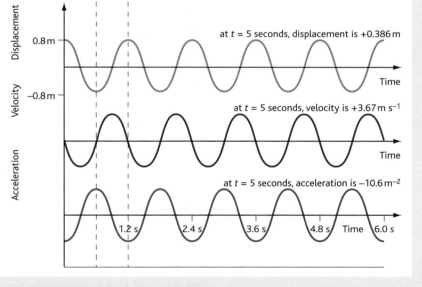

at t = 5 seconds, displacement is +0.386 m

at t = 5 seconds, velocity is +3.67 m s^{-1}

at t = 5 seconds, acceleration is −10.6 m^{-2}

fig. 6.1.6 SHM graphs for a giant tuning fork.

SHM energy

The kinetic energy of a pendulum varies during its swinging motion. At each end of the swing, the bob is momentarily stationary, and it therefore has zero kinetic energy at these points. The kinetic energy then increases steadily until it reaches a maximum when the bob passes through the central position and is moving with its maximum speed. The kinetic energy then decreases to reach zero at the other end of the swing. This cycle repeats continuously. However, once swinging, the pendulum system cannot gain or lose energy. The varying kinetic energy must be changing back and forth into another form of energy. In this example, the other form is gravitational potential energy as the pendulum rises to a maximum height, where it has maximum GPE, and drops to minimum GPE as it passes through the lowest point at the centre of its swing.

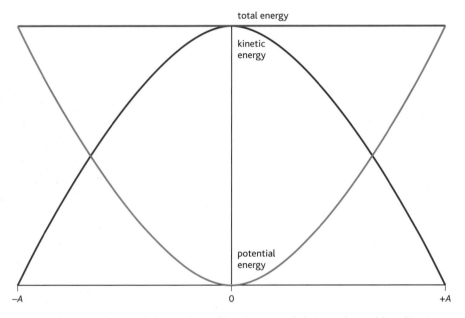

fig. 6.1.7 The energy in a simple harmonic oscillator is constantly being exchanged from kinetic to potential and back again, whilst the total remains constant as the sum of the kinetic and potential energies.

The result shown in **fig. 6.1.7** is exclusively for a system which cannot lose any energy. The closest we can get to such a system is a pendulum in a vacuum, which would be almost free from energy losses. However, air resistance will act on real pendulums. In the next chapter we shall see what happens when energy can be lost from, or added into, an oscillating system.

Worked example

A forest playground has a tyre hanging from a tree branch (**fig. 6.1.8**). The tyre behaves like a pendulum, with a rope of 4.0 metres length, and the tyre mass 15 kg. A child of mass 45 kg swings on the tyre by pulling it 3.0 metres to one side and leaping on. What is the maximum height that the tyre will reach above its equilibrium position?

$$T = 2\pi \sqrt{\frac{l}{g}}$$

$$= 2\pi \sqrt{\frac{4}{9.81}}$$

$$= 4.0\,s$$

$$\omega = \frac{2\pi}{T} = 1.6\,\text{rad}\,s^{-1}$$

Maximum velocity

$$v_{max} = A\pi = 3.0 \times 1.6$$

$$= 4.7\,m\,s^{-1}$$

Maximum kinetic energy

$$E_{kmax} = \frac{1}{2}\,m{v_{max}}^2$$

$$= \frac{1}{2} \times (45 + 15) \times (4.7)^2$$

$$= 660\,J$$

Maximum potential energy

$$E_{pmax} = mgh_{max} = E_{kmax} = 660\,J$$

$$\therefore \quad h_{max} = \frac{660}{mg} = 1.1\,m$$

fig. 6.1.8 Converting potential energy into kinetic energy can be fun!

Questions

1   A pendulum bob has a mass of 0.6 kg and a time period of 4 seconds. If it is released from an amplitude position of 5 cm, what is its kinetic energy after eight seconds? What is its maximum kinetic energy?

2   If no energy were lost, a bungee jumper would continue to oscillate up and down forever. Describe the energy changes the bungee jumper would undergo. Discuss kinetic energy, different types of potential energy, and the total energy. Conclude by explaining why in real life this does not happen.

3   Suggest how energy might be lost from a pendulum swinging in a vacuum.

4   A grandfather clock has a 2 m long pendulum to keep time. If the owner set it at noon by setting the hands and starting the pendulum from an amplitude of 10 cm, calculate the position, velocity and acceleration of the pendulum bob at 6 seconds after noon.

6.2 Damped and forced oscillations Spec 123, 124

Free and forced oscillations

Releasing a pendulum from its maximum amplitude and letting it swing freely (preferably in a vacuum) is an example of free oscillation. The situation is set up for a continuous exchange of potential and kinetic energy, caused by a restoring force which is proportional to the displacement. Any oscillating system has a **natural frequency**, which is the frequency at which it naturally oscillates when left alone.

However, oscillators can be forced to behave in a different way to their natural motion. If, as a pendulum swung one way, you were to push in the opposite direction, it would turn back. By repeated application of forces from your hand in different directions, you could force the pendulum to oscillate at some other frequency. This would then be **forced oscillation**, and the frequency you were causing it to swing at would be the **driving frequency** (**fig. 6.2.1**).

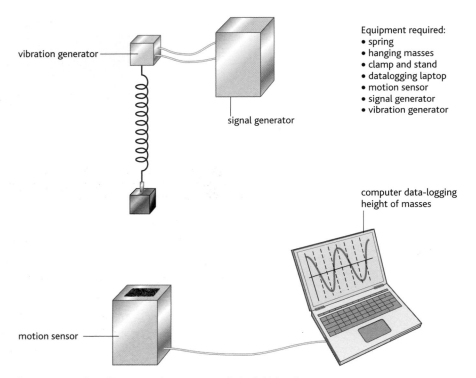

Equipment required:
- spring
- hanging masses
- clamp and stand
- datalogging laptop
- motion sensor
- signal generator
- vibration generator

fig. 6.2.1 Forced oscillations can be set up at a desired driving frequency.

Forcing oscillations involves adding energy to a system whilst it oscillates. Unless this is done at the natural frequency, the system is unlikely to undergo SHM and will dissipate the energy quite quickly. This is what happens if you push a child on a swing at the wrong moment in the oscillation.

Damped oscillations

Damped oscillations suffer a loss in energy in each oscillation and this reduces the amplitude over time (**fig. 6.2.2**).

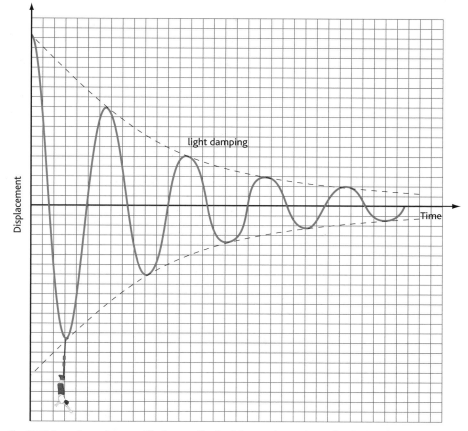

fig. 6.2.2 Damping reduces oscillation amplitude. A bungee jumper's amplitude decreases because elastic stresses in the rubber rope dissipate energy as heat, and air resistance removes kinetic energy. Note that the dissipation of sound energy by screaming will not reduce the amplitude as this does not come from the oscillation energy!

If a system is performing SHM at its natural frequency, its energy may still be dissipated through a friction force acting on the system. If a pendulum is left to swing without interference, its amplitude will decrease with each swing owing to air resistance, and internal stresses due to flexing of the material of the string. Note that although the amplitude decreases, the period remains constant throughout. These effects would be amplified if we were to attach a small sail to the pendulum to catch the air. Artificially increasing the air resistance in this way is an example of **damping**.

The amount of damping may vary, which will change how quickly the amplitude is reduced (**fig. 6.2.3**). If the oscillator completes several oscillations, the amplitude will decrease exponentially. This is known as underdamping. Alternatively, the amplitude of oscillation may drop so rapidly that the oscillator does not even complete one cycle. This is known as overdamping. Swinging a pendulum in a bowl of water will result in overdamping. If the damping is such that the oscillator returns to its equilibrium position in the quickest possible time, without going past that position (known as overshooting), then it is critically damped.

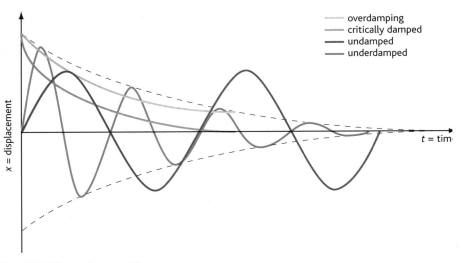

fig. 6.2.3 Different degrees of damping.

Overdamping is useful in many situations, like car suspension systems, but too much overdamping would cause the oscillator to take a very long time to return to its equilibrium position. You can appreciate this if you imagine a pendulum swung through treacle – an example of extreme overdamping!

Effects of damping

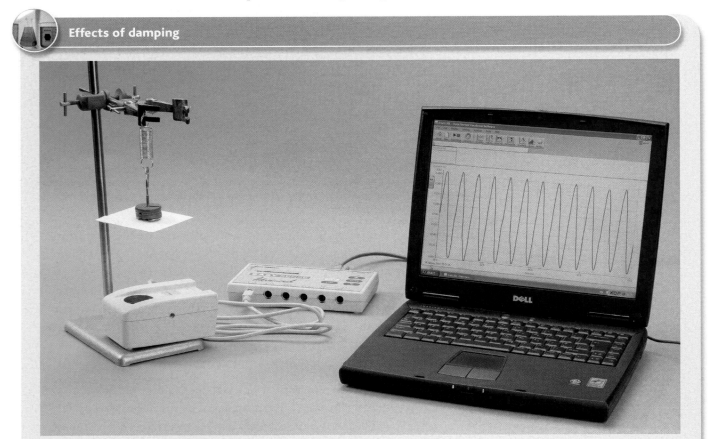

fig. 6.2.4 How does damping affect oscillations?

The setup shown in **fig. 6.2.4** can be used to investigate the effects of different degrees of damping. The card sail will provide air resistance, and altering its size will change its damping effect, making the amplitude decrease more or less rapidly. Can you make a card sail that provides critical damping?

Resonance

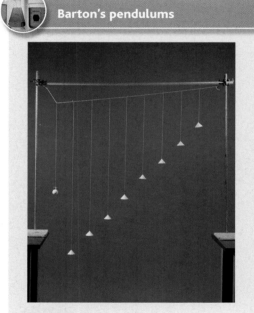

fig. 6.2.5 Damping in a washing machine lessens the effects of vibration.

If a system or object is forced to vibrate at its natural frequency, it will absorb more and more energy, which increases the amplitude of the oscillations. This is called **resonance**. If your washing machine is very noisy during one part of the wash cycle, it will be when the motor is spinning at a certain frequency. This drives vibrations in the machine which are at the natural frequency of one of the washing machine panels. This causes the panel to vibrate with increasing amplitude, making a loud noise, and may even cause the machine to move across the floor (**fig. 6.2.5**). During the rest of the wash cycle, the motor rotates at frequencies which do not match the natural frequency of any part of the machine, and it is much quieter.

Barton's pendulums

A simple setup of several pendulums can demonstrate resonance. The heavy swinging ball acts through the suspension wire to drive all the other pendulums at its natural frequency. Only the pendulum with the same natural frequency vibrates with a large amplitude. This pendulum has the same length of wire as the driving pendulum. The other pendulums show little movement, because the driving frequency does not match their natural frequency.

fig. 6.2.6 Barton's pendulums.

Solutions to real problems, like the noisy washing machine, can be designed using the principles of damping. As objects will be inclined to oscillate with large amplitudes at their natural frequency, this is generally the frequency at which these engineering solutions are aimed. Creating damping systems which provide the right level of damping is a difficult problem in many real situations, especially as many objects have several natural frequencies.

Questions

1 Give a real life example of:
  a forced oscillations **b** free oscillations
  c damping **d** resonance

2 Explain why an accelerating car may go through a brief period when a part of the dashboard rattles annoyingly.

3 Describe, using scientific terminology, how the problem in question 2 could be overcome.

4 Explain the differences between overdamping, underdamping and critical damping.

Resonance problems and damping solutions Spec 123, 124, 125

As the driving frequency applied to an oscillating system changes, it will pass through natural frequencies of the system which cause large amplitude vibrations. The size of the vibrations at resonant frequencies can be so great that they damage the system. This is just what happens when an opera singer breaks a wine glass by singing loudly at just the right pitch (**fig. 6.2.7**).

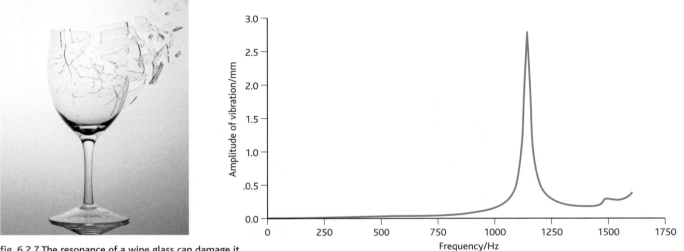

fig. 6.2.7 The resonance of a wine glass can damage it.

For some oscillators, such as clocks, we want damping to be at a minimum. For others, such as the shock-absorbing system on a mountain bike (**fig. 6.2.8**), we want oscillations to stop as quickly as possible. To make this happen requires the system to have critical damping so that it returns to equilibrium without overshooting.

fig. 6.2.8 The suspension on a mountain bike has springs to accept some movement, and shock absorbers to critically dampen any oscillations.

HSW Breaking bridges

In 1850, over 220 French soldiers died as the bridge they were crossing collapsed into the river at Angers. There is some debate as to the importance of the wind on that stormy night, but it is generally agreed that the rhythmic marching of the soldiers hit a natural frequency of some part of the bridge and overstressed already corroded cables until they failed. This disaster, along with a similar bridge collapse at Broughton Bridge near Manchester 23 years previously, led to the introduction of military units breaking step, where each soldier walks at their own pace, when crossing bridges.

fig. 6.2.9 Resonance from wind turbulence driving forces caused the collapse of the Tacoma Narrows bridge.

A similar disaster happened in 1940 to a road bridge in Tacoma, Washington, USA (**fig. 6.2.9**). Its design led to resonance as wind turbulence generated a driving frequency that matched the natural frequency at relatively low wind speeds. For the first four months it was open, it gained the nickname 'Galloping Gertie' due to its tendency towards large oscillations. On 7 November, the wind pattern hit the resonant frequency such that after several hours of twisting with an amplitude of several metres, the concrete of the bridge deck eventually failed and most of the bridge fell into the Tacoma Narrows channel. Ever since, bridge designs have been modelled in wind tunnels.

London's 'Wobbly Bridge'

fig. 6.2.10 London's Millennium Bridge opened for a single day before resonance problems meant that it had to be closed for the installation of 91 dampers.

To celebrate the new millennium in 2000, a pedestrian bridge was built across the Thames in London (**fig. 6.2.10**). It opened on 10 June, and it is estimated that between 80 000 and 100 000 people crossed on that opening day. At its busiest, there were over 2000 people on the bridge. According to a report from the Ove Arup Partnership, who designed and built the bridge, 'Unexpected movements occurred'. In fact, different parts of the bridge suffered excessive sideways wobbling, to such a degree that many pedestrians struggled to continue walking and had to hold onto the railings. Some even reported feeling seasick.

There was no problem with vertical movements, but the bridge also had lateral and twisting modes of vibration and these had resonances at several different frequencies below 1.5 Hz. Normal walking pace is between 1.6 and 2.4 Hz, but sightseers may move more slowly. The big problem was that once the bridge began to move with a tiny swinging action, people started to walk in step with the swings, and so their driving frequency matched the natural frequency. Steve Strogatz of Cornell University published a paper on the bridge in the scientific journal *Nature*. He suggested that the problem 'was one of crowd dynamics as much as engineering. The bridge surpassed standards for withstanding weight and wind. Every nonhuman element had been tested.'

In their investigation of the problems, Ove Arup, the bridge's engineers, did some experiments in which they organised a large crowd of people to walk up and down the deck of the bridge in various ways and at various speeds. Only 166 people were needed in one part of the bridge to make it suffer serious sideways movements. The analysis of the experimental data, including accelerometer and video data, determined that only under certain conditions would the resonances occur, and thus the engineers were able to design and install specific solutions. One option was to make the bridge stiffer so that its oscillations would naturally have a smaller amplitude for the forces involved. However, this was considered too difficult and expensive to install. So, the decision was taken to add horizontal and vertical dampers, rather like car shock absorbers, in various places throughout the structure (**fig. 6.2.11**). These have changed the resonant frequencies so that crowds of people cannot generate a driving frequency that matches them. The wobbly-bridge phenomenon stopped, and it was re-opened to pedestrians on 27 February 2002.

fig. 6.2.11 A pattern of dampers installed on the Millennium Bridge have reduced oscillation amplitudes by altering the resonant frequencies.

Investigating damping

A signal generator can be connected to a vibration generator to produce driving forces with a changeable frequency. This can then be used to investigate the effects of damping on oscillations. You could set up a model of an earthquake shaking a building and see how dampers could be attached to the model, either internally or externally, to reduce the damage caused by resonance (**fig. 6.2.12**).

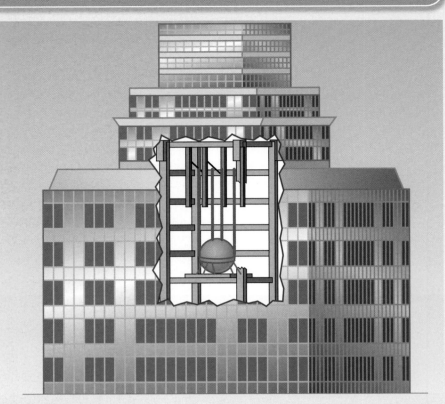

fig. 6.2.12 In the Taipei 101 skyscraper in Taiwan, a giant steel pendulum, with a mass of 728 tonnes, is tethered by giant shock absorbers. It is the world's largest earthquake-induced vibration damper.

Professional research institutions will use large-scale models on shaking tables to test new designs for skyscraper protection (**fig. 6.2.13**). In a school laboratory, a structure made of straws or struts of wood could be tested with foam padding dampers and a vibration generator.

fig. 6.2.13 Vibration testing of a model skyscraper to simulate earthquakes.

HSW Bungee rope or climbing rope?

As we saw in the materials topic of AS Physics, climbing ropes need to be made of a material which will stretch slightly, without breaking, to stop a climber from falling. We can consider this as a damped oscillating system. A climber hanging on a rope is much like a mass hanging on a spring. If they fall, the oscillation must be critically damped so that the climber begins to oscillate but does not bounce several times before stopping. For this reason, bungee cord would not make a suitable climbing rope! The stiffness and construction of the rope must be a perfect combination of stretchy so as to avoid a painful fall, and stiff to bring the climber to a halt. To achieve this, climbing ropes are made from many individual strands woven together in the form of a spiral. After a fall, a climbing rope has been permanently damaged and must be replaced. The rope material is ductile and suffers a plastic deformation which acts to reduce the amplitude of oscillations. A less stiff material could avoid replacement but would not damp the oscillations safely. In effect, the plastic deformation of the ductile rope material provides the critical damping. Potential oscillations are stopped before they start.

Questions

1 Explain why the Angers bridge collapsed in 1850.

2 Explain how a damper between girders in a skyscraper could reduce damage caused by an earthquake.

3 Explain how some dance music which has an inaudible bass frequency of between 5 and 10 Hz can get clubbers moving to the music.

4 If an oscillating system is made to perform *forced oscillations* at a frequency close to its *natural frequency*, then *resonance* occurs.

   Describe how you could demonstrate qualitatively the meanings of the terms in italics. Include a diagram of the apparatus you would use.

Examzone: Topic 6 Oscillations

1 Define simple harmonic motion. **(2)**

The curve labelled A shows how the displacement of a body executing simple harmonic motion varies with time.

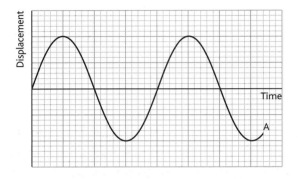

Sketch the graph above and add the following:

i) A curve labelled B showing how the acceleration of the same body varies with time over the same time period.

ii) A curve labelled C showing how the velocity of the same body varies with time over the same time period. **(4)**

Which pair of curves illustrates the definition of simple harmonic motion?

Explain your answer. **(3)**

(Total 9 marks)

2 A child of mass 21 kg sits on a swing of length 3.0 m and swings through a vertical height of 0.80 m.

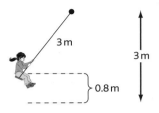

Calculate the speed of the child at a moment when the child is moving through the lowest position. **(2)**

Calculate the force exerted on the child by the seat of the swing at a moment when the child is moving through the lowest position. **(3)**

Explain why, as the amplitude of the motion increases, children may lose touch with the seat of the swing. **(2)**

(Total 7 marks)

3 The diagram shows one piston of an internal combustion engine.

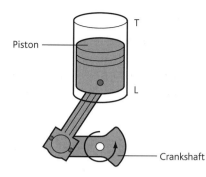

Piston

T

L

Crankshaft

As the crankshaft rotates through 360°, the top of the piston moves from L to T and back to L. The distance LT is 8.6 cm and the crankshaft rotates at 6000 revolutions per minute.

Calculate the frequency of oscillation *f* of the piston. **(1)**

State the amplitude of this oscillation. **(1)**

The oscillations of the piston are approximately simple harmonic. Calculate the maximum acceleration of the piston. **(2)**

At which position(s) in the movement of the piston will this acceleration be zero? **(1)**

Suggest why the motion of the piston *is not* perfectly simple harmonic. **(1)**

(Total 6 marks)

4 The graph shows the variation of acceleration *a* with displacement *x* for a body oscillating with simple harmonic motion.

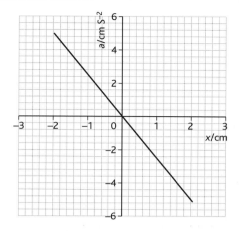

Calculate the period of oscillation of the body. **(2)**

At time *t* = 0 the body is momentarily at rest.

Copy the axes below and sketch a graph to show how acceleration of the body varies with time. Add a scale to the acceleration axis.

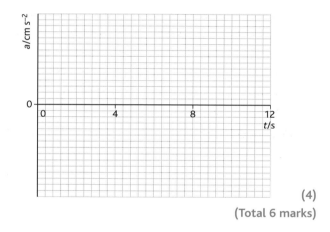

(4)

(Total 6 marks)

5 A motorist notices that when driving along a level road at 95 km h^{-1} the steering wheel vibrates with an amplitude of 6.0 mm. If she speeds up or slows down, the amplitude of the vibrations becomes smaller.

Explain why this is an example of resonance. **(3)**

Calculate the maximum acceleration of the steering wheel given that its frequency of vibration is 2.4 Hz. **(2)**

(Total 5 marks)

Topic 7 Astrophysics and cosmology

This topic covers the physical interpretation of astronomical observations, the formation and evolution of stars, and the history and future of the Universe.

What are the theories?

Gravity is the driving force behind development and evolution of cosmic scale bodies like stars and galaxies. The first chapter in this topic introduces gravitational field strength and Newton's universal law of gravitation. A comparison is drawn between gravitational and electric fields, as their governing equations are very similar.

The brightness of stars, and the distance to them, are vital pieces of information for astronomers. The topic discusses how these are measured. This leads on to a treatment of stars as black body radiators, which allows us to classify them by size, temperature and luminosity. This classification confirms our theories of the evolution of stars throughout their lives. Finally, the Doppler effect observed in the light from galaxies helps us to work out the structure of the whole Universe, as well as providing us with suggestions for its future.

What is the evidence?

The only information we can gain from objects outside our Solar System comes from observing the light (or electromagnetic radiation) we receive from them. Various pieces of ingenious physics allow us to take the light arriving here on Earth and confirm many theories about the stars and galaxies.

What are the implications?

This final topic takes us to the very limits of science. Some of the conclusions border on the philosophical. The topic examines ideas about the creation of the Universe, which means the creation of existence itself. And what of the future? The topic deals with the possibilities for the Universe in the very long term. It is little wonder that physics was originally called natural philosophy.

The map opposite shows you the knowledge and skills you need to have by the end of this topic, and how they are linked together. The numbers refer to the sections in the Edexcel specification.

Chapter 7.1

use the expression $F = \frac{Gm_1m_2}{r^2}$ (126)

derive and use the expression $g = \frac{-Gm}{r^2}$ for the gravitational field due to a point mass (127)

recall similarities and differences between electric and gravitational fields (128)

Chapter 7.2

recognise and use the expression $L = \sigma T^4 \times$ surface area (for a sphere $L = 4\pi r^2 \sigma T^4$) (Stefan–Boltzmann law) for black body radiators (132)

recognise and use the expression: $\lambda_{max}T = 2.898 \times 10^{-3}$ m K (Wien's law) for black body radiators (133)

recognise and use a simple Hertzsprung–Russell diagram to relate luminosity and temperature (131)

use a Hertzsprung–Russell diagram to explain the life cycle of stars (131)

◀ From Topic 5 (136, 137, 138)

Chapter 7.3

recognise and use the expression relating flux, luminosity and distance $F = \frac{L}{4\pi d^2}$; understand its application to standard candles (129)

explain how distances can be determined using trigonometric parallax and by measurements on radiation flux received from objects of known luminosity (standard candles) (130)

recognise and use the expressions $z = \frac{\Delta\lambda}{\lambda} \approx \frac{\Delta f}{f} \approx \frac{v}{c}$ for a source of electromagnetic radiation moving relative to an observer and $v = H_0d$ for objects at cosmological distances (134)

be aware of the controversy over the age and ultimate fate of the Universe associated with the value of the Hubble constant and the possible existence of dark matter (135)

7.1 Gravitational fields Spec 126, 127, 128

From apples to galaxies

The attraction of the stars

The current theories about the formation of the galaxies, stars and planets are all driven by one fundamental underlying force – **gravity**. The idea is that every particle with mass attracts every other particle with mass. So, if the Big Bang spread tiny particles across space, they would all attract each other. The acceleration generated by these tiny forces might be exceedingly small, but the Universe has plenty of time. Slowly but surely, the particles move towards each other and clump together. This effect is more pronounced for particles nearer to each other, as they attract each other more strongly than those separated by larger distances. These clumps of matter will continue to attract other nearby particles or clumps that have formed, and **accrete** into larger and larger bodies of material. This collection of matter might become a planet, or if enough material gets packed together densely enough, nuclear fusion may start and a star is born (**fig. 7.1.1** and **fig. 7.1.2**).

fig. 7.1.1 **Stars are being formed from clouds of gas in the Carina Nebula.**

A particle that has mass will feel a force when it is in a gravitational field. Like electric fields created by charged particles, a massive particle will generate a radial gravitational field around itself. Unlike electric fields, gravity is always attractive.

The force that a body will feel is the strength of the **gravitational field** (g) multiplied by the amount of mass (m), as given by the equation:

$$F = mg$$

From this force equation, we can also see how quickly a massive particle would accelerate. From Newton's second law we know that $F = ma$, so we can equate the two equations:

$$F = mg = ma$$

So:

$$a = \frac{mg}{m}$$
$$= g$$

Thus the **acceleration due to gravity** is the same as the **gravitational field strength**, g. On Earth, g has the value $9.81 \, \mathrm{m \, s^{-2}}$ or $9.81 \, \mathrm{N \, kg^{-1}}$.

fig. 7.1.2 Gravity drives star formation in the Tarantula Nebula, as photographed by the Hubble Space Telescope.

Worked example

What force will a two-tonne elephant feel when it is in the Moon's surface gravitational field, which has a strength of $1.6 \, \mathrm{N \, kg^{-1}}$?

$$F = mg = 2\,000 \times 1.6$$
$$= 3.2 \times 10^3 \, \mathrm{N}$$

Newton was the first scientist to determine the equation that gives us the gravitational force between two masses, m_1 and m_2, which are separated by a distance, r, between their centres of gravity.

$$F = \frac{-Gm_1m_2}{r^2}$$

where G is the gravitational constant, which has the value $6.67 \times 10^{-11}\,\mathrm{N\,m^2\,kg^{-2}}$.

In practice, we often ignore the minus sign that should be present in calculations of gravitational force as gravity is always attractive.

[411]

aut corpus aliud quodcunque vel gravitate omnino deftitueretur vel pro quantitate materiæ fuæ minus gravitaret, quoniam id non differt ab aliis corporibus nifi in forma materiæ, poffet idem per mutationem formæ gradatim tranfmutari in corpus ejufdem conditionis cum iis quæ pro quantitate materiæ quam maximè gravitant, (per Hypoth. III.) & viciffim corpora maxime gravia, formam illius gradatim induendo, poffent gravitatem fuam gradatim amittere. Ac proinde pondera penderent à formis corporum, poffentque cum formis variari, contra quam probatum eft in Corollario fuperiore.

Corol. 3. Itaque Vacuum neceffariò datur. Nam fi fpatia omnia plena effent, gravitas fpecifica fluidi quo regio aeris impleretur, ob fummam denfitatem materiæ, nil cederet gravitati fpecificæ argenti vivi, vel auri, vel corporis alterius cujufcunque denfiffimi; & propterea nec aurum neque aliud quodcunque corpus in aere defcendere poffet. Nam corpora in fluidis, nifi fpecificè graviora fint, minimè defcendunt.

Corol. 4. Gravitatem diverfi generis effe à vi magnetica. Nam attractio magnetica non eft ut materia attracta. Corpora aliqua magis trahuntur, alia minus, plurima non trahuntur. Eftque vis magnetica longe major pro quantitate materiæ quam vis gravitatis: fed & in eodem corpore intendi poteft & remitti; in receffu verò à magnete decrefcit in ratione diftantiæ plufquam duplicata; proptere quod vis longe fortior fit in contactu, quam cum attrahentia vel minimum feparantur ab invicem.

Prop. VII. Theor. VII.

Gravitatem in corpora univerfa fieri, eamque proportionalem effe quantitati materiæ in fingulis.

Planetas omnes in fe mutuò graves effe jam ante probavimus, ut & gravitatem in unumquemque feorfim fpectatum effe reciprocè ut quadratum diftantiæ locorum à centro Planetæ. Et inde confequens eft

Bbb 2

[412]

eft, (per Prop. LXIX. Lib. I. & ejus Corollaria) gravitatem in omnes proportionalem effe materiæ in iifdem.

Porrò cum Planetæ cujufvis *A* partes omnes graves fint in Planetam quemvis *B*, & gravitas partis cujufque fit ad gravitatem totius, ut materia partis ad materiam totius, & actioni omni reactio (per motus Legem tertiam) æqualis fit; Planeta *B* in partes omnes Planetæ *A* viciffim gravitabit, & erit gravitas fua in partem unamquamque ad gravitatem fuam in totum, ut materia partis ad materiam totius. Q. E. D.

Corol. 1. Oritur igitur & componitur gravitas in Planetam totum ex gravitate in partes fingulas. Cujus rei exempla habemus in attractionibus Magneticis & Electricis. Oritur enim attractio omnis in totum ex attractionibus in partes fingulas. Res intelligetur in gravitate, concipiendo Planetas plures minores in unum Globum coire & Planetam majorem componere. Nam vis totius ex viribus partium componentium oriri debebit. Siquis objiciat quod corpora omnia, quæ apud nos funt, hac lege gravitare deberent in fe mutuò, cùm tamen ejufmodi gravitas neutiquam fentiatur: Refpondeo quod gravitas in hæc corpora, cum fit ad gravitatem in Terram totam ut funt hæc corpora ad Terram totam, longe minor eft quam quæ fentiri poffit.

Corol. 2. Gravitatio in fingulas corporis particulas æquales eft reciprocè ut quadratum diftantiæ locorum à particulis. Patet per Corol. 3. Prop. LXXIV. Lib. I.

Prop. VIII. Theor. VIII.

Si Globorum duorum in fe mutuò gravitantium materia undique, in regionibus quæ à centris æqualiter diftant, homogenea fit: erit pondus Globi alterutrius in alterum reciprocè ut quadratum diftantiæ inter centra.

Poftquam inveniffem gravitatem in Planetam totum oriri & componi ex gravitatibus in partes; & effe in partes fingulas reciprocè pro-

fig. 7.1.3 **Much of modern science builds on the work of Sir Isaac Newton – for example the law defining the force of gravity between two objects.**

Worked example

a What force will exist between two neutrons in the Tarantula Nebula that are separated by a distance of two metres?

$$F = \frac{-Gm_1m_2}{r^2}$$

$$= \frac{-6.67 \times 10^{-11} \times 1.67 \times 10^{-27} \times 1.67 \times 10^{-27}}{2^2}$$

$$= 4.65 \times 10^{-65}\,\mathrm{N}$$

Note that the minus sign has been omitted from the answer.

b How quickly will the neutrons accelerate towards one another (ignoring the effects of all other particles)?

$$a = \frac{F}{m}$$

$$= \frac{4.65 \times 10^{-65}}{1.67 \times 10^{-27}}$$

$$= 2.78 \times 10^{-38}\,\mathrm{m\,s^{-2}}$$

c Why is it difficult to calculate how long they would take to reach each other?

The acceleration is inversely proportional to the square of the distance between them. Thus the acceleration is constantly increasing as they get closer together. Our usual equations of motion require constant acceleration.

HSW Weighing the Earth

Newton pondered on how the Moon knows the Earth is there, when he suggested that gravity keeps the Moon in orbit around the Earth. The answer to Newton's question is still not fully understood by scientists, but his formula can be used to great effect. It was of vital importance to NASA scientists when they made calculations in order to launch the nine Apollo Moon missions some forty years ago.

Even before space travel, it was possible to use data about the Moon's orbit to work out the mass of the Earth (fig. 7.1.4). The time period of the Moon's orbit around the Earth is 27.3 days, or $T = 2.36 \times 10^6$ s. The average orbital radius for the Moon is 384 000 km, or $r = 3.84 \times 10^8$ m. From this data, we can calculate the mass of the Earth:

Gravitational attraction between Moon and Earth, $F = \dfrac{-Gm_E m_M}{r^2}$

Centripetal force required to keep Moon in orbit, $F = \dfrac{-m_M v^2}{r}$

Gravity is the cause of the centripetal force, so these two forces are equal:

$$\frac{-Gm_E m_M}{r^2} = \frac{-m_M v^2}{r}$$

$$\frac{Gm_E}{r^2} = \frac{v^2}{r}$$

$$\frac{Gm_E}{r} = v^2$$

$$m_E = \frac{rv^2}{G}$$

The speed of the Moon comes from the time it takes to orbit:

$$v = \frac{2\pi r}{T}$$

$$= \frac{2\pi \times 3.84 \times 10^8}{2.36 \times 10^6}$$

$$= 1020 \, \text{m s}^{-1}$$

Thus:

$$m_E = \frac{3.84 \times 10^8 \times 1020^2}{6.67 \times 10^{-11}}$$

$$m_E = 6.02 \times 10^{24} \, \text{kg}$$

fig. 7.1.4 Weighing the Earth by observing the Moon.

Questions

1 Explain why the weight of an object on the Earth is found by multiplying its mass in kilograms by 9.81.

2 Calculate the gravitational force between two π^0 particles in deep space, if they are 8 metres apart. The mass of a neutral pion is 2.40×10^{-28} kg.

3 Calculate the gravitational force between the Earth and the Moon if the Moon's mass is 7.35×10^{22} kg.

4 Calculate the average distance of the Earth from the Sun, if the mass of the Sun is 2.0×10^{30} kg.

Gravitational fields Spec 127, 128

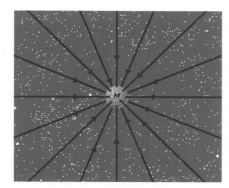

fig. 7.1.5 **The radial gravitational field around a point mass.**

Radial fields

Any mass will generate a gravitational field that will exert a force on any mass within the field. As gravity is always attractive, the field produced by a point mass will be radial in shape and the field lines will always point towards the mass (**fig. 7.1.5**).

Gravitational field strength

The radial field produced by a point mass naturally has its field lines closer together nearer the mass, as a result of its geometry (see **fig. 7.1.5**). This means that the strength of the field decreases with increasing distance from the mass causing it. The decrease is significant, and in outer space, as far as it is possible to be from a galaxy or other particles, there will be regions where there is virtually no gravity. This can be explained mathematically by the formula that tells us the strength of a gravitational field at a certain distance, r, from a mass, M. We have already seen that the force on a mass, m, caused by a gravitational field is $F = mg$. Also, the gravitational force on a mass, m, exerted by another mass, M, is given by Newton's expression:

$$F = \frac{-GMm}{r^2}$$

These two expressions are calculating the same force, so must themselves be equal:

$$F = \frac{-GMm}{r^2} = mg$$

Therefore:

$$g = \frac{-GM}{r^2}$$

i.e. the field strength is independent of the object being acted upon.

Worked example

A geostationary satellite orbits at a height, h, of 35 800 km above the surface of the Earth. Calculate the gravitational field strength caused by the Earth at this distance. The radius of the Earth, R_E, is 6400 km.

Distance from the Earth's centre:

$r = R_E + h$

$= 42\,200\,km$

$= 4.22 \times 10^7\,m$

$g = \dfrac{-GM}{r^2} = \dfrac{-6.67 \times 10^{-11} \times 6 \times 10^{24}}{(4.22 \times 10^7)^2}$

$g = 0.22\,N\,kg^{-1}$

Electric and gravitational fields

You may have noticed something familiar about the equations we have been using to calculate gravitational forces and fields. Mathematically, they are of exactly the same form as those we used to calculate the force on charged particles and electric field strength. The only differences are the symbols we use to represent the quantities causing the fields, and the constants of proportionality (**table 7.1.1**). The similarities come from the fact that both types of field are radial from a point. The constants of proportionality depend upon the way the forces interact with the fabric of the Universe, and with the unit system that we use in the calculations.

Quantity	Gravitational field	Electric field
Force	$F = \dfrac{-Gm_1m_2}{r^2}$	$F = \dfrac{kq_1q_2}{r^2}$
Field strength	$g = \dfrac{-Gm}{r^2}$	$E = \dfrac{kq}{r^2}$

table 7.1.1 Gravitational and electrical fields compared. Remember, $k = \dfrac{1}{4\pi\varepsilon_0}$.

Although the force and field strength of the gravitational and electric fields share the same form, they do differ in some significant ways. Whilst the gravitational field is always attractive, the electric field is not. As electrical charges can be either positive or negative, the electric field can be either attractive or repulsive. In addition, the electric field is significantly stronger than the gravitational field.

Worked examples

At what distance from a proton would its gravitational attraction for an electron be the same as its electrostatic attraction for that electron when held 10 metres away? Comment on the answer.

Electrostatic force:

$$F = \frac{kq_1q_2}{r^2}$$

$$= \frac{8.99 \times 10^9 \times 1.6 \times 10^{-19} \times -1.6 \times 10^{-19}}{(10)^2}$$

$$= -2.3 \times 10^{-30}\,\text{N} \quad \text{(a force of attraction)}$$

Gravitational attraction:

$$F = \frac{-Gm_1m_2}{r^2}$$

$$= -2.3 \times 10^{-30}\,\text{N}$$

$$r^2 = \frac{-Gm_pm_e}{-2.3 \times 10^{-30}}$$

$$= 4.41 \times 10^{-38}$$

$$r = 2.1 \times 10^{-19}\,\text{m}$$

The distance between the two centres of gravity therefore is smaller than the radius of a proton, so it would be impossible for the electron to get this close. Gravity is an extremely weak force in comparison to the other three forces in nature, but it affects all matter, not just things that are charged.

HSW The clockwork Universe

Combining Newton's Laws of Motion with his Law of Universal Gravitation led to the philosophical notion of the Universe as a clockwork mechanism. By this we mean that if we were able to determine precisely the positions and velocities of every particle in the Universe, it would theoretically be possible to calculate their future (and past) positions and interactions, and thus calculate the future. Ultimately, we could plot the future course of life, and society, on Earth. This idea has been extremely uncomfortable to scientists and philosophers.

Fortunately for those who find this difficult, the advent of quantum mechanics has released the Universe back to an unknown future history by insisting that there is a random nature to the movement of particles. However, this is also a philosophically prickly concept. To suggest that given the same initial conditions, a particle might behave in two different ways on two separate occasions, goes somewhat against the axioms upon which science is built. Experimental repeatability, or 'Determinism', as defined 200 years ago by the French scientist Laplace, enables us to produce laws fixed across space and time. This is the very aim of scientific inquiry, and is a principle deeply ingrained in many scientists. Einstein refused to accept some of the ramifications of Heisenberg's Uncertainty Principle, and the fledgling quantum mechanics, when he wrote in 1926 to Max Born: '[God] does not throw dice'.

Stephen Hawking more recently has confirmed that the Universe does have a random element, and his work on black holes has also led to the problem that sometimes the outcome cannot even be observed. He concluded that: 'Not only does God definitely play dice, but He sometimes confuses us by throwing them where they can't be seen.'

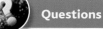 Questions

1   Calculate the gravitational field strength at the orbit of a polar satellite that travels at 900 km above the surface of the Earth.

2   Compare the magnitudes of the force of electrostatic attraction between an electron and a proton in a hydrogen atom (radius = 0.25×10^{-10} m) with the gravitational attraction of the Sun on Pluto. Pluto has a mass of 1.29×10^{22} kg and orbits at a distance of 5900 million kilometres from the Sun.

3   What would the mass of the Moon have to be for the Earth's gravity to exert the same force of attraction on it as the electrostatic attraction of the proton for the electron in a hydrogen atom?

4   There is a point on the line between the centres of the Earth and the Moon where their gravitational fields have equal magnitude but are in opposite directions, effectively creating a point of zero gravity. Calculate the distance of this point from the centre of the Earth.

7.2 Starshine Spec 131, 132, 133

Stellar properties

The attraction of the stars

One star differeth from another star in glory

from the Bible, first book of Corinthians, chapter 15, verse 41.

Modern astronomers have not yet defined the 'glory' of a star, but to distinguish one from another, we can measure various stellar properties. These allow us to classify stars into various groups that have quite enigmatic names, like **red giant**, **white dwarf** and **blue supergiant**. You should remember that because stars are at such enormous distances from the Earth, the only information we have about them is the electromagnetic radiation we receive from them (**fig. 7.2.1**). They are much too far away for us to send probes to them, or even to send signals to in the hope of detecting reflections. However, scientists have managed to determine an enormous amount of detailed information from even the faintest glows in the night sky. Incredibly, the EM emissions from stars can tell us their temperature, chemical composition, speed of movement, approximate age, size and much more.

fig. 7.2.1 Starlight is the only information we have about the stars.

The Stefan–Boltzmann law

How bright is a star? Observing stars with the naked eye, we are only able to distinguish six different levels of stellar brightness (**fig. 7.2.2**). This is insufficient for scientific use as many stars of differing brightness would appear identical to our eyes. Astronomers, therefore, use a more precise measure to classify the brightness of stars, known as **luminosity**.

fig. 7.2.2 Can you identify the brightest and dimmest stars in this star cluster, NGC 290?

We define luminosity as the rate at which energy of all types is radiated by an object in all directions. This depends upon both its size and, more importantly, its temperature. All objects emit electromagnetic radiation. Infrared cameras can detect radiation from our bodies, but with our eyes we can only see visible electromagnetic radiation from hot objects, for example the red glow from a fire.

The electromagnetic radiation is given off across a very large range of wavelengths. A perfect radiator is called a **black body** and will give off energy across the entire electromagnetic spectrum following a distribution like those in **fig. 7.2.4**. This distribution is given by the **Stefan–Boltzmann law**. This tells us that the power output from a black body is proportional to its surface area and the fourth power of its temperature in kelvin.

$$L = \sigma T^4 \times \text{surface area}$$

where σ is the Stefan–Boltzmann constant, $\sigma = 5.67 \times 10^{-8} \, \text{W} \, \text{m}^2 \, \text{K}^{-4}$.

So:

$$L = \sigma A T^4$$

which for a sphere would become:

$$L = 4\pi r^2 \sigma T^4$$

Working on the assumption that a star acts like a black body emitter, which is a very good approximation, this equation describes the luminosity of a star.

Worked example

a What is the luminosity of the Sun, given that it has a radius of 7.0×10^8 m and its surface temperature is 6000 K?

Luminosity of the Sun:

$L = \sigma A T^4$

$= \sigma 4\pi r^2 T^4$

$= 5.67 \times 10^{-8} \times 4\pi (7 \times 10^8)^2 \times 6000^4$

$= 4.52 \times 10^{26}$ W

b What would be the surface temperature of a star of radius 14.0×10^8 m with the same luminosity as the Sun?

$A_{star} = 4\pi r^2$

$\qquad = 4\pi \times (14.0 \times 10^8)^2$

$\qquad = 2.46 \times 10^{19}$ m^2

$T_{star} = \sqrt[4]{\dfrac{L}{\sigma A}}$

$\qquad = \sqrt[4]{\dfrac{4.52 \times 10^{26}}{(5.67 \times 10^{-8} \times 2.46 \times 10^{19})}}$

$T_{star} = 4240$ K

So a bigger star can be at a lower temperature and yet have the same luminosity, i.e. it looks as bright.

Wien's law

To calculate luminosity, we needed to know the temperature of the star. There are various methods for determining the temperatures of stars, but we will focus on one which uses the wavelengths of light given off by a star. When we examine the range of wavelengths emitted by a star, known as its spectrum, we find that some wavelengths are given off with more intensity than others.

The graph in **fig. 7.2.3** shows how the intensity of the light emitted by the Sun varies for the different wavelengths in its spectrum. Comparing this with the curves in **fig. 7.2.4**, you can see that the Sun acts very much like a black body radiator (although not exactly). The Sun emits a lot of electromagnetic radiation in the visible region, with a peak at about 470 nm.

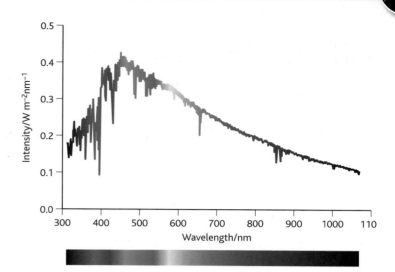

fig. 7.2.3 The spectrum of light emitted by the Sun.

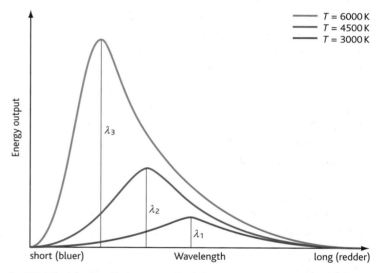

fig. 7.2.4 Black body radiation curves for different temperatures.

We saw from the Stefan–Boltzmann law that as the temperature of a black body increases, it emits more energy. **Fig. 7.2.4** shows how the amount of energy emitted at different wavelengths changes with temperature. At higher temperatures the curve has a more pronounced peak, and the wavelength of the peak output gets shorter as the temperature rises. The relationship between the peak output wavelength and temperature is described by **Wien's law**:

$$\lambda_{max} T = 2.898 \times 10^{-3} \text{ m K}$$

The number 2.898×10^{-3} m K is known as Wien's constant.

Worked example

Looking at the spectrum of light from Betelgeuse, in the constellation of Orion, its peak wavelength is at 9.35×10^{-7} m. What is the surface temperature of Betelgeuse?

$$\lambda_{max}T = 2.898 \times 10^{-3}$$

$$T = \frac{2.898 \times 10^{-3}}{\lambda_{max}}$$

$$T = \frac{2.898 \times 10^{-3}}{9.35 \times 10^{-7}}$$

$$= 3100\,K$$

Questions

1 What is the luminosity of the star Sirius, which has a surface temperature of 12 000 K and a diameter of 2 220 000 km?

2 a The Sun's surface temperature has been measured as 5700 K. Calculate the peak wavelength of the solar spectrum.

 b The peak wavelength from the Sun is in fact measured on Earth as being 470 nm. Why is the measured value different from your calculated value from part **a**?

3 Calculate the peak wavelength output we would expect of Bellatrix if its surface temperature is 21 500 K.

4 a From **fig. 7.2.5**, calculate the temperatures of Antares and Spica.

 b What is the significance of the difference in the area underneath each curve?

5 a Stars β Ori and α Cet have temperatures of approximately 11 000 K and 3600 K respectively. Calculate the wavelength at which the intensity of radiation from each star is a maximum. Give your answers in nanometres.

 b Use the Stefan–Boltzmann law to calculate the power emitted per square metre of surface, measured in $W\,m^{-2}$, for β Ori.

 c The power emitted per square metre of surface for α Cet is $1.0 \times 10^{7}\,W\,m^{-2}$.

 Copy the axes in **fig. 7.2.6** and sketch two graphs, showing how this emitted power is distributed over different wavelengths for each star. Label your graphs Ori and Cet.

 d The visible spectrum extends from approximately 400 nm to 700 nm. Use your graphs to explain why β Ori is a bluish star, while α Cet is reddish.

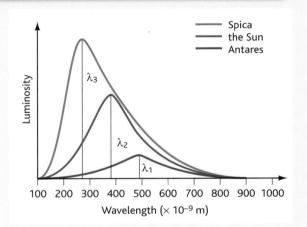

fig. 7.2.5 Spectral emission curves for three stars.

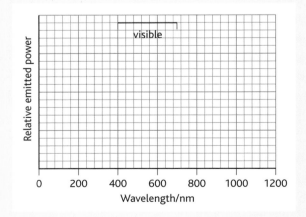

fig. 7.2.6

Classifying stars Spec 131, 132, 133

Star classes

Astronomers have classified stars into groups according to their temperature. This is a useful property to use since stars with similar temperatures tend to share many other features. As we saw from Wien's law, the temperature determines the spectral output of the star, but it can also suggest chemical composition and age.

Spectral class	Effective temperature/ K	Colour	M/M_{Sun}	R/R_{Sun}	L/L_{Sun}	Main sequence lifespan
O	28 000–50 000	Blue	20–60	9–15	90 000–800 000	1–10 Myr
B	10 000–28 000	Blue-white	3–18	3.0–8.4	95–52 000	11–400 Myr
A	7500–10 000	White	2.0–3.0	1.7–2.7	8–55	400 Myr–3 Gyr
F	6000–7500	White-yellow	1.1–1.6	1.2–1.6	2.0–6.5	3–7 Gyr
G	4900–6000	Yellow	0.85–1.1	0.85–1.1	0.66–1.5	7–15 Gyr
K	3500–4900	Orange	0.65–0.85	0.65–0.85	0.10–0.42	17 Gyr
M	2000–3500	Red	0.08–0.05	0.17–0.63	0.001–0.08	56 Gyr

table 7.2.1 Spectral class summary.

The spectral star classes are labelled by letters (table 7.2.1). The usual mnemonic for remembering the letters, in order from hottest to coolest, is:

Oh Be A Fine Girl (or Guy), Kiss Me!

You will notice a number of trends in the data in table 7.2.1. The hotter stars tend to have more mass and are more luminous. The larger gravitational pressure at the centre of a massive star makes the nuclear fusion reactions within the star run very fast, producing a lot of energy and using the hydrogen fuel in the star at an incredible rate. In addition, more massive stars are also larger. Therefore, with large size and high temperatures, the hotter stars are very luminous, giving off a great deal of energy. At the same distance away these will then appear very bright in the night sky, compared with a smaller, cooler star.

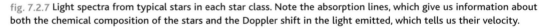

fig. 7.2.7 **Light spectra from typical stars in each star class. Note the absorption lines, which give us information about both the chemical composition of the stars and the Doppler shift in the light emitted, which tells us their velocity.**

Table 7.2.1 also shows the change in colour that goes along with changing stellar class. This is a direct result of the variation in output curve for different temperatures we saw associated with Wien's law (fig. 7.2.4). If we combine together equal intensity output of the colours of the visible spectrum, this will produce white light. The extra emissions above this white basic emission – the peak of the curve on the graph in fig. 7.2.4 – determine the colour the star appears. This is illustrated by the spectra in fig. 7.2.7. The electromagnetic radiation given out by an O class star appears quite blue, whereas when the spectrum of colours emitted by an M class star is combined the star will appear overall quite red. Given the decreasing size pattern we have seen, it will come as little surprise to find out that blue supergiants are generally O class stars, whereas **red dwarf** stars are usually M class.

The Hertzsprung–Russell diagram

If you were to plot a graph of luminosity against star temperature to confirm the trend of **table 7.2.1**, you would find that there is a general negative correlation. However, the more data you add, the more complex the picture becomes. We must also remember that the temperature measurement assumes the star behaves as a black body, and the luminosity is similarly often not as accurate as we would like. In general, luminosity has to be determined from a calculation that includes the distance to the star, and measuring the distances to stars is by no means an exact science (see **chapter 7.3** for more details). Such a plot can give us some very useful insights, but is not a graph in the true sense. It is known as a **Hertzsprung–Russell diagram** (**fig. 7.2.8**).

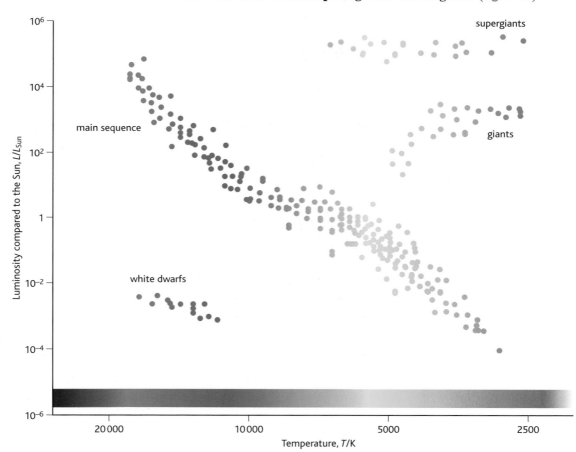

fig. 7.2.8 A Hertzsprung–Russell diagram.

Most stars we observe fall on a diagonal line across the Hertzsprung–Russell diagram, which is called the **main sequence**. These are stable stars that will exist in this state for the majority of their lifetime. Their negative correlation represents the connection between brightness and high temperature. Note that the plot is always drawn with hotter temperatures on the left hand side. There are also other stages in a star's evolution, which appear in other places on the diagram, but these are much shorter than its stable period. Thus there are far fewer stars in those parts of the H–R diagram. For example, as blue supergiants burn out in just a few million years, most of these have already done so, and we don't see many; the top left area of the H–R diagram is lightly populated.

Stellar evolution

The majority of material in the Universe is hydrogen ($\approx 78\%$) or helium ($\approx 21\%$), and it is from these elements that stars are initially formed. From an accreting collection of these gases, called a **protostar**, the life cycle of a star follows a number of stages, with the star ending its life as a white dwarf, **neutron star** or **black hole**. As the star undergoes nuclear fusion, the binding energy differences of the nuclei before and after fusion mean that the process releases energy, often as electromagnetic radiation, to heat the star. The pressure from the vibration of its particles, and the electromagnetic radiation trying to escape, hold up the structure of the star against gravitational collapse. It is this constant battle between the outward pressure and gravity that drives the evolution of a star throughout its lifetime. The initial mass of the star is a critical factor in determining how the battle wages, and thus which of the possible life cycles a star will follow (**fig. 7.2.9**).

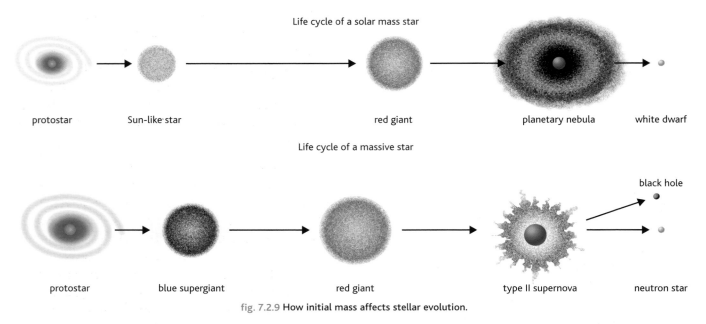

fig. 7.2.9 **How initial mass affects stellar evolution.**

The multiple possible life cycles for stars are usually grouped together into just two paths in which the outcomes are similar. These are the life cycle for low-mass stars (like our Sun) and the life cycle for massive stars, which have at least four times the mass of our Sun.

Low-mass stars

Once it has accreted about the mass of our Sun, a low-mass star will start to undergo nuclear fusion of hydrogen, converting it into helium. This is a stable stage of life in which radiation pressure and gravity are in equilibrium. The star will remain in this state for billions of years. Eventually, it will run low on hydrogen fuel, but will have produced so much energy that it will expand slightly. This expansion causes the temperature to fall and the star becomes a red giant. Our Sun is expected to undergo this change in another 4–5 billion years, when it will expand beyond the orbit of Venus. Once most of the hydrogen fuel is used, the star will start fusing helium nuclei. This complex process can cause an explosion that throws some material from the star out into space, forming a **planetary nebula**. As the fuel to produce energy to support the star runs out, the outward pressure from fusion drops and gravity takes hold, causing the star to contract to a much smaller size. This heats up the star significantly and it becomes a white dwarf. As time continues, the star will slowly run out of energy and die, passing through the red dwarf stage to become a **black dwarf**. Note that the black dwarf stage is theoretical, as it takes a white dwarf longer than the current age of the Universe to cool this much, so there has not yet been time for any to develop.

Massive stars

If a protostar has more than four times the mass of our Sun, the star begins life as a blue supergiant. As with low-mass stars, nuclear fusion begins and the star enters a stable stage of life in which heat pressure and gravity are in equilibrium. However, the fusion processes happen at much higher temperatures than in lower mass stars. The core of the Sun may be at 15 million kelvin, whereas a large star could have a core temperature of 40 million kelvin. This means that it burns very quickly, and the conditions make it possible for further fusion of some of the larger atoms it produces to occur. The fusion of helium can produce a variety of the larger elements, which have mass numbers that are multiples of helium's four nucleons, such as carbon, oxygen and silicon. There will then be stages of carbon and oxygen burning. A high-mass star is likely to be on the main sequence for only up to a billion years. When the material of such a star has been fused to the point where it is mostly iron, it can no longer undergo nuclear fusion and it stops producing energy. This happens even more abruptly than in a low-mass star, and with the enormous gravitational forces produced by the large mass, it undergoes an incredible collapse. This sudden increase in density produces a sudden huge burst of energy, effectively bouncing the collapse back out. This explosion is called a (Type II) supernova and is the most immense burst of energy ever witnessed. It is so bright, at about 10 billion times the luminosity of the Sun, that you can see the change in the night sky with the naked eye (**fig. 7.2.10**).

fig. 7.2.10 The remains of supernova N63A Menagerie.

Within a supernova explosion there is so much energy that nuclear reactions occur which produce the elements above iron in the periodic table. The natural occurrence of these elements is evidence that supernovae must have occurred in the past, as the binding energies of these heavy elements are such that they cannot be created in other natural processes in the Universe.

After a high-mass star has exploded as a supernova, the entire star may be completely shattered. If there remains a central core of stellar material, this will either be a neutron star (if the core was up to 3 solar masses) or a black hole (if the core retained more than 3 solar masses). Neither of these are easy to detect, as they emit little or no light, and they are not plotted on the Hertzsprung–Russell diagram. A neutron star consists almost entirely of neutrons, packed as densely together as the nucleons within the nucleus of an atom. They can hold three times the mass of the Sun but are only about 10 km in diameter. Black holes are even smaller and hold even more matter than neutron stars. This means that their gravitational pull is immense – so strong that even things travelling at the speed of light cannot escape.

You will see from **fig. 7.2.9** that during its life a given star develops along a sequence from one type of star to another. If we observe it at each of these points in its life, they would be plotted in different places on the H–R diagram. Thus, we can plot the life cycle of a star as a movement around the H–R diagram (**fig. 7.2.11**).

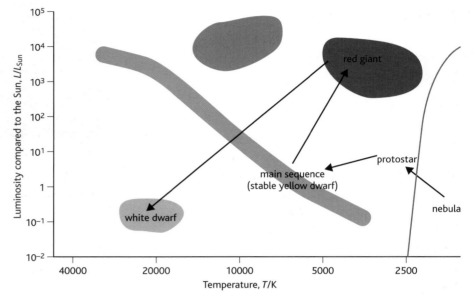

fig. 7.2.11 The Sun's life cycle will move it around the H–R diagram.

Questions

1 The mass of the Sun is 2.0×10^{30} kg. If we assume that it is entirely composed of protons, how many protons is this? If the Sun fuses all its protons over the course of its estimated nine billion year lifetime, how many protons are undergoing nuclear fusion every second?

2 Draw a flow chart showing the life cycles of:

a a star that starts out with six times the mass of the Sun

b a star that starts out with twice the mass of the Sun.

3 Calculate the gravitational field strength at the surface of a black hole, if it has five times the mass of the Sun and a diameter of 10 cm. How does this compare to the Earth's gravitational field strength?

4 a From memory, make a quick sketch of the Hertzsprung–Russell diagram and mark on the path taken by a star with the same mass as our Sun, as it develops through the various stages of its life cycle.

b Mark on your sketch the life cycle path taken by a blue supergiant if it starts out with a mass 8 times that of the Sun.

5 Why do the nuclear fusion processes within stars tend to produce elements with a mass number that is a multiple of four, such as carbon-12, oxygen-16 and silicon-20?

6 a Why can't the nuclear fusion in stars produce elements higher in the periodic table than iron-56?

b How do heavier elements than iron-56 exist, when the Big Bang produced an initial Universe composed of only hydrogen and helium?

7 a When a star moves off the main sequence, it initially becomes a red giant. Describe the processes occurring which result in it becoming 'giant-sized'.

b Use Wien's law to explain why these giant stars look red compared with their appearance when they were on the main sequence.

c Use Stefan's law to explain why a red giant has greater luminosity than when it was a main sequence star.

7.3 Hubble's law Spec 129, 130

Distances to the stars

Big distance units

Astronomical distances are very large. Our nearest neighbour is the Moon, and yet that is nearly 400 000 000 m away. The Sun is 150 000 000 000 m away, and the distance to the orbit of Pluto is 5 750 000 000 000 m. Measuring across space quickly generates very large values. Using standard form notation helps with this, but astronomers have defined a number of alternative distance units to cut down the magnitudes of the numbers involved.

You have probably already heard of the **light year**. This is the distance that light can travel in one year, which is about 10^{16} m. We also use the **astronomical unit (AU)**, which is the radius of the Earth's orbit around the Sun, $1\,\text{AU} = 1.5 \times 10^{11}$ m. Later we will also consider distances in parsecs.

Trigonometric parallax

To measure the distance to relatively close stars, astronomers use a method that is commonly used in surveying, known as **trigonometric parallax**. As the Earth moves around the Sun, a relatively close star will appear to move across the background of more distant stars. This optical illusion is used to determine the distance of the star. The star itself does not move significantly during the course of the observations. To determine the trigonometric parallax you measure the angle to a star, and observe how that changes as the position of the Earth changes. We know that in six months the Earth will be exactly on the opposite side of its orbit, and therefore will be two astronomical units from its location today.

fig. 7.3.1 You can observe the principle behind parallax measurements using your fingers to represent near and distant stars.

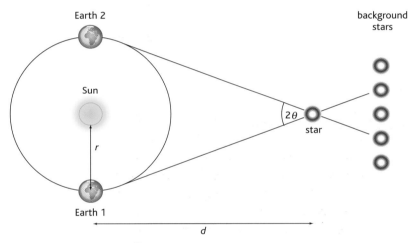
fig. 7.3.2 Trigonometric parallax measurements.

Using observations of the star to be measured against a background of much more distant stars, we can measure the angle between the star and the Earth in these two different positions in space, six months apart. As we know the size of the Earth's orbit, geometry allows calculation of the distance to the star.

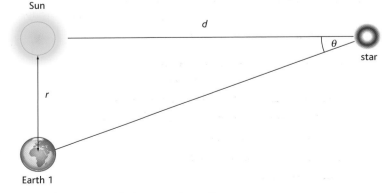
fig. 7.3.3 The geometry of trigonometric parallax.

By taking the picture of **fig. 7.3.2** and cutting it in half, we get a right-angled triangle formed as shown in **fig. 7.3.3**, showing the **parallax angle**, θ.

$$\tan \theta = \frac{r}{d}$$

$$d = \frac{r}{\tan \theta}$$

The distance, d, will come out in the same units used to measure r. This method is only accurate up to a distance of about 650 light years.

Seconds of arc

When making measurements for the trigonometric parallax of stars, astronomers often need to be able to measure very small differences in the angles. Remember that each degree can be split into 60 minutes, and each minute of arc (an arc is a part of a circle) can be split into 60 seconds.

1 degree = 60 minutes = 3600 seconds

$1° = 60' = 3600''$

HSW The parsec

A **parsec (pc)** is a measure of distance. It is an abbreviation of 'parallax second'. It is the distance a star must be from the Sun in order for the angle Earth–star–Sun to be 1 arcsecond.

$$1 \, \text{parsec} = \frac{1.5 \times 10^{11}}{\tan(1/3600)}$$

$$= 3.09 \times 10^{16} \, \text{m}$$

$$1 \, \text{light year} = 3 \times 10^8 \times 365 \times 24 \times 60 \times 60$$

$$= 9.46 \times 10^{15} \, \text{m}$$

$1 \, \text{parsec} = 3.26 \, \text{light years}$

Worked example

Astronomers measuring the parallax angle to Alpha Centauri found that the angle measured after a six month period was 1.52 seconds of arc different from that measured at first. How far is Alpha Centauri from Earth?

$2\theta = 1.52''$

$\theta = \dfrac{1.52}{2} = 0.76''$

$\theta = 0.76 \times \dfrac{1}{3600}$

$\theta = 2.11 \times 10^{-4}°$

$r = 1.5 \times 10^{11} \, \text{m}$

$d = \dfrac{r}{\tan \theta}$

$\quad = \dfrac{1.5 \times 10^{11}}{\tan(2.11 \times 10^{-4})}$

$\quad = \dfrac{1.5 \times 10^{11}}{3.68 \times 10^{-6}}$

$\therefore \quad d = 4.07 \times 10^{16} \, \text{m}$

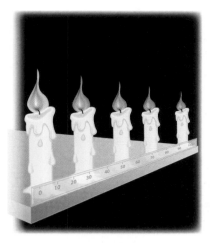

fig. 7.3.4 **At increasing distance, a light source will look dimmer.**

Standard candles

We saw previously that the brightness of a star was linked to its size and its temperature. However, the Stefan–Boltzmann law only deals with the power output of the star at its surface. How bright it looks to us, or how much energy we receive from it, depends upon how far away the star is (**fig. 7.3.4**). It follows, then, that if we knew the power output of a star, how bright it appears to us on Earth would give away its distance.

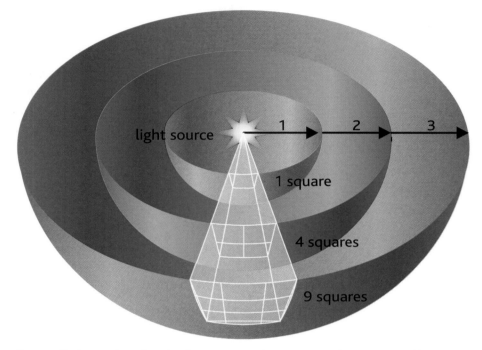

fig. 7.3.5 **The inverse square law, showing energy spread over greater and greater areas with increasing distance from a star.**

The inverse square law means that the energy emitted by a star will spread out in all directions over the surface of an ever-increasing sphere (**fig. 7.3.5**). As the surface area of a sphere is $4\pi r^2$, this gives us an equation for the radiant energy flux at a certain distance, d, from a star:

$$F = \frac{L}{4\pi d^2}$$

where L is the luminosity in watts.

Worked example

The Sun has a luminosity of $L = 3.8 \times 10^{26}$ W. What is the radiant energy flux from the Sun at the surface of the Earth?

$d = 1.5 \times 10^{11}$ m

$F = \frac{L}{4\pi d^2}$

$= \frac{3.8 \times 10^{26}}{4\pi \, (1.5 \times 10^{11})^2}$

$F = 1300$ W m^{-2}

Some stars, including some variable stars and supernovae, have properties that mean their luminosity can be determined quite separately from other measurements. These are known as **standard candles**. If we have a figure for the luminosity, and measure the energy flux (brightness) of the star reaching the Earth, we can then calculate how far away it is, by comparing it with a standard candle with the same luminosity.

Worked example

The luminosity of Betelgeuse is 5.4×10^{30} W. Its radiant energy flux at the Earth is $1.1 \times 10^{-8}\,W\,m^{-2}$. How far away is Betelgeuse?

$$F = \frac{L}{4\pi d^2}$$

$$d^2 = \frac{L}{4\pi F}$$

$$d = \sqrt{\frac{L}{4\pi F}}$$

$$= \sqrt{\frac{5.4 \times 10^{30}}{4\pi\,(1.1 \times 10^{-8})}}$$

$$d = 6.2 \times 10^{18}\,m$$

or $\quad d = 660\,ly$

or $\quad d = 200\,pc$

HSW Variable stars

Over a period of years at the beginning of the twentieth century, Henrietta Leavitt, working at the Harvard College Observatory, catalogued a huge number of stars in the nearby Magellanic Clouds. She monitored them over time and found that their brightness changed, varying in a repeating cycle. The time period of this oscillation in brightness was constant and, importantly, was in direct proportion to the luminosity of each star (**fig. 7.3.6**).

It was possible to calculate the intrinsic luminosity of these stars, as they were close enough to use trigonometric parallax to find their distance. Leavitt had discovered the period–luminosity relation. A longer time period for oscillation meant an intrinsically brighter star. Astronomers then took this relationship and used it to determine the luminosity of variable stars at much greater distances. From the luminosity, the distance to

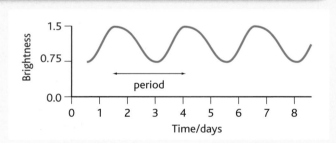

fig. 7.3.6 The brightness variation typical of RR Lyrae variable stars. These are stars that have left the main sequence, but have not yet exhausted all of their nuclear fuels. They alternately expand and contract, causing their brightness to vary repeatedly.

these stars can be determined using our expression for the radiant energy flux observed here on Earth. While Leavitt particularly studied RR Lyrae stars, there are two types of Cepheid variable stars for which the period–luminosity relationship is even stronger, and nowadays these are more commonly the standard candles astronomers will use.

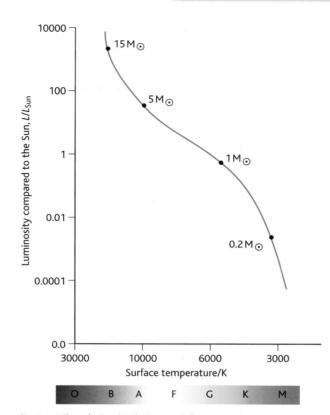

fig. 7.3.7 **The relationship between stellar size and temperature gives luminosity, which in turn can give distance.**

One of the simplest methods of determining the luminosity of a star is simply to look at its spectrum. The peak wavelength gives the temperature from Wien's law, and from the width of spectral lines you can determine whether or not it is a main sequence star. If it is, and you find its place on the main sequence of the H–R diagram as shown in **fig. 7.3.7**, you can read the luminosity from the y-axis. However, this is one of the least reliable standard candle methodologies.

Questions

1   How far away is Alpha Centauri in parsecs?

2   The parallax angle to Barnard's Star is 0.545". How far away is Barnard's Star in
    a   metres   c   parsecs
    b   light years   d   astronomical units?

3   The luminosity of Rigel is 3.9×10^{31} W. At the Earth, Rigel's radiant energy flux is 5.42×10^{-8} W. How far away is the star?

4   Explain why we must know a star's luminosity in order to determine its distance if it is more than 200 pc away. Why is this more complicated than just looking at how bright the star is in the sky?

5   Jupiter's orbit is 5.2 AU from the Sun. If Jupiter is considered as a black body with a temperature of 110 K and radius 69 900 km, calculate:
    a   the maximum radiant energy flux at the surface of the Earth due to Jupiter's electromagnetic emissions (*Hint*: You will first need to calculate the luminosity)
    b   the peak wavelength of Jupiter's energy output.
    c   How does the energy we receive from Jupiter compare with that we get from the Sun?

The age of the Universe Spec 134, 135

The Doppler effect

At AS level, we met the idea of the Doppler effect in which the wavelength of waves is altered by the relative movement of their source compared with an observer. The Doppler effect causes the sound of moving vehicles to change as they pass us. It also makes stars and galaxies appear to be a different colour because they are moving away from the Earth. The light we receive from them has a longer wavelength than when it was originally emitted; it has been red shifted. We saw previously how this led the American astronomer Edwin Hubble to suggest that nearly all galaxies are moving away from us, and that the further they are away, the faster the galaxies are receding.

Doppler red shift

laboratory spectrum

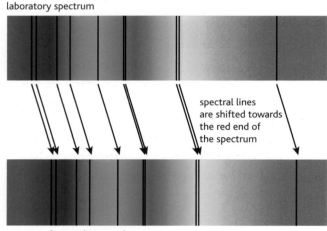

spectral lines are shifted towards the red end of the spectrum

spectrum from a distant galaxy

fig. 7.3.8 Comparison of light from distant galaxies with light produced in (stationary) Earth-based experiments can allow calculation of how fast the galaxy is moving away from the Earth.

The amount of red shift a galaxy exhibits, z, allows us to calculate how fast it is moving (**fig. 7.3.8**). This can be done using measurements of either wavelength or frequency changes.

$$z = \frac{\Delta\lambda}{\lambda} \approx \frac{\Delta f}{f} \approx \frac{v}{c}$$

Worked example

In a laboratory sample, the hydrogen alpha spectral line is at a wavelength of 656.285 nm. In the spectrum from a nearby star, this line is observed at a wavelength of 656.315 nm. How fast is this star moving, and in which direction?

The wavelength from the star is longer than it should be, so the star is moving away.

$$\Delta\lambda = 656.315 - 656.285 = 0.030 \, \text{nm}$$

$$\frac{\Delta\lambda}{\lambda} = \frac{v}{c}$$

$$v = c \times \frac{\Delta\lambda}{\lambda}$$

$$= \frac{3 \times 10^8 \times 0.030}{656.285}$$

$$= 13\,700 \, \text{m s}^{-1}$$

$$v = 13.7 \, \text{km s}^{-1}$$

Hubble's law

Local motions can affect the red shift in a confusing way, but considering the speeds of objects at cosmological distances, there is a simple relationship between them. This is known as Hubble's law:

$$v = H_0 d$$

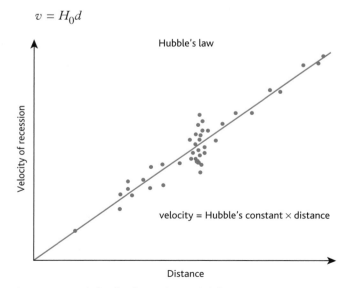

fig. 7.3.9 As virtually all galaxies show red shift in their spectra, Hubble concluded that all the galaxies must be moving apart from each other, and thus the Universe must be expanding.

So, the recession velocity of a galaxy is directly proportional to its distance away from us. The constant of proportionality, the Hubble constant, can be found from the gradient of the graph of **fig. 7.3.9**. This has had many values over the years, which demonstrates the immense difficulties involved in accurately determining astronomical distances. Since the launch of the Hubble Space Telescope, the uncertainty in measurements, and hence the uncertainty in the Hubble constant, has reduced significantly. The best modern value is considered accurate to within 5% and is $H_0 = 71\,\mathrm{km\,s^{-1}\,Mpc^{-1}}$. With an accurate value for H_0, astronomers can now use Hubble's law to determine distances to newly observed objects.

Worked example

A supernova appears in the night sky, and astronomers find that it has a red shift of $z = 0.45$. How far away is the supernova?

$$z = \frac{v}{c}$$

$$v = z \times c$$

$$= 0.45 \times 3 \times 10^8$$

$$= 1.35 \times 10^8\,\mathrm{m\,s^{-1}}$$

$$= 1.35 \times 10^5\,\mathrm{km\,s^{-1}}$$

According to Hubble's law:

$$v = H_0 d$$

$$d = \frac{v}{H_0}$$

$$= \frac{1.35 \times 10^5}{71}$$

$$d = 1900\,\mathrm{Mpc}$$

Note that the speed was found in $\mathrm{km\,s^{-1}}$ as we have the Hubble constant in $\mathrm{km\,s^{-1}\,Mpc^{-1}}$.

How old is the Universe?

As all distant objects show a red shift, they are all moving away from us. This implies that the Universe as a whole is expanding. If we imagine time running backwards from the present, then the Universe would contract until a moment where everything was in the same place. This would be the time of the Big Bang, when everything first exploded outwards from that single point. Thus, if we can find the Hubble constant, it will tell us how quickly the Universe is expanding. From this we can work out when it all started (**fig. 7.3.10**).

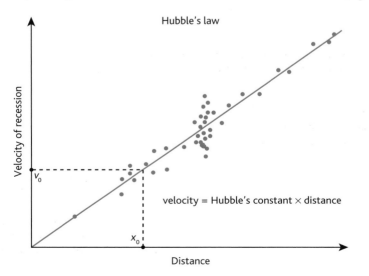

Hubble's law

velocity = Hubble's constant × distance

v_0

x_0

Velocity of recession

Distance

fig. 7.3.10
Simple mechanics determines the age of the Universe.

For an object to travel a distance d_0 from the beginning of time, at a speed of v_0, the time taken, T_0, can be calculated from the basic equation for speed:

$$\text{speed} = \frac{\text{distance}}{\text{time}}$$

$$v_0 = \frac{d_0}{T_0}$$

$$T_0 = \frac{d_0}{v_0}$$

If we consider the gradient of the Hubble graph, $H_0 = \frac{v_0}{d_0}$.

$$T_0 = \frac{1}{H_0}$$

Note that in this calculation you should use the same units for the distance and for the length component of the units for recession velocity. Usually, the Hubble constant is quoted in units of $\text{km s}^{-1}\,\text{Mpc}^{-1}$.

$$H_0 = 71\,\text{km s}^{-1}\,\text{Mpc}^{-1} = 71\,000\,\text{m s}^{-1}\,\text{Mpc}^{-1}$$

$$1\,\text{pc} = 3.08 \times 10^{16}\,\text{m}$$

$$1\,\text{Mpc} = 3.08 \times 10^{22}\,\text{m}$$

$$\therefore\ H_0 = \frac{71\,000}{3.08 \times 10^{22}}$$

$$= 2.31 \times 10^{-18}\,\text{m s}^{-1}\,\text{m}^{-1}$$

$$H_0 = 2.31 \times 10^{-18}\,\text{s}^{-1}$$

So, $\quad T_0 = \frac{1}{H_0}$

$$= \frac{1}{2.31 \times 10^{-18}}$$

$$\therefore\ T_0 = 4.33 \times 10^{17}\,\text{s}$$

This value for T_0 gives the age of the Universe as 13.7 billion years.

Questions

1 The galaxy NGC 7320C has a red shift value of $z = 0.02$.

   a At what wavelength would you expect to find the hydrogen alpha line in the spectrum of light from NGC 7320C?

   b Use the best modern value for Hubble's constant to calculate the distance to NGC 7320C in megaparsecs.

2 The value for the Hubble constant has varied over the years, from $50\,\text{km s}^{-1}\,\text{Mpc}^{-1}$ to $100\,\text{km s}^{-1}\,\text{Mpc}^{-1}$, as different star data were used to draw the graph. Calculate the range of ages of the Universe that this represents.

3 Use the data shown in **fig. 7.3.11** to answer these questions.

   a Calculate the recession velocity of each galaxy.

   b What would be the rest wavelength for a CIV spectral line?

   c What would be the frequency of the SiIV spectral line in galaxy i)?

4 Hubble's law can be represented by the formula $v = H_0 d$.

   a State the unit of the Hubble constant H_0.

   b Show how the age of the Universe can be estimated by using the above formula. State an assumption that has to be made.

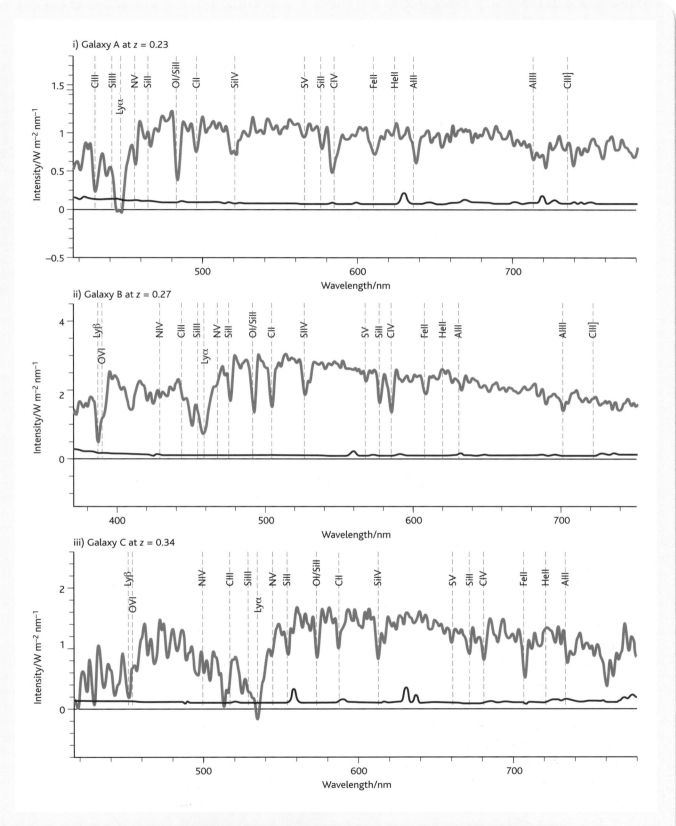

fig. 7.3.11 Spectral intensities of light from three different galaxies. The dotted line labels show the wavelength positions of various spectral lines, corresponding to electron transitions in different elements.

The fate of the Universe Spec 135

fig. 7.3.12 **Our position within existence can only be guessed at.**

The Universe is expanding. Will this change in future? The answer to this question depends critically on the mass of the Universe, and more specifically on the density of matter. Gravity is the force that could slow the expansion down to a stop, and possibly even then start to cause the Universe to contract back inwards (**fig. 7.3.13**). This might eventually end in a **Big Crunch**. The force of gravity between particles decreases with the square of the distance. Thus if the matter in the Universe is only sparse, then the gravitational forces between particles, stars and galaxies will be generally weak. The Universe will continue expanding forever. However, if the matter in the Universe has more than a critical density then the gravitational forces will succeed in causing the Big Crunch.

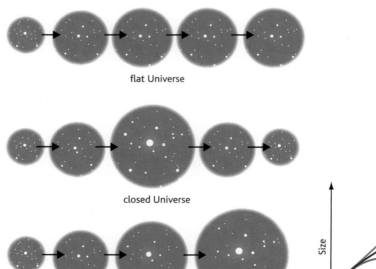

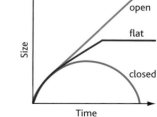

fig. 7.3.13 **Our Universe could expand forever, expand to a constant size, or stop expanding and then collapse again.**

Dark matter

To determine the fate of the Universe, scientists have been trying to work out its density. However, they have hit upon some big problems. Galaxies emit a certain amount of light. We can measure this by measuring their apparent brightness and accounting for the inverse square decrease in this caused by the distance to the galaxy. From the actual luminosity of a galaxy, we can estimate the mass of all its stars. Galaxies rotate and this means that all the stars they contain must be experiencing a centripetal force towards the centre of the galaxy's rotation. When astronomers measure the rotational speed of the stars in the galaxies, they find that the mass suggested by the luminosity calculations is not nearly enough to create the centripetal force needed to keep the galaxy spinning (**fig. 7.3.14**). In fact, the mass of the stars is generally only about 10% of that needed. This suggests that galaxies must contain a lot of mass that does not emit light.

Astronomers have not yet discovered what the dark matter could be. Most stars will have a planetary system, but the mass of all these planets is not nearly enough to hold a galaxy together. Similarly, black holes, or interstellar gases are good candidates for dark matter, but these (and other similar suggestions) are also not observed in sufficient quantities. We can account for a lot of dark matter with straightforward things like these, but scientists are convinced that the majority of dark matter is of another as yet unknown form.

fig. 7.3.14 The mass of stars lighting up a galaxy is not nearly enough to provide a gravitational centripetal force strong enough hold the stars in place against their rotational velocity.

Questions

1 a What is meant by the Doppler effect when applied to light?

  b Edwin Hubble reached a number of conclusions as a result of observations and measurements of red shift. State two of these conclusions.

  c **Fig. 7.3.15** gives values of wavelength for part of the electromagnetic spectrum.

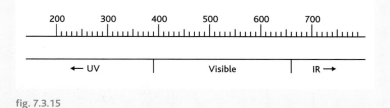

fig. 7.3.15

  A very hot distant galaxy emits violet light just at the edge of the visible spectrum. Estimate the maximum velocity the galaxy could have so that visible light could still be detected as it moves away from the Earth.

  d The fate of the Universe is dependent on the average mass–energy density of the Universe. What is meant by the critical density of the Universe?

Examzone: Topic 7 Astronomy and cosmology

1 a The graph shows the best-fit line obtained when recessional velocity is plotted against distance from Earth for a large number of galaxies.

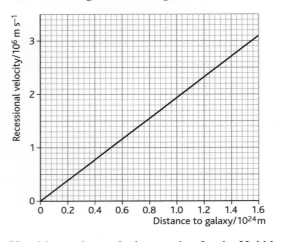

Use this graph to calculate a value for the Hubble constant. **(2)**

A spectral line measured using a laboratory source has a wavelength of 372.7 nm. The same line, measured in light from a distant galaxy, has an apparent wavelength of 410.0 nm. Estimate the distance of this galaxy from Earth. **(4)**

b The diagram shows a deflated balloon. It has three dots on its surface, labelled P, Q and R. Draw the balloon as it would appear when fully inflated. Mark the new positions of the three dots.

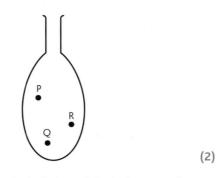

(2)

Explain how the inflation of the balloon can be used to model the expansion of the Universe. You may be awarded a mark for the clarity of your answer. **(4)**

(Total 12 marks)

2 a i) State Newton's law for the gravitational force between point masses. **(2)**

ii) Use this law to show that the gravitational field strength g at a distance r from the centre of the Earth, where r is greater than or equal to the radius R of the Earth, is given by

$$g = \frac{GM}{r^2}$$

where M is the mass of the Earth. **(1)**

iii) Use the axes below as a guide to plot a graph to show how g varies as the distance r increases from its minimum value of R to a value of $4R$.

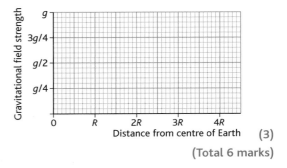

(3)

(Total 6 marks)

3 Spectrum A shows two emission lines of hydrogen obtained in a laboratory; spectrum B shows the same lines as obtained from light from a distant galaxy. Use these spectra to determine the **velocity** of this galaxy. (The diagrams are not to scale.)

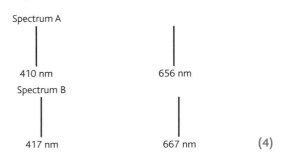

(4)

Using a value for the Hubble constant of $1.8 \times 10^{-18}\,\text{s}^{-1}$, estimate the distance of this galaxy from Earth. **(2)**

(Total 6 marks)

4 a The graph shows the relative intensity of the energy distribution in the spectrum of a body radiating at a temperature of 6000 K (the approximate temperature of the Sun).

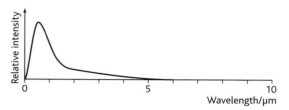

Estimate the wavelength at which the intensity of radiation from the Earth is a maximum. (2)

Copy the graph and add a second curve to the graph to show the approximate energy distribution in the radiation emitted by the Earth in the range 0–10 μm. (2)

b Here is a Hertzsprung–Russell diagram showing the main sequence.

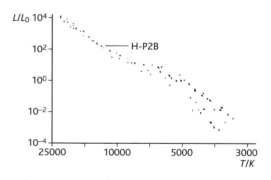

Copy the diagram and mark regions on the diagram where you would find (i) giant stars (ii) white dwarfs. (2)

L_0, the luminosity of the Sun, is 3.9×10^{26} W. Estimate the temperature of the Sun. (1)

Use the graph to estimate the luminosity of the star H-P 2B. (2)

Calculate the surface area, and hence the radius of H-P 2B. (4)

c Our Sun is on the main sequence. Outline its past and expected life story, starting from the time it was first on the main sequence. You may be awarded a mark for the clarity of your answer. (4)

(Total 17 marks)

5 Using the usual symbols write down an equation for

i) Newton's law of gravitation

ii) Coulomb's law (2)

State one difference and one similarity between gravitational and electric fields. (2)

A speck of dust has a mass of 1.0×10^{-18} kg and carries a charge equal to that of one electron. Near to the Earth's surface it experiences a uniform downward electric field of strength $100 \, \text{N C}^{-1}$ and a uniform gravitational field of strength 9.8 N kg^{-1}.

Draw a free-body force diagram for the speck of dust. Label the forces clearly. (2)

Calculate the magnitude and direction of the resultant force on the speck of dust. (4)

(Total 10 marks)

6 a The intensity of solar radiation at the top of the Earth's atmosphere is 1.4 kW m^{-2}. The Sun's average distance from the Earth is 1.5×10^{11} m.

Show that the luminosity of the Sun is approximately 4×10^{26} W. (3)

Why is the intensity at the top of the Earth's atmosphere used in this calculation? (1)

The Sun's energy is produced when hydrogen 'burns' to form helium. Four protons are required to make each helium nucleus. Use the data below to estimate the energy released for each helium nucleus created. (Your answer will be only approximate as it ignores the positrons which are also released in the process.)

Data: mass of proton = 1.67×10^{-27} kg

mass of helium nucleus = 6.64×10^{-27} kg (4)

Show that the number of helium nuclei created per second in the Sun is approximately 1×10^{38}. (1)

Hence estimate the mass of hydrogen burned per second in the Sun. (2)

b The graphs show the sensitivity of a particular brand of photographic film and that of a charge coupled device, CCD, to different parts of the electromagnetic spectrum.

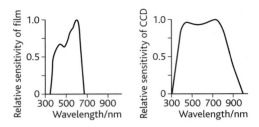

The surface temperature of a star can be calculated once the wavelength of the peak of its spectrum (λ_{max}) is known. Use the graphs to explain why photographic film would be less suitable than CCDs for determining λ_{max} of a star which radiates mainly in the visible region (400 nm–700 nm) of the electromagnetic spectrum. (3)

State one other advantage of using CCDs suggested by these graphs. (1)

c State what happens to the hydrogen 'burning' process in a star as it moves off the main sequence to become a red giant. (2)

Why is a red giant more luminous than the main sequence star from which it originated, even though its temperature is lower? (1)

d Describe how observations of Cepheid variable stars are used to estimate the distance to nearby galaxies. You may be awarded a mark for the clarity of your answer. (5)

e Read the short passage below and answer the questions about it.

> In a simple binary system two stars move in circular orbits of different radii about a common centre. The two stars take the same time T to complete one revolution. If the binary system is viewed more or less edge-on the stars periodically pass in front of one another, reducing the amount of light that reaches us. Such a system is called an eclipsing binary and can be detected from its light curve, which is a plot showing how the observed light intensity varies with time. Once the orbital period T has been determined the total mass M of the binary system can be calculated from the relationship $M = 4\pi^2 d^3 / GT^2$

where d is the sum of the radii and G is the gravitational constant.

[Adapted from TRUMP *Astrophysics Project*]

Explain the meaning of the term **binary system**. (1)

The light curve for an eclipsing binary consisting of a small very bright star and a much larger star is shown below. The system is being viewed edge-on. Diagrams B and D (not to scale) show the relative positions of the small and large star at two times between the dips in the light curve.

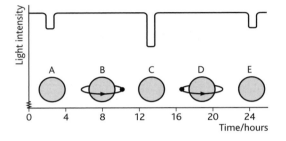

Copy and complete diagrams A, C and E to show the positions of the small bright star at the times of the dips in the light curve. (2)

Explain why the dip in the curve at A is smaller than the dip at C. (2)

Estimate the orbital period of this binary. (1)

Approximately how long does it take the small star to cross the disc of the larger one? (1)

On the light curve above show how the observed light intensity varies with time when this system is viewed perpendicular to the plane of the orbits. (2)

(Total 32 marks)

7 Draw a labelled diagram to illustrate the principle of how the distance to a nearby star can be measured using the annual parallax method. (4)

Why is this method only suitable for nearby stars? (1)

(Total 5 marks)

8 State two ways in which a white dwarf star differs from a main sequence star. (2)

Describe what happens to a star after it has become a white dwarf. (2)

A Hertzsprung-Russell diagram showing the main sequence is drawn below. The luminosity of the Sun = L_o

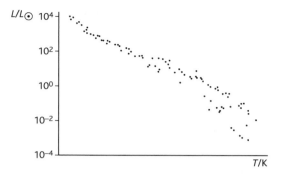

Sketch the graph and add a scale to the temperature axis. (2)

Identify one star on the diagram which has a luminosity very similar to that of the Sun. Label this star X. (1)

Shade in a region on the diagram where white dwarf stars are located. Label this region W. (1)

Label with an M the region on the diagram where the most massive main sequence stars are located. (1)

Explain why the most massive main sequence stars have the shortest lifetimes. You may be awarded a mark for the clarity of your answer. (4)

Two stars, Deneb and Vega, are similar in colour. What can be deduced about the surface temperatures of the two stars? Explain your answer. (2)

Star	Luminosity/W	Distance from Earth/m
Deneb	2.5×10^{31}	1.5×10^{19}
Vega	1.9×10^{28}	2.3×10^{17}

The table gives some information about the two stars.

Which star has the greater surface area? Justify your answer. (3)

Which star will have the higher intensity and therefore appear brighter as seen from the Earth? Show all your working. (4)

(Total 22 marks)

Index

Pearson Education Limited

Edinburgh Gate

Harlow

Essex CM20 2JE

© Pearson Education Limited 2009

The right of Miles Hudson to be identified as the author of this work has been asserted by him/them in accordance with the Copyright, Designs and Patents Act of 1988.

ISBN 978-1-4082-0608-9

Design   320 Design Ltd.

Illustration   Oxford Designers and Illustrators

Index   Richard Howard

Printed and bound by Scotprint Ltd., Haddington, UK

The publisher's policy is to use paper manufactured from sustainable forests.

Acknowledgements

The publishers are grateful to Richard Laird for his collaboration in reviewing this book.

Photo acknowledgements

The publisher would like to thank the following for their kind permission to reproduce their photographs:

(Key: b-bottom; c-centre; l-left; r-right; t-top)

3B Scientifc GmbH, Hamburg: 65; **Alamy Images:** Steve Allen Travel Photography 28; Phil Degginger 60; fine art 26; Kalicoba 14t, 20b; William S. Kuta 31; Mark Nemeth 25; Sciencephotos 51; Skyscan Photolibrary 142; A. T. Willett 141; **Art Directors and TRIP photo Library:** Helene Rogers 55, 162b; © **CERN:** 76 (icon), 91r, 92, 94, 95; **CartoonStock Ltd:** 85; **Trevor Clifford:** 17, 21, 30, 42, 44, 50, 62, 64, 68, 69, 117, 134, 160, 187 (icon); **Corbis:** Bettmann 29; Jeff Christensen/Reuters 15; Pawel Libera 164; Christian Liewig 10l; **Courtesy of the Archives, California Institute of Technology:** 48; **Courtesy Zettl Research Group, Lawrence Berkeley National Laboratory and University of California at Berkeley:** 63r; **DK Images:** Andy Crawford 120, 121; Jamie Marshall 72; **EFDA-JET:** 139; **Getty Images:** 10r; Steve Bronstein/ Stone 162t; Marsi/Stone 157; Steve Taylor/Photographer's Choice 20t; **GreenLearning's Re-energy.ca (www.greenlearning.ca):** 73b; **Alex Helman, Physics Department, UCSC:** 84; **iStockphoto:** Matthew Cole 36 (icon); Erick Nguyen 8 (icon); Serghei Velusceac 112 (icon); **Jupiter Unlimited:** Comstock Images 170 (icon); Stockxpert 126 (icon), 148 (icon); **Nick Kim:** 196; **NASA:** ESA, HEIC, and The Hubble Heritage Team (STScI/AURA) 185; European Space Agency/NASA/E. Olszewski (University of Arizona) 178t; NASA and A. Riess (STScI) 178b; **No Trace:** 33; **PA Photos:** AP 163; Barry Batchelor/ PA Archive 166; **Philosophiae Naturalis Principia Mathematica by Isaac Newton:** 11, 173; **Photolibrary. com:** Hisham F Ibrahim/Digital Vision 14b; **Reprinted with permission from the American Journal of Physics vol32, p551, 1964, American Association of Physics Teachers:** 86; **Rex Features:** c.Paramount/Everett 98; Dave Penman 165; **Science Photo Library Ltd:** Carl Anderson 93; CERN 91l; Dr David Wexler, coloured by Dr Jeremy Burgess 83; Robert Gendler 172r; Andrew Lambert Photography 161; Lawrence Berkeley Laboratory 99; Peter Menzel 63l; NASA/ESA/N. SMITH(University of California, Berkeley)/Hubble Heritage Team(STSCL/AURA) 172l; NASA/ESA/STScI 197; NASA/JPL-CALTECH/UMD 22; Antonia Reeve 38; RIA NOVOSTI 144; Royal Astronomical Society 115; **Scientific American, December 20 1890:** 73t; **Mike Vetterlein:** 41

Cover images: *Front:* **Photolibrary.com:** Oxford Scientific/Jon Heras

All other images © Pearson Education

Picture Research by: Louise Edgeworth

We are grateful to the following for permission to reproduce copyright material:

The ATLAS Experiment at CERN for an extract from "What must a detector be capable of doing?" *Experiment Tour* on http://www.atlas.ch/etours_exper/experiment-12.html, copyright © The ATLAS Experiment at CERN; Danish Wind Industry Association for an extract and photo about Charles F. Brush http://www.windpower.org/en/ pictures/index.htm, reproduced with permission; Edexcel Limited for Edexcel exam questions between June 1995 and June 2006 copyright © Edexcel Limited; EFDA-Jet for the video 'An Introduction to EFDA-JET (EFDA-JET 2003)' http://www.jet.efda.org/pages/multimedia/movies/ index.html (460x360 (WMV 13MB), reproduced with permission; European Nuclear Society for data on Uranium mining www.euronuclear.org in Table 5.2, copyright © European Nuclear Society, 2003; GreenLearning Canada for "Build your own Wind Turbine" pdf designed by Dave Mussell http://www.re-energy.ca/pdf/wind-turbine. pdf. These materials have been used with permission from GreenLearning Canada, www.greenlearning.ca, www. re-energy.ca; NASA for the animation of the deep space collision http://www.nasa.gov/mov/120426main_ge-062405. mov, source NASA; The Nobel Foundation for an extract from Professor Siegbahn, Swedish Academy of Sciences, 1960 source www.nobelprize.org; Princeton University Press for an extract by Stephen Hawking from the series of six lectures with Roger Penrose on the nature of space and time sponsored by Princeton University Press http://arxiv.org/abs/ hep-th/9409195, reproduced with permission; and Professor A. Zettl, University of California at Berkeley for the video and animation of the Berkeley nanomotor section http://www. physics.berkeley.edu/research/zettl/projects/Rotorpics.html, reproduced with permission.

Examzone section © Edexcel Ltd 2009

Single User Licence Agreement:
Edexcel A Level Science: A2 Physics ActiveBook CD-ROM

Warning:
This is a legally binding agreement between You (the user or purchasing institution) and Pearson Education Limited of Edinburgh Gate, Harlow, Essex, CM20 2JE, United Kingdom ('PEL').

By retaining this Licence, any software media or accompanying written materials or carrying out any of the permitted activities You are agreeing to be bound by the terms and conditions of this Licence. If You do not agree to the terms and conditions of this Licence, do not continue to use the Edexcel A Level Science: A2 Physics ActiveBook CD-ROM and promptly return the entire publication (this Licence and all software, written materials, packaging and any other component received with it) with Your sales receipt to Your supplier for a full refund.

Intellectual Property Rights:
This Edexcel A Level Science: A2 Physics ActiveBook CD-ROM consists of copyright software and data. All intellectual property rights, including the copyright is owned by PEL or its licensors and shall remain vested in them at all times. You only own the disk on which the software is supplied. If You do not continue to do only what You are allowed to do as contained in this Licence you will be in breach of the Licence and PEL shall have the right to terminate this Licence by written notice and take action to recover from you any damages suffered by PEL as a result of your breach.

The PEL name, PEL logo, Edexcel name, Edexcel logo and all other trademarks appearing on the software and Edexcel A Level Science: A2 Physics ActiveBook CD-ROM are trademarks of PEL. You shall not utilise any such trademarks for any purpose whatsoever other than as they appear on the software and Edexcel A Level Science: A2 Physics ActiveBook CD-ROM.

Yes, You can:
1. use this Edexcel A Level Science: A2 Physics ActiveBook CD-ROM on Your own personal computer as a single individual user. You may make a copy of the Edexcel A Level Science: A2 Physics ActiveBook CD-ROM in machine readable form for backup purposes only. The backup copy must include all copyright information contained in the original.

No, You cannot:
1. copy this Edexcel A Level Science: A2 Physics ActiveBook CD-ROM (other than making one copy for back-up purposes as set out in the Yes, You can table above);

2. alter, disassemble, or modify this Edexcel A Level Science: A2 Physics ActiveBook CD-ROM, or in any way reverse engineer, decompile or create a derivative product from the contents of the database or any software included in it:

3. include any materials or software data from the Edexcel A Level Science: A2 Physics ActiveBook CD-ROM in any other product or software materials;

4. rent, hire, lend, sub-licence or sell the Edexcel A Level Science: A2 Physics ActiveBook CD-ROM;

5. copy any part of the documentation except where specifically indicated otherwise;

6. use the software in any way not specified above without the prior written consent of PEL;

7. Subject the software, Edexcel A Level Science: A2 Physics ActiveBook CD-ROM or any PEL content to any

derogatory treatment or use them in such a way that would bring PEL into disrepute or cause PEL to incur liability to any third party.

Grant of Licence:
PEL grants You, provided You only do what is allowed under the 'Yes, You can' table above, and do nothing under the 'No, You cannot' table above, a non-exclusive, non-transferable Licence to use this Edexcel A Level Science: A2 Physics ActiveBook CD-ROM.

The terms and conditions of this Licence become operative when using this Edexcel A Level Science: A2 Physics ActiveBook CD-ROM.

Limited Warranty:
PEL warrants that the disk or CD-ROM on which the software is supplied is free from defects in material and workmanship in normal use for ninety (90) days from the date You receive it. This warranty is limited to You and is not transferable.

This limited warranty is void if any damage has resulted from accident, abuse, misapplication, service or modification by someone other than PEL. In no event shall PEL be liable for any damages whatsoever arising out of installation of the software, even if advised of the possibility of such damages. PEL will not be liable for any loss or damage of any nature suffered by any party as a result of reliance upon or reproduction of any errors in the content of the publication.

PEL does not warrant that the functions of the software meet Your requirements or that the media is compatible with any computer system on which it is used or that the operation of the software will be unlimited or error free. You assume responsibility for selecting the software to achieve Your intended results and for the installation of, the use of and the results obtained from the software.

PEL shall not be liable for any loss or damage of any kind (except for personal injury or death) arising from the use of this Edexcel A Level Science: A2 Physics ActiveBook CD-ROM or from errors, deficiencies or faults therein, whether such loss or damage is caused by negligence or otherwise.

The entire liability of PEL and your only remedy shall be replacement free of charge of the components that do not meet this warranty.

No information or advice (oral, written or otherwise) given by PEL or PEL's agents shall create a warranty or in any way increase the scope of this warranty.

To the extent the law permits, PEL disclaims all other warranties, either express or implied, including by way of example and not limitation, warranties of merchantability and fitness for a particular purpose in respect of this Edexcel A Level Science: A2 Physics ActiveBook CD-ROM.

Termination:
This Licence shall automatically terminate without notice from PEL if You fail to comply with any of its provisions or the purchasing institution becomes insolvent or subject to receivership, liquidation or similar external administration. PEL may also terminate this Licence by notice in writing. Upon termination for whatever reason You agree to destroy the Edexcel A Level Science: A2 Physics ActiveBook CD-ROM and any back-up copies and delete any part of the Edexcel A Level Science: A2 Physics ActiveBook CD-ROM stored on your computer.

Governing Law:
This Licence will be governed by and construed in accordance with English law.

© Pearson Education Limited 2009